THE *Penetone* HANDBOOK

A COLLECTION OF USEFUL
TABLES AND INFORMATION

PUBLISHED BY

AMERACE-ESNA CORPORATION

CHEMICAL SPECIALTIES DIVISION

Printed in the U.S.A.

FOREWORD

TO OUR GOOD FRIENDS, CUSTOMERS, AND SUPPLIERS: With the publication of the second edition of the Penetone Handbook, may we once again take the opportunity to express our appreciation for your patronage and cooperation over the last three decades, through which we have achieved a leadership position in the specialty chemical field.

The Chemical Specialties Division of Amerace-Esna Corporation combines the scientific research, technical developments, and manufacturing and marketing experience of five industry leaders in the specialty chemical industry — five companies with a background of more than 175 years in the cleaning, metal finishing, laundry, and maintenance fields.

It is interesting to note that the origins of the American Specialty Chemical Industry can be linked directly to the foundations of the Penetone, Patek, Yosemite, Wilco, and Allegheny companies. In 1875, when lye soap was the only product available to the laundry trade, the Patek Company successfully pioneered in the development of a complete line of commercial laundry products including sours, bleaches, and easy-to-use starches. Over three decades ago, the Penetone Company developed the first liquid synthetic detergent as a replacement for hard-to-handle soaps and highly alkaline products then in use in industrial cleaning. Through the years, these companies have maintained their reputation for product innovation and improvement through continual research and product development.

Today, C.S.D.'s diversified line of products and services are available in virtually every part of the globe. On the domestic scene, manufacturing facilities in the United States and Canada, plus warehousing and distribution points in major industrial centers, assure ample stocks and prompt deliveries. In Europe, the Far East, and Latin America, identical products are manufactured in strict accordance with domestic formulations by a network of licensees.

We are all aware that the need for new products and new processes to satisfy industries' ever-increasing demands is a never-ending challenge. Now, as in the past, our research efforts yield new and improved products for industry. At the hub of our research activities is a team of graduate chemists and technicians who conduct basic and applied research on new and existing product applications.

Through years of product innovation and improvement, we have developed a reputation for pioneering the development of safer products for industry. Our search continues for substitutes to replace caustic, toxic, and hazardous industrial finishing and maintenance ingredients.

Presently, more than 300 industrial and related products are manufactured in plants located in Los Angeles, California; Tenafly, New Jersey; and Scarborough, Ontario, Canada. In addition, a modern liquid and powdered silicate facility operates in Butler, New Jersey. Rigid production standards govern every step of the manufacturing process assuring continuous product performance. All feed stocks are checked against established specifications prior to acceptance. Additionally, production control chemists supervise ingredient blending to insure that the factors of time, temperature, and agitation are identical in every production run.

For customer convenience, all 300 of C.S.D.'s industrial, institutional, metal finishing, and laundry products are introduced and demonstrated by a network of field Sales Representatives located in principal cities in the United States and Canada. They are available at all times to help you determine the most effective material for a particular application, to show you the proper in-use procedure, pass on new product information, and gather data to help solve your special problems.

Our Technical Services Laboratory stands ready to develop workable economic solutions for any customer problem. All customer problems are analyzed, a solution developed, trial tested, and then presented to the customer with on-site demonstration by a field service technician.

Many products originally developed to solve a specific customer problem are widely used in industry today. Perhaps the best known is Navee 42®, a product developed at the government's request, for removing carbonized oil deposits and residue from damaged ships at Pearl Harbor.

We hope the preceding sketch helps you to better understand the organization, workings, and services of the Chemical Specialties Division of Amerace-Esna Corporation. If you have any questions, problems, or comments about the Division and products it makes, we shall be happy to be of assistance in any way we can.

Since this handbook was first published, we have received a number of requests for additional information. We have included many of these requests in the following pages. We sincerely hope that this edition of the Penetone Handbook continues to serve your needs, as well as the Chemical Specialties Division itself.

Sincerely,

H. I. Etelman
General Manager

ACKNOWLEDGMENTS

We wish to thank the firms listed below for their kind permission to reproduce or adapt for use in this Handbook a number of tables and articles that have appeared in various publications of theirs:

North America Companies (p. 1)
Association of Casualty and Surety Companies (pp. 2, 3)
General Electric Company (p. 19)
American Medical Association (pp. 21, 29)
American Red Cross (p. 26)
National Safety Council (pp. 34, 35)
Texaco, Inc. (pp. 35, 46, 52, 55, 60, 61, 64, 65)
Fisher Scientific Co. (pp. 42-43)
Allied Chemical Corp. (pp. 44, 97)
New Departure Division of General Motors (pp. 45, 48, 90, 92, 94)
Industrial Research Service (pp. 50-51)
Platecoil Division of Tranter Manufacturing, Inc. (pp. 53, 70, 76, 78, 147, 150)
Bowser Technical Refrigeration (p. 59)
Posey Iron Works (pp. 60, 96, 105, 106, 135, 143)
Monsanto Chemical Company (pp. 73, 74)
National Wood Tank Institute (p. 102)
Lukens Steel Company (p. 104)
Universal Atlas Cement (pp. 132, 133, 134)
American Iron and Steel Institute (pp. 166, 167)
Institute of Radio Engineers (p. 171)
W. B. Conkey Company (p. 179)
Bankers Trust Company (p. 186)

We also acknowledge the use of materials from four books published by Prentice-Hall, Inc.: *Builder's Vest Pocket Reference Book* compiled by William J. Hornung; *Electrician's Vest Pocket Reference Book* by Henry B. Hansteen; *Mechanic's Vest Pocket Reference Book* by John H. Wolfe and Everett R. Phelps; and *Pipefitter's and Plumber's Vest Pocket Reference Book* compiled by George K. Bachmann.

MAJOR PRODUCT GROUPS OF
THE CHEMICAL SPECIALTIES DIVISION

INDUSTRIAL PRODUCTS
Liquid Detergents
Powdered Cleaners
Safety Solvents
Emulsion Cleaners
Degreasers
Acid Cleaners
Corrosion Inhibitors
Carbon Removers
Metal Finishing Compounds
Paint Strippers
Floor Finishes
Sealers
Waxes

LAUNDRY PRODUCTS
Liquid & Powdered Wash Room Formulations
Bleaches
Sours
Stain Removers
Fabric Softeners
Linen Handling Equipment
Finishing Products

LIQUID ALKALINE CLEANERS

SENIOR

Heavy-duty formulation of Penetone. Nontoxic, nonflammable. Used for general maintenance cleaning or for the degreasing of machinery and parts. Safe for use on all metals including aluminum. Excellent as a coolant.

STEAM KLEEN

Noncaustic, water-soluble cleaning concentrate developed especially for steam cleaning — also used for dip tank degreasing. Nonflammable, nontoxic. Helps prevent cloggage of steam cleaning equipment.

FORMULA 611

Heavy-duty formulation of Steam Kleen for extra-hardened deposits of soil requiring powerful cleaning action. Nontoxic, nonflammable. Also used for heavy-duty dip tank degreasing.

PC-6

A disinfectant cleaner providing in a single product the most effective germ-killing properties with all-purpose cleaning power — safe for all surfaces. Leaves no lingering disinfectant smell.

POWER CLEANER

Low foaming, liquid cleaner, designed especially for use in power scrubbers. Safe on common floor surfaces. Excellent wax and floor dressing stripper, when used at higher concentrations. Excellent steam cleaner.

CQ-832

Liquid car wash designed for autolaundries. Floats off soil and dirt, no streaking after the water rinse. Will not dissolve wax or automobile polish, nor will it harm the finest finish. CQ-832 will not harm any surface not harmed by water. Exceptionally high and stable suds.

SHAMP

Odorless, nonflammable, nontoxic liquid shampoo for rugs and upholstery. Ideal for public carriers. Produces dry stable suds. Safe — mild to personnel and surfaces.

SUPAR

A concentrated detergent with solvent additives. Used for extra heavy-duty general maintenance cleaning. Safe on aluminum and magnesium, vinyl, asphalt, paint and rubber surfaces.

FORMULA Y 55

Concentrated mildly alkaline general purpose cleaner, containing penetrating and emulsifying agents combined in a single-phase liquid. It is nontoxic, nonflammable and has a slight odor.

BLAND

A low foam, liquid steam cleaning compound which combines high cleaning ability with highest safety standards. Sequestrant content guarantees performance in hardest water.

POWDERED ALKALINE CLEANERS

PENESOLVE #1 BLUE

Gentle, yet powerful all-purpose cleaner. For general maintenance, metal cleaning and light steam cleaning. Safe for all metals, including aluminum. For cleaning in a soak or electrolytic tank. Moderate sudsing.

PENESOLVE 5

Moderately alkaline, universal, powdered degreaser. Safe on all metals. Powerful emulsifying, penetrating, wetting, and grease dissolving properties. Excellent steam cleaning detergent. Noncaustic, no fumes. Moderate sudsing.

PENESOLVE L-707

A white dustless powder, used as a hot tank cleaner for all types of sheet aluminum. It removes oils, protective coatings, including manufacturers stamping inks.

PENESOLVE 814

Powdered alkaline rust and scale stripper. Penesolve 814 can be used in any container made of ordinary iron or steel. Cannot cause hydrogen embrittlement. Also cleans sludge, paint, carbon, and scale at the same time as it removes rust and scale.

PENESOLVE 902

Rapid acting paint stripper and heavy-duty degreaser. Will not corrode or etch iron or steel. Used in hot soak tank. Processed to reduce dusting when handled in its powdered form. Moderate sudsing.

PENESOLVE Y-1162

Hot tank motor block degreaser and carbon remover. In addition, it has rust removal properties and is an excellent copper and brass radiator cleaner.

TUFF

A nonflammable, yellow, dustless, high strength, low odor, granular compound for cleaning greasy soiled concrete flooring and ramps.

PENESOLVE E-Z

Medium duty powdered, dustless steam cleaning compound containing no harsh caustic. Safe on all metals, plastic, rubber, and painted surfaces.

SAFETY SOLVENTS

INHIBISOL®

Safety solvent replacement for carbon tetrachloride. Formulated from Penolene 643 with inhibitor added for absolute safety on aluminum. Nonflammable. Same safety, efficiency, and drying time as Penolene 643. Also available in 12 oz. aerosol spray can.

FORMULA 602

Safety solvent replacement for poisonous carbon tetrachloride. Dries twice as fast as mineral spirits. Flashpoint — 135°F. Twenty-four times safer than carbon tet. Good solvent powder.

EXOLVE

Safety solvent replacement for carbon tetrachloride. Dries four times faster than mineral spirits. High flashpoint — 230°F., no fire point. Twelve times safer than carbon tet.

SOLUTE

A blend of special solvents designed to replace highly toxic carbon tetrachloride and other extremely hazardous chlorinated solvents. Its high flashpoint also makes Solute a safer replacement for gasoline and mineral spirits.

TPC SOLVENT

Odorless solvent degreaser for room temperature cleaning. Use for degreasing in large dip tanks or production line and bench cleaning of parts. High flashpoint — 130°F. Safe on all metals. Also available as Type 724 with higher flashpoint of 185°F.

724 SOLVENT

Same as TPC Solvent except higher flashpoint, very slight odor and somewhat slower drying. Flash is 155°F. closed cup and 175°F. open cup.

PENOLENE 643

Safest of all safety solvent replacements for carbon tetrachloride. Dries as rapidly as carbon tetrachloride. Nonflammable, 120 times safer than carbon tet.

FORMULA 676

A free flowing, light bodied solvent, neutral in composition, nonflammable, and noncorrosive. Used for dissolving greases, oils, and stripping rubber, latex, paints and plastics.

CARBON REMOVERS

FORMULA 423

Solvent stripper with water seal for cold tank degreasing of parts and equipment. Removes paint, tars, gums, resins, carbon, rubber, and grease. Nonflammable — safe on metals including aluminum.

DUNKIT

Concentrated cold tank stripper. You add protective water seal before using. Strips paints, carbon, synthetic rubber, plastic, and almost all organic materials. Nonflammable, safe on all metals including aluminum.

AQUA SEAL

Solvent carbon remover. Nonflammable, nonexplosive, noncorrosive. Strips tar, gum, rubber, and paint. Cuts rust. Liquid seal makes it economical and safer to use.

FORMULA Y CR #1

Two phase cold tank cleaner for fast removal of carbon, oil, grease, dirt, sludge, and lead deposits from automotive engine parts. It contains no phenols or cresols.

PEN-STRIP CR

A liquid diphase stripper formulated with emulsifying agents and corrosion inhibitors. Safe on most metals. Particularly effective on a variety of vinyls, acrylics, modified epoxies, and alkyds. Apply by hot tank immersion with 5% water seal. Mild steel equipment is suitable.

BRAWN

Heavy duty-paint and carbon stripper. Viscous, semi-jell "digests" or dissolves paint, causing it to become soluble in water, and leaves no skins. Safe for use on all ferrous metals. Use on aluminum only if over-all etch is desired. No fume hazard, safe for use in confined areas.

METAL FINISHING

AE 1009

Highly alkaline powdered stripper formulated to remove chemically resistant finishes. Generally recommended with special additive Pen-Strip A. Removes paint film left by many paint strippers. Excellent rinsing. Recommended for ferrous metals, magnesium, and copper alloys.

NUTRAL 1010

A specially blended acidic material, neutralizes any etchant remaining on surfaces. Quickly removes characteristic gray smut that develops on the aluminum during the etching operation and restores the aluminum to its original luster.

PENESOLVE 997

A heavy–duty spray washing material which combines selected wetting agents with the right degree of alkalinity. Designed for use on ferrous metals.

PENESOLVE 1022

A balanced spray washing compound, designed for aluminum surfaces. Low foaming, the material quickly emulsifies soils.

PAINT-LOC 995

A premium grade iron phosphatizer expressly developed for application by power spray washer. Ideal for low temperature phosphating where soil conditions permit.

PENESOLVE 996

An iron phosphatizer material for application by immersion. Improved cleaning ability melts away tenacious soils without the aid of mechanical agitation.

PENESOLVE 1056

A new concept in water wash paint spray booth treatments. Designed to float or digest the newest finishes. Prevents paint from sticking to booth walls.

SOLVENT EMULSION PRODUCTS

NAVEE 42®

Powerful, self-emulsifying, solvent degreaser with an extra margin of safety. For tough and stubborn grease and oil removal. Nonexplosive. Coast Guard Safety Certificated.

OLD SALT

Solvent emulsion degreaser, mild and safe on almost every type of surface, and will not irritate the skin. Flashpoint is above 160°F. No strong odor, no toxic solvents, and is completely free rinsing.

FORMULA 861

Odorless, solvent emulsion degreaser. Nonacidic, nonalkaline. Quickly dissolves and emulsifies grease, oil, and tar-like substances which can be easily rinsed away with water. Used in wipe, dip, or spray applications for tank cleaning, removal of buffing rouge, and as a cleaner prior to heat treating.

BUXITE

Solvent emulsion degreaser. Removes oil, grease, buffing and polishing compounds from machines and parts. For cold soak tank or parts washer. High flashpoint — no toxic fumes.

FORMULA 925

Solvent emulsion degreasing concentrate. Diluted with water or solvent for wipe, dip, or spray cleaning of carbon, oil, and grease from machinery and equipment, especially automotive. High flashpoint.

NAVEE 427

Similar to Navee 42 but especially formulated for cleaning carbon exhaust stains from airplane hulls and cowlings. Nonexplosive. Safe for use on aluminum and magnesium.

PAINT STRIPPERS

PEN-STRIP G

A low odor, easy to apply viscous paint stripper. Lifts paints from metal. Meets performance requirements of MIL-R-25134 and MIL-R-8633A.

PEN-STRIP PT

Safe on all metal surfaces, this fast acting viscous paint stripper meets the performance requirements of MIL-R-25134 and MIL-R-8633A. Heavy-duty stripper for most epoxies.

PEN-STRIP NPX

Nonphenolic, nonchromated, heavy-duty stripper recommended for operations where chromates or phenols cannot be used. Composed of a unique blend of solvent acid ingredients, Pen-Strip NPX is very effective in removing baked-on acrylics, epoxies, vinyls, & polyurethane.

PEN-STRIP WX

A room temperature tank immersion stripper designed for removing oven cured epoxies and other highly resistant finishes. A water seal of 5% by volume may be added. Extra long tank life. Can be used in mild steel tanks.

PEN-STRIP TX

Viscous version of Pen-Strip X. Will handle the toughest upright stripping jobs. Leaves metal surfaces film free and ready for repainting.

RIPPLE

Rapid paint stripper for metal or wood. Viscous liquid, mild odor. Safe on aluminum. Contains no acids, does not damage skin. Applied by brush or spray. Blisters or "ripples" paint. Easily water-rinsed, leaves film-free surface.

STRYPTONE

Viscous, clinging stripper for removing carbon, paint, and almost all organic materials from upright surfaces or parts which cannot be immersed in a tank. Nonflammable, safe on aluminum and all metals.

PEN-STRIP LC

A highly potent solvent caustic paint stripper for removing all types of paint from steel, magnesium, and copper alloys. Nonphenolic Pen-Strip LC presents no disposal problems. Used concentrated at temperatures of 200-230°F.

PEN-STRIP A

Liquid stripper additive for use with AE 1009, Penesolve 814, and Penesolve 902. Recommended as an additive for removing exceptionally tough epoxy, urethane, vinyl, and acrylic paints. Normally used at 2 to 3% by volume of stripping bath.

PEN-STRIP Y 44

General purpose, water rinsible nonflammable paint remover for all woods and metals.

PEN-STRIP Y 1421

An evaporation retarded, water rinsible liquid for the removal of photo resistant paints and Warno paint from etched circuit boards.

PEN-STRIP 1242

Cresylic acid type cold tank paint stripper developed to remove tough epoxy, Day Glo, and many vinyl paints from all metals including magnesium.

ACID CLEANERS

FORMULA 990

An inhibited liquid rust and scale remover. Possesses excellent lime solubilizing characteristics. Removes rust and scale without attacking sound base metal.

FORMULA 991

Powdered inhibited acid. Mixed with water and heated to remove corrosion and hard water scale. Easy to handle.

LUMABRITE

Cleans and brightens aluminum truck bodies, and aircraft. Removes grease, oil, road grime, exhaust stains, and leaves surface bright and protected. Nontoxic, nonflammable. Economical and safer to use.

FORMULA Y 34

Specially balanced oxide and corrosion dissolvent used for brightening brass and copper alloys.

GALVANPRIME

A dual-purpose, double-action, prepaint conditioner and etchant for all galvanized iron surfaces, as well as a phosphatizer for ferrous metals.

SILVER BRIGHT

Mildly acidic brightener for kitchenware, copper, silver, and gold. Also used as a tarnish and light corrosion remover before soldering or metal plating operations.

FERROTONE

Rust and scale remover. Contains no hydrochloric acid, so brief skin exposure is not injurious. No toxic fumes. Removes rust stains from painted surfaces without harming paint.

RUST PREVENTIVES

TYPE C

Protects metals against rust and corrosion in hot or cold climates, damp or corrosive atmospheres. Equally effective in or outdoors, for at least one year. Dry, waxy-brown film resists moisture and weather.

TYPE D

Provides up to 6 months metal protection against rust and corrosion during indoor storage. Deposit a dry, invisible, thin protective film on all metals. Resists the attack of acid fumes.

TYPE R

Specially treated safety solvent. Degreases metals and deposits an invisible coating which prevents rust and corrosion. Provides 2 months indoor storage protection. Used for all metals and electrical equipment.

TYPE S

Diluted with water, Type S is used as a rinse after degreasing. Deposits a thin, invisible film on metals. Protects against rust and corrosion up to 2 months during indoor storage. Also used in water-soluble grinding and cutting fluids, and to protect circulatory cooling systems where mild foam is not objectional.

SPECIAL PRODUCTS

SLIX

Oil slick disperser for eliminating fire and slip hazard from oil or gasoline spills. Ideal for spills on water or roadways. Nonflammable, nontoxic, odorless. Slix treated oil or solvents will not burn and are easily water-hosed away. Absolutely safe on all surfaces including asphalt.

FORMULA Y 169 CONCENTRATE

A highly polar type compound which when diluted with solvent can be used as either a rust preventive, film-forming compound, or as a water displacement compound.

FORMULA Y 1547

A photo resist stripper that is designed to remove any photo resist in 35 seconds without damaging the printed circuit board medium.

SPILL-AWAY

A gel type oil spill remover which is non toxic to marine life. Its unique gelling action allows oil spill to be easily removed from salt and fresh water. Renders petroleum products nonflammable on contact.

FORMULA 867

Automatic tank and marine wash. Can pull grease and oil deposits from behind rust and corrosion. Stable in hard, soft, salt or acid water. Contains no solvents; is nontoxic, odorless, and nonflammable.

FLOOR SEALS & FINISHES

DURAGLO 58

A durable, lasting, brilliant finish that outwears ordinary waxes and synthetic finishes. Contains famous anti-slip ingredient, Ludox. Scuff and water resistant. Contains 100% carnauba wax.

TREDFAST 10

Extra heavy duty polymer floor wax gives highest possible gloss without buffing. Wears like a coat of iron. Formulated with acrylic and vinyl plastic base. May be rebuffed again and again at signs of wear. Reduces need for frequent waxing.

TREDFAST 66

A new, high gloss floor wax, which dries to a durable slip-resistant finish on all types of flooring. Formulated with anti-slip properties. Tredfast 66 provides surefooted traction as well as a durable, long lasting scuff resistant finish.

PUFF

A newly-developed, clear, polyurethane floor finish, Puff is a one-step treatment to floor perfection. Applied by roller, brush, or mop, floors can be completely coated with Puff in less time than it takes to apply a conventional sealer or varnish.

TERAZOTONE

Transparent seal and preservative for terrazzo floors. Leaves crystal clear, satin lustre protective coating.

NEWVAR

Penetrating floor seal. Especially suitable for wood. Seals and finishes in one operation. Toughens wood fibers with a hard coating which absorbs wear.

VARNOLITE

Solvent, synthetic polymer-base seal and finish coating for concrete, masonry, metal. Tough, durable finish. Resists acids, alkalines, and oils. Prevents dusting. Dries in 2 hours.

INDUSTRIAL SILICATES

BRITESIL

A complete line of liquid sodium silicates with properties that vary with the ratio of silica to sodium oxide.

BRITESORB

A finely divided precipitated magnesium silicate with a high absorbency and high surface to volume ratio.

GLOSSARY OF LAUNDRY PRODUCTS

VITEX

Exclusive line of nylon press covers and pads manufactured by C.S.D.

PATEX PRESS PADS

Exclusive line of metal press pads specifically designed for use with the VITEX product line.

SPEEDLITE "20 PLUS" BLEACH

Powdered organic laundry bleach containing minimum 20% available chlorine and fortified with phosphates to regenerate soap and aid rinsing.

SPEEDLITE SOUR-BLU

Laundry sour with high available neutralizing power. Contains fluorescent brighteners and laundry bluing.

SPEEDLITE FABRIC SOFTENER

Cationic quaternary ammonium fabric softener and bacteriostatic agent. Imparts soft feel and reduces static electricity.

SPEEDLITE SOFT-I-SAN

Combination powdered cationic fabric softener and sanitizer formulated to make linens soft and bacteriostatic.

SPEEDLITE HI-LITE

A unique chelating agent which increases the detergency of wash formulations.

SPEEDLITE BF-811

Liquid fabric softener and sanitizer. Powerful cationic action leaves wash loads bacteriostatic.

GLASTRUX

A complete line of materials handling tanks, trucks, boxes and baskets. Fabricated of heavy duty fiberglass reinforced resin. Available in a wide variety of sizes and colors.

CONTENTS

PART ONE — INDUSTRIAL SAFETY AND FIRST AID

PART TWO — MATHEMATICAL TABLES AND CONVERSION FACTORS

CONTENTS

PART THREE — PHYSICAL PROPERTIES OF MATTER

PART FOUR — METAL WORKING AND MECHANICAL DATA

CONTENTS

Part Four—Metal Working and Mechanical Data (Continued)

PART FIVE — BUILDING AND CONSTRUCTION

CONTENTS

CONTENTS

PART EIGHT — BUSINESS METHODS

INDUSTRIAL SAFETY AND FIRST AID

EXIT SAFETY

EXIT AVAILABLE IN REASONABLE TRAVEL DISTANCE

High fire hazard	75 feet
Average hazard	100 feet
Sprinklered building	150 feet

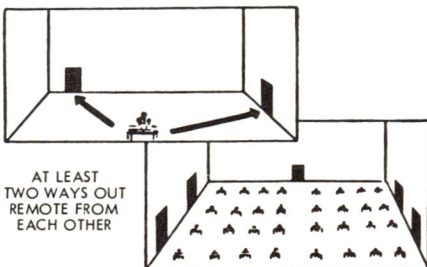

AT LEAST
TWO WAYS OUT
REMOTE FROM
EACH OTHER

Additional exits according to number
of persons and relative fire danger

THIS WAY OUT → EXIT

TO BASEMENT NOT AN EXIT

EXIT TO STREET

**EXIT PATHS MARKED,
UNOBSTRUCTED,
WELL LIGHTED**

**FIRE EXIT DRILLS WELL PLANNED,
FREQUENTLY PRACTICED**

PLAN VIEWS OF FAVORED TYPES OF EMERGENCY EXITS

Stair enclosure, usually of masonry, prevents fire on any floor trapping persons above. Smokeproof tower is better as opening to air at each floor largely prevents chance of smoke in stairway. Horizontal exit provides a quick refuge, lessens need of hasty flight down stairs. All doors shown are fire retardant doors.

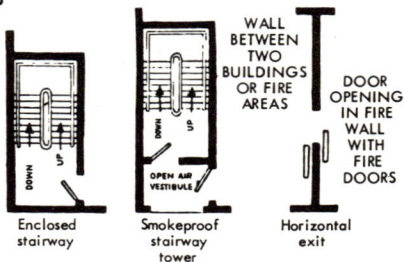

WALL
BETWEEN
TWO
BUILDINGS
OR FIRE
AREAS

DOOR
OPENING
IN FIRE
WALL
WITH
FIRE
DOORS

DOWN

UP

OPEN AIR
VESTIBULE

Enclosed
stairway

Smokeproof
stairway
tower

Horizontal
exit

Fire may make fire escapes useless as this picture, drawn from photograph of actual fire, shows.

FIRE ESCAPES ARE MAKESHIFTS, OFTEN DANGEROUS

There's little safety where occupants have to clamber over window-sills to flimsy, steep, and weather-swept outside fire escapes. Substantial outside stairs and approved slide escapes may be used to provide exits lacking on existing buildings.

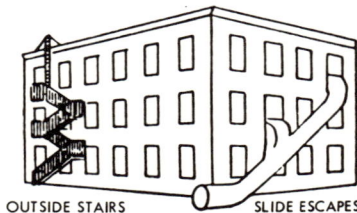

OUTSIDE STAIRS

SLIDE ESCAPES

Association of Casualty and Surety Companies

2

Many forms of personal protective equipment are indicated here. Obviously, all the protection mentioned is neither necessary nor desirable in many instances.

Thorough knowledge of the hazards involved in each operation and the merits of the equipment offered should be applied by a responsible individual when contemplating the adoption of one or more of the items.

PERSONAL PROTECTIVE EQUIPMENT

EQUIPMENT

HEAD PROTECTION
- HARD HATS
- ASBESTOS HOODS
- FIBRE HOODS
- LEATHER HOODS
- RUBBER HOODS

EYE PROTECTION
- CLEAR GLASS GOGGLES
- COLORED GLASS GOGGLES
- GAS-ACID TIGHT GOGGLES

RESPIRATORY PROTECTION
- CHEM. CARTR. RESPIRATOR
- MECH. FILTER RESPIRATOR
- GAS MASK-HOSE MASK

COATS, CAPES, APRONS
- ASBESTOS
- CHROME LEATHER
- FIREPROOFED DUCK
- RUBBER
- REINFORCED CANVAS
- WIRE MESH APRONS

LEG PROTECTION
- ASBESTOS
- CHROME LEATHER
- FIRE-PROOFED DUCK
- GLASS-FIBRE CLOTH
- FIBRE METAL ALLOYS
- SHIN GUARDS

ARM PROTECTION
- ASBESTOS
- CHROME LEATHER
- FIRE PROOFED DUCK
- GLASS FIBRE CLOTH
- FIBRE METAL ALLOYS
- RUBBER SLEEVES

HAND PROTECTION
- ASBESTOS GLOVES
- CHROME LEATHER GLOVES-PADS
- RUBBER GLOVES
- RUBBERIZED COTTON GLOVES
- METAL-MESH FINGER GUARDS
- STEEL FINGER GUARDS

FOOT PROTECTION
- REINFORCED TOE SHOES
- SEWN SOLE SHOES
- WOODEN SOLE SHOES
- CHROME LEATHER SHOES
- RUBBER BOOTS OR SHOES
- RUBBER INSULATED SHOES
- CONGRESS TYPE SHOES
- STEEL TOE GUARDS
- PROTECTIVE CREAMS

HAZARD
- SPARKS
- HOT SOLIDS
- HOT LIQUIDS
- RADIANT HEAT
- DUST
- FUMES-GASES
- SMOKE
- ELECTRICITY
- MOISTURE
- ACIDS, CAUSTICS, ETC.
- FALLING OBJECTS
- FLYING CHIPS, ETC.
- OTHER FLYING OBJECTS
- ROUGH OBJECTS
- ELECTRIC SHOCK
- WELDING ARC
- CUTS
- BLOWS
- PUNCTURES
- BLAST CLEANING
- DERMATITIS

SPECIAL NOTES: Women's Hazard: All women working around machinery should wear a cap (enclosing all hair), slacks and breast guards. Explosive Gases & Vapors: The equipment used should be non-static producing and free from spark-producing fittings. Oxygen or supplied air breathing apparatus should be worn when the atmosphere has insufficient oxygen to sustain life. Life belts and life lines should be worn where there is a possibility of falling from high places or into pits, etc. Kapok vests should be worn where there is a possibility of falling from structures or boats into water.

3

RAMPS, STAIRS & LADDERS: PREFERRED ANGLES

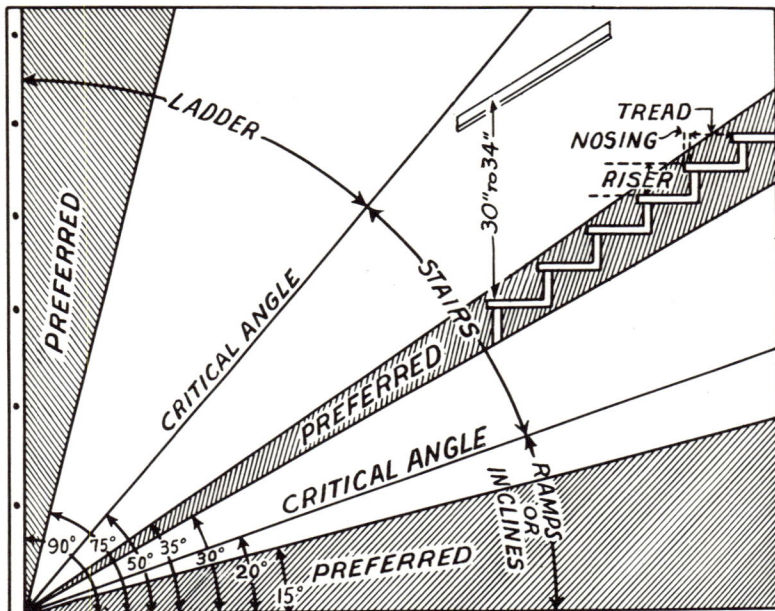

Courtesy National Safety Council.

4

CHARACTERISTICS OF COMMON FIRE EXTINGUISHERS

TYPE	CAPACITY	SUITABLE FOR: Class A Fires (Wood, Paper, Textiles, Rubbish, etc.)	SUITABLE FOR: Class B Fires (Oil, Gasoline, Grease, Paint, etc.)	SUITABLE FOR: Class C Fires (Electrical Equipment)	UNIT CLASSIFICATION	APPROXIMATE HORIZONTAL RANGE OF STREAM	APPROXIMATE TIME OF DISCHARGE	APPROXIMATE WEIGHT WHEN FULLY CHARGED	YEARLY INSPECTION	SUBJECT TO FREEZING	USUAL METHOD OF OPERATION	METHOD BY WHICH CONTENTS ARE DISCHARGED	CONTENTS OF EXTINGUISHER
SODA-ACID	1¼-1½ Gal.	YES	NO	NO	A-2	30-40 Ft.	35 Seconds	20-25 Lbs.	Discharge and Refill	YES	Invert	Carbon dioxide gas formed by chemical reaction	Sodium Bicarbonate Solution and Sulfuric Acid
FOAM	1¼-1½ Gal. / 2½-5 Gal.	YES	YES	NO	A-2, B-2 / A-1, B-1	30-40 Ft.	35-40 Sec. / 60 Seconds	20-25 Lbs. / 35-70 Lbs.	Discharge and Refill	YES	Invert	Carbon dioxide gas formed by chemical reaction	Solutions of Sodium Bicarbonate, Aluminum Sulfate and Foam Stabilizer
CARBON DIOXIDE	2-2½ Lbs. / 4- Lbs. / 7½-15 Lbs. / 15-25 Lbs.	NO (But may be effective on small fires)	YES	YES	B-4, C-4 / B-2, C-2 / B-2, C-1 / B-1, C-1	3 Ft. / 4 Ft. / 6-8 Ft.	12-15 Sec. / 15-20 Sec. / 20-45 Sec. / 35-85 Sec.	9-12 Lbs. / 15-20 Lbs. / 20-50 Lbs. / 40-65 Lbs.	Weigh Extinguisher	NO	Turn hand wheel, pull trigger or squeeze handle	Release of gas which is under pressure	Carbon Dioxide
DRY CHEMICAL	2-6½ lbs. / 7½-10 lbs. / 15-25 lbs.	NO (But may be effective on small fires)	YES	YES	B-2, C-2 / B-2, C-1 / B-1, C-1	8-12 Ft. / 10-14 Ft. / 10-14 Ft.	8-15 Sec. / 13-20 Sec. / 13-50 Sec.	7-15 Lbs. / 20-25 Lbs. / 30-50 Lbs.	Weigh Gas Cartridge, Check Dry Chemical	NO	Pull pin and open valve or press lever. Then squeeze nozzle handle	Pressure of stored Carbon Dioxide Gas	Specially Treated Sodium Bicarbonate and Cartridge of Carbon Dioxide
VAPORIZING LIQUID (Pump Type)	1-2½ Qt. / 1-3½ Gal.	NO (But may be effective on small fires)	YES	YES	B-2, C-2 / B-2, C-1	20-30 Ft. (Dependent on Operator)	45-150 Sec. / 60-100 Sec. (Dep. on Opr.)	7-21 Lbs. / 25-75 Lbs.	Discharge Partly	NO	Turn Handle and pump	Pumping	Specially Treated Carbon Tetrachloride
VAPORIZING LIQUID (Stored Pressure Type)	2 Qt. / 1 Gal. / 3 Gal.	NO (But may be effective on small fires)	YES	YES	B-2, C-2 / B-2, C-1 / B-2, C-1	20-30 Ft.	30 Sec. / 50-75 Sec. / 150-190 Sec.	16 lbs. / 25-35 Lbs. / 75 Lbs.	Weigh Gas Cartridge	NO	Open Valve	Pressure of stored Air or Carbon Dioxide Gas	Specially Treated Carbon Tetrachloride
LOADED STREAM	1 Gal. / 2½ Gal.	YES	YES	NO	A-2, B-4 / A-1, B-2	30-40 Ft.	35 Sec. / 55-60 Sec.	20-25 Lbs. / 40 lbs.	Weigh Gas Cartridge	YES (Unless Anti-freeze solution is used)	Invert and bump on floor	Pressure of Stored Carbon Dioxide Gas	Special Solution of Alkali Metal Salts
WATER (Stored Pressure Type)	2½ Gal.	YES	NO	NO	A-1	30-40 Ft.	50-60 Sec.	35-40 Lbs.	Weigh Gas Cartridge	YES	Invert and bump on floor	Pressure of Stored Carbon Dioxide Gas	Water
ANTI-FREEZE (Stored Pressure Type)	2½ Gal.	YES	NO	NO	A-1	30-40 Ft.	50-60 Sec.	40 lbs.	Weigh Gas Cartridge	NO	Invert and bump on floor	Pressure of Stored Carbon Dioxide Gas	Water Solution of Calcium Chloride
WATER (Pump Tank)	2½-5 Gal.	YES	NO	NO	A-1	30-40 Ft. (Dependent on Operator)	60-120 Sec. (Dependent on Operator)	40-65 Lbs.	Discharge and Refill	YES (Unless Anti-freeze solution is used)	Pumping	Pumping	Water (with Calcium Chloride if anti-freeze type)
WATER PAILS	10 Qt. / 12 Qt.	YES	NO	NO	A-6 / A-5	Dependent on Operator	Dependent on Operator	23 Lbs. / 27 Lbs.	Empty Refill	YES (Unless Anti-freeze solution is used)	Throw	Throwing	Water (with Calcium Chloride if anti-freeze type)

Courtesy North America Companies

5

HOW SAFE ARE THE "SAFETY SOLVENTS"*

THERE MUST BE more than a thousand different solvent cleaners which identify themselves as safety solvents. It would be helpful if their names would provide some hint as to their composition. Then, at least, you would be in a fair position to set up suitable safety practices for using them. But no, you're faced with names like Solvo-Kleen, Electro-Solv, Electri-Kleen, Electrolene, Carbo-Solv, Carbon Met, Saf-tee-Solv, Formula 602, and so on.

Probably many of us have often longed for the good old days when, if a solvent cleaner were needed, we would simply drag out either carbon tetrachloride or gasoline and that would be the end of it . . . sometimes the end of us too! At least in those days the safety man (if there was one) knew what chemical he was dealing with. Of course, you sometimes find that one of these so-called modern "safety solvents" is nothing more than disguised carbon tetrachloride. A friend of mine, who is a plant manager, often teases safety solvent salesman by asking—"What kind of carbon tetrachloride are you selling today?"

Now don't get me wrong. I have nothing against carbon tetrachloride, because it's a darn good solvent and has many important uses. As a matter of fact, you can often feel quite secure when using it because nowadays people are so well aware of its hazards that proper precautions are usually taken in handling it.

An old timer once asked, "What have you chemists done to carbon tetrachloride? How come it's so much more toxic now than it used to be in the old days?" The people in safety can take that as a tribute to their good work in insisting on suitable safety practices with toxic materials. The industrial hygienists are to be commended for gradually bringing the M.A.C. limits of these harzardous products down to a safe working level.

It is almost certain that someone in every industrial organization is using a safety solvent. Perhaps the electrical department is spraying or dipping electrical instruments, motors, switchboards, or generators, or doing general cleaning, maintenance and overhaul work on electrical equipment. Perhaps your office personnel are using a safety solvent to clean typewriters, business machines, or dictating equipment. If you do metal forming, drilling, grinding, lathe work, buffing or polishing, your plant may be removing the various lubricating fluids, cutting compounds, or light oils with a safety solvent.

---

*Based on an address presented at 28th All-Ohio Safety Congress April 22, 1958, by Melvin Z. Poliakoff of The Penetone Company.

6

"SAFETY SOLVENTS"

If you maintain a fleet of trucks or do any work on automotive equipment, chances are someone is wiping down a chassis or dipping parts into a solvent of some type. If a product is being assembled or otherwise put into some completed form ready for delivery, you are no doubt using some type of solvent cleaner for final cleaning. If your work involves precision instruments, such as ball bearings, gyros, and electronic devices, a safety solvent is probably used for removing the various oils, greases, and faintest possible traces of foreign matter.

If you are in the textile or dry cleaning business, a solvent of some type which falls in the category we are discussing is being used.

We could go on and on in this way and, I am certain, cover every type of industry. My point is simply that most of us are confronted with these solvents and so it will pay us to take a closer look at their various properties and hazards, in order to determine how best they can be used safely.

In choosing a safety solvent, you look for a product which will do the job required most efficiently, with minimum harm to equipment and personnel and at minimum cost. Production people must concern themselves with such questions as whether it will harm electrical insulation, plastics, varnishes, or other painted and enameled surfaces; whether it removes soils rapidly enough; whether it leaves a residue-free surface; whether the residue is conductive or non-conductive; whether the residue will react with oxygen; whether the solvent evaporates fast enough or perhaps too fast, and a host of other questions concerned with the efficiency of a solvent for a particular job. While extremely important, these questions fall outside the scope of our discussion of safety aspects here.

One thing we know for sure about safety solvents is that all of them are at least a little toxic, so let's examine this feature for a while.

What is toxicity? A good definition is simply the expression "too much."

When a solvent has been used over a long period of time, we get to know a lot about it because of the kind of experience we have had with it. For a fairly toxic material, for example, the Medical Archives may periodically report deaths, illnesses, skin problems, lung problems, etc. It is based on this kind of information and experience that the American Conference of Governmental Industrial Hygienists is able to establish what they call "A threshold limit"* for a chemical. This threshold limit

---

*See pp. 33-37 for Threshold Limit Values

7

is the maximum average atmospheric concentration, usually expressed as parts per million (ppm) of contaminant, to which workers may be exposed for an 8-hour working day without injury to health.

The threshold limit value is commonly referred to as Maximum Allowable Concentration, abbreviated M.A.C. You will recall a moment ago my comment about the old timer who claimed that modern science has caused carbon tet to become more toxic. Actually perhaps he was guided by the M.A.C. which was previously recorded at somewhere around 100 ppm for carbon tet and is currently listed as 25 ppm. The same thing has happened to benzene which, at one time, was up around 150 and now is listed as 35 ppm. Thus you see, the more familiar we become with these various chemicals, the more exact the industrial hygienists can be in setting a threshold limit.

One problem, however, about this M.A.C. value or threshold limit value, is that many of us are inclined to lean too heavily on the M.A.C. without taking into consideration other factors associated with a chemical's potential hazard. The M.A.C. tells us how much of the solvent we can safely breathe; in other words, this measurement is concerned with the toxicity of the material itself. It tells us nothing about the tendency of this chemical or safety solvent to contaminate the atmosphere and thus become a hazard.

Let me illustrate this —

Suppose we have a Chemical "A", which has an M.A.C. of 10 and a Chemical "B" which has an M.A.C. of 500. You notice immediately that it is possible to breathe in 500 ppm of Chemical B and still feel secure about it. As far as Chemical A is concerned, you would be darn careful with it and make sure that you didn't breathe in much of its vapor because even 10 parts per million parts of air will represent a hazard. Chemical A is therefore much more toxic.

Now let's assume that Chemical B is a fast evaporating or volatile solvent like gasoline, and that Chemical A is a waxy substance which will not evaporate unless it is heated to a very high temperature. Under normal conditions, at room temperature, Chemical A remains a wax and will not contaminate the air we breathe at all, while Chemical B evaporates most readily and in a confined area will easily reach its 500 ppm M.A.C. in a short time.

Under those conditions, the hazard associated with Chemical A is far lower than the hazard associated with Chemical B, even though the M.A.C. for Chemical B is far lower than for Chemical A.

"SAFETY SOLVENTS"

Don't you agree, then, that it is extremely important to consider carefully the conditions under which a product is used, so that its tendency to reach its M.A.C. under those conditions can be evaluated?

Certainly a fast evaporating solvent will quickly disappear into the atmosphere and contaminate the air we breathe. Vapor Pressure is the technical term which refers to tendency to evaporate. A high vapor pressure represents a rapid rate of evaporation, and a low vapor pressure characterizes a slight tendency to volatilize or evaporate.

You may say, then—"This is easy. Let's choose a safety solvent that has a high M.A.C. and a low vapor pressure." That would be fine, except for the fact that a low vapor pressure would mean that a solvent would not want to evaporate and might remain as an oily film on the surface being cleaned. The production department would throw you out if you made such a recommendation! Your production department will usually want to work with a safety solvent cleaner that will evaporate or dry fairly quickly. So your problem will be to make sure that for whatever solvent is chosen, the M.A.C. is not exceeded—and this can be done by providing suitable ventilation.

Howard Gadberry of the Midwest Research Institute published some excellent information on this subject in *National Safety News*, Dec. 1954. He explains a ventilation rate equation which enables you to calculate the amount of ventilation required to maintain a safe working atmosphere.

$$\frac{\text{cu. ft. per minute}}{\text{gallons per hour}} = \frac{53.7 \times \text{Spec. Gravity} \times 10^6}{\text{Mol. Wt.} \times \text{M.A.C.}}$$

In using this equation, one would have to determine by actual experience or experiment how many gallons of the safety solvent are evaporated per hour under the conditions of use. One easy way to determine this would be to take a measurement of the tank or drum of safety solvent before and after one hour's use and determine how much was lost. This could be considered evaporation.

We might run through a calculation of this type very quickly. Let's take carbon tetrachloride, for example.

Molecular weight is 153.84
Specific Gravity is 1.595
M.A.C. is 25

Substituting these in the equation, we obtain as an answer 22,300 cu. ft. per minute per gallon of carbon tetrachloride used.

"SAFETY SOLVENTS"

This means that if the consumption of carbon tet is one gallon per hour, you would have to install exhaust fans, fume hoods or other ventilating equipment capable of moving 22,300 cu. ft. of air per minute. That may seem like a lot of air movement where just one gallon of solvent is being consumed per hour; and that brings me to my next point.

Folks don't usually realize how little of a toxic liquid is needed to create a hazardous atmosphere, or to exceed its M.A.C. In Table I below, we have listed the quantity of solvent required to reach its M.A.C. in an unventilated room 10' x 10' x 10' or 1000 cubic feet.

Table I
Volume in ML Required to Reach
M.A.C. in a Room 10'x10'x10'

SOLVENT	VOLUME (ml)
Carbon Tetrachloride	2.8
Benzene	3.62
Methyl Alcohol (wood alcohol)	9.42
Trichloroethylene	20.8
Toluene	24.7
Methyl Ethyl Ketone	26.1
1, 1, 1, Trichloroethane	58.4
Ethyl Alcohol	67.8
Acetone	85.5

Recall for a moment that a teaspoon contains approximately 4 ml. and you will realize how easy it is to exceed the safe working limit for a solvent in confined areas. It takes less than a teaspoon of Carbon Tetrachloride or benzene to create a health hazard in your average-size home room or small office.

Let us reflect—when your people clean a typewriter or remove a spot with a dry cleaning fluid, how much solvent do you think they use? It's worth thinking about.

In considering health hazards, we should also know something about the effect of temporary over-exposure to solvent fumes. For example in the case of Carbon Tetrachloride, we know that continuous exposure to more than 25 ppm may be harmful, but acute poisoning can result when a person is exposed to 5000 parts per million for only 5 minutes. Longer exposures to this concentration, or even very short exposures to concentrations above 24,000 ppm, usually result in eventual death. This type of temporary over-exposure occurs often enough to warrant closer study. Recently, in a well-known coffee plant, a coffee extracting kettle was being heated during a cleaning process. Someone opened the wrong valve and trichloroethylene was allowed to flow into this hot empty kettle. The entire plant area was almost instantly blanketed with trichloroethylene fumes far in excess of its M.A.C. One death and several serious illnesses resulted!

Wherever solvents are used for cleaning purposes in a hand operation, dermatitis can become a problem. Many safety solvents are non-irritating but they are excellent degreasers. Continuous contact with the skin may cause dryness and possible cracking, which could easily lead to dermatitis especially where unsanitary practices exist. Where workers must clean by hand, plastic-coated gloves should be available so that prolonged contact with the skin is avoided. Frequent use of good lanolin-containing skin creams is recommended in order to counteract dryness. Skin protective creams while helpful are seldom adequate. We find that the frequency of such dermatitis outbreaks is usually greater when cold weather starts. The normal tendency of the skin to become chapped, together with the drying effect of the solvent, lead to this condition.

Now, what about fire hazards? For far too long, safety people have relied on flashpoint as the sole criteria for evaluating flammability. True, flashpoint is an indication of how readily vapors of a solvent will ignite, for the flashpoint, as you will recall, is the lowest temperature at which enough vapors are given off to form a flammable mixture of vapors and air immediately above the liquid surface. Flashpoint determinations, using the Cleveland open cup, Tag closed cup, Pensky-Marten closed cup methods, frequently vary by as much as 10 to 25°.

One trouble with the use of flashpoint as a guide to flammability is that many people assume that so long as the temperature in the working area is not above the flashpoint of the solvent, no fire hazard exists. For example, if you are using mineral spirits with a flashpoint of 105°F. in a room with an average temperature of 68 to 80°F., it is wrong to assume that a fire hazard doesn't exist. In every room or working area, there is a point where the flashpoint of 105° is probably exceeded. It may be on the surface of an electric light bulb, the presence of a spark from a motor, or static electricity. Solvent vapors can ignite at any of these points.

"SAFETY SOLVENTS

Many of the useful properties of solvents depend on rapid evaporation or fast drying or, as we have seen, on high vapor pressure. A solvent with a rapid rate of evaporation produces a high concentration of solvent vapors in the air surrounding the liquid. This vapor air mixture will ignite more easily than the liquid itself; thus the speed of evaporation, although very desirable for many purposes, often introduces increased fire hazard. This is true for almost all solvents except some of the halogenated solvents. Included in this class are such chlorinated materials as carbon tetrachloride and trichloroethylene, which are not flammable, but don't make the mistake of assuming that all chlorinated solvents are not flammable.

Another reason why flashpoint does not usually provide sufficient measure of fire hazard is that many safety solvents are complex mixtures of various ingredients. By introducing a small amount of non-flammable chlorinated solvent into the mixture, one can produce a product which will show no flashpoint by conventional methods of test, and yet still be highly flammable.

Thus, a manufacturer of such a product might state on his label "Flashpoint—none," and the user on reading this would assume he was dealing with a non-flammable solvent. A rag soaked with such a product would, however, burn readily if a match were touched to it. This type of blended safety solvent can be detected by the fact that the various ingredients evaporate at different rates. The chlorinated or non-flammable ingredient is usually the fastest evaporating portion of such a mixture. Since the flashpoint determination only measures the flammability of the vapors produced initially, it does not warn us of fire hazard which exists in the use of the whole product.

To safeguard yourselves against this type of non-uniform mixture, flashpoint tests should be repeated after evaporation of 50% of the solvent. If flashpoint before and after evaporation of 50% of the solvent remains approximately the same, you can be reasonably certain that the safety solvent is a uniformly evaporating material and does not change its flammability properties as it dries.

If a product will burn, whether its flashpoint is high or low, it should be treated as potentially hazardous.

Some of the ideas which we are discussing here today were effectively demonstrated during tests which we ran at a large railroad engine overhaul station. The purpose of the study was to establish ventilation requirements during the cleaning of diesel engines and electrical equipment, in order to assure a safe working atmosphere. Ventilation needs were calculated and set up, using the equation mentioned earlier.

A Davis halide meter was used to measure the concentration of chlorinated solvent in the vicinity of the operator's face. The operator was spraying a safety solvent based on 1, 1, 1 trichloroethane, using a shop-made solution-lifting gun with a $\frac{1}{2}''$ home-made spray nozzle operated by air pressure at $90\#$ per sq. in. Immediately after the operation started, the halide meter registered far in excess of 500 ppm. Close study of the situation indicated that this crude spray device was causing coarse droplets of fluid to bounce off the work back into the operator's face. By simply changing the shop-constructed spray device to a suitable atomizer, the spray droplets were reduced in size and effectively handled

Table II
Characteristics of Commonly Used Industrial Solvents

SOLVENT	MOLECULAR WEIGHT	VAPOR PRESSURE (mm. Merc. room temp.)	THRESHOLD LIMIT ppm (MAC)	SPECIFIC GRAVITY	FLASH POINT F (Tag CC))
Acetone	58.08	186	1000	0.792	0
Benzene	78.11	75.5	35	0.879	12
Carbon Tetrachloride	153.84	91.3	25	1.595	none
Chloroform	119.39	150	100	1.489	none
Ethyl Acetate	88.1	72.8	400	0.901	24
Ethyl Alcohol	46.07	44	1000	0.79	55
Methyl Alcohol	32.04	98.3	200	0.792	52
Methylene Chloride	89.94	355	500	1.336	none
Methyl Ethyl Ketone	72.1	71	250	0.806	24
Mineral Spirits	142	7	500	0.76	105
Nitrobenzene	123.11	—	1	1.1987	190
Octane	114.23	120	500	0.706	63
Perchloroethylene	165.85	14.4	200	1.631	none
Tetrachloroethane	167.86	9	5	1.588	none
Toluene	92.13	22	200	0.866	40
1, 1, 1 Trichlorethane	133.42	101	500	1.33	none
Trichloroethylene	131.4	56	200	1.47	none
Turpentine	136	4.4	100	0.865	95

13

by the existing ventilation. The atmosphere in the neighborhood of the operator's face now never rose above 200 ppm, which is safely within the 500 ppm M.A.C. listed for 1, 1, 1 trichloroethane.

An interesting sidelight in this series of tests was the rapid development of static electricity in the shop-made spray nozzle due to the rapid movement of air and solvent through the nozzle. Sparking was clearly evident between the nozzle and various parts of the metal surfaces being cleaned. This certainly would have constituted a severe fire hazard if a flammable cleaning solvent were used, and serves to point up the general need for grounding such cleaning systems, or wherever flammable liquids are dispensed.

It also demonstrates how the body can be subjected to the action of the liquid cleaning solvent through ingestion of liquid droplets, even though ingestion of a liquid is not usually considered a serous industrial hazard.

Fortunately in this case existing data indicates that the body is capable of throwing off effects of 1, 1, 1 trichloroethane, and that it does not build up and cause damaging effects on the liver, kidneys and circulatory system as do many other chlorinated solvents.

When solvents are sprayed in various types of cleaning operations and painting procedures, we must be constantly aware of the increased fire hazard that exists. Here we are not only concerned with the flammability of the vapors produced but also of the liquid droplets. Sprayed droplets of solvent are usually flammable; furthermore, such droplets vaporize faster, giving rise to greater concentration of vapors in the

atmosphere. The illustration shows the ease with which a high flash-point solvent will ignite when sprayed in the vicinity of a flame. (The lit cigarette lighter was placed near the spray for demonstration purposes.)

Manufacturers of substitutes for carbon tetrachloride — indeed all those who sell industrial chemicals — should assume the responsibility of seeing that their products are used with safety. Over-enthusiasm and the desire for volume sales must not lead to irresponsible promotion tactics. In many cases, manufacturers are hesitant about placing warning notices or precautionary measures on their labels for fear of discouraging sales.

Too little information on a label is almost as dangerous as incorrect information. It is essential that a manufacturer provide enough information to the users of his product so that intelligent decisions can be made with regard to safe handling of the solvent. Users of so-called "safety solvents" have a right to know precisely under what conditions those solvents are safe, and under what conditions a hazard might exist. No product should be accepted in any plant unless this information is provided.

PROPERTIES OF INDUSTRIAL LIQUIDS, GASES AND SOLIDS

The code numbers in the last column indicate the following extinguishing agents: (1) Water (See Note A below), (2) Foam, (3) Carbon dioxide or dry chemical, (4) See Note B below (Gas fires), (5) Approved dry compound for metal fires. For explanation of code numbers under "Effect On Skin" and "Relative Toxicity," see the article "Toxicity Of Solvents" immediately following this table.

Name	Effect On Skin	Relative Toxicity	Flash Point °F. Closed Cup	Flash Point °F. Open Cup	Explosive Limits % by Vol. in Air Lower	Explosive Limits % by Vol. in Air Upper	Auto-ignition Temp. °F.	Susceptibility to Spontaneous Heating	Specific Gravity (Water = 1.00)	Vapor Density (Air = 1.00)	Suitable Extinguishing Agents
Acetic Acid (Glacial)	—	—	104	110	4.0	—	1050	No	1.05	2.07	1,3
Acetone	1,2	1	0	15	2.15	13.0	1000	No	0.792	2.00	3
Acetylene	—	—	gas	—	2.5	80	635	No	—	0.91	4
Aluminum (Powder)	—	—	—	—	—	—	—	No	—	—	5
Ammonia (Anhydrous)	—	—	gas	—	16.0	25.0	1204	No	—	0.587	4
Amyl Acetate-n	1,2	2	76	80	1.1	—	714	No	0.879	4.49	3
Amyl Alcohol-n	—	—	91	120	1.2	—	621	No	0.817	3.04	3
Aniline	5	3	168	—	—	—	1418	No	1.022	3.22	2,3
Asphalt (typical)	—	—	400+	535+	—	—	905	No	0.95-1.1	—	1,2,3
Benzene	1,2,5	4	12	—	1.4	8	1076	No	0.88	2.77	2,3
Bronzing Liquid	—	—	<80 (may be)	—	—	—	—	—	—	—	2,3
Butane-n	—	—	76	gas	1.6	8.5	806	No	0.599	2.046	4
Butyl Acetate-n	1,2	2	72	90	1.7	15	790	No	0.88	4.00	3
Butyl Alcohol-n	1,2	2	84	110	1.7	—	693	No	0.806	2.55	1,3
Butyl Carbitol	—	—	172	200	—	—	442	No	0.955	5.58	1,3
Butyl Cellosolve	—	—	141	165	—	—	472	No	0.902	4.07	1,3
Butyl Lactate	—	—	—	160	—	—	720	No	0.968	5.04	2,3
Butyl Stearate-n	—	—	320	385	—	—	—	—	0.855	—	1,2,3
Butyric Acid-n	1	1	170	—	—	—	—	No	0.960	3.04	1,3
Carbitol	—	—	201	215	—	—	—	No	0.99	4.62	1,3
Carbon Disulfide	1,2,5	4	-22	—	1.0	50	257	No	1.256	2.64	1,3
Carbon Tetrachloride	—	4	non-flammable		—	—	—	No	1.595	5.3	—
Castor Oil	—	1	445	545	—	—	840	Yes	0.96	—	1,2,3
Cellosolve	1,5	1	104	120	2.6	15.7	460	No	0.931	3.10	3
Charcoal	—	—	—	—	—	—	—	Yes	3.51	—	1
Chloroform	—	—	non-flammable		—	—	—	No	1.489	4.13	—
Coal Tar Oil	—	—	<80	—	—	—	—	—	<1	—	2,3
Coal Tar Pitch	—	—	405	490	—	—	—	—	—	—	1,2,3
Coconut Oil	—	—	420	510	—	—	—	Yes	0.91	—	1,2,3
Creosote Oil	—	—	165	185	—	—	637	No	>1	—	1,2,3

16

Cresylic Acid	3,5	3	187	—	—	—	1038	No	1.04	3.72	1,3
Cyclohexanol	1,2,5	2	154	—	—	—	—	No	0.962	3.45	1,2,3
Cyclohexanone	1,2,5	2	147	—	1.1 @ 212°F.	2.6	847	No	0.947	3.38	3
Decane-n	—	1	115	—	—	—	>500	No	0.730	4.90	2,3
Denatured Alcohol - 95%	1	1	60	—	0.67	—	750	No	0.82	1.60	3
Diacetone	1,2	1	136	145	—	—	1190	—	0.93-0.94	—	1,3
Dibutyl Phthalate-n	—	—	315	335	—	—	757	No	1.045	9.58	1,2,3
o-Dichlorobenzene	—	—	151	165	—	—	—	No	1.325	5.07	1,2,3
p-Dichlorobenzene	—	—	150	165	—	—	—	No	1.458	5.07	1,2,3
Diethanolamine	—	—	—	280	—	—	1224	No	1.097	3.65	1,3
Diethylene Glycol	1	1	255	290	1.97	—	444	No	1.119	3.66	1,3
Diethylene Oxide Dioxane	1,2	2	54	65	2.2 @ 212°F.	22.2	356	—	1.035	3.03	3
Dimethyl Formamide	—	—	136	155	—	—	833	—	0.945	—	1,2,3
Dioctyl Phthalate	—	2	—	390	—	—	—	—	0.986	13.45	1,2,3
Dipentine	1,2,3	—	126	—	—	—	—	Yes	0.852	4.7	2,3
Dipropylene Glycol	1	1	—	280	—	—	—	No	1.040	—	1,3
Duplicator Fluid	2	1	54	—	—	—	—	No	—	—	3
Ethane	—	—	gas	—	3.3	10.6	950	No	—	1.035	4
Ethyl Acetate	1	1	24	30	2.18	11.5	907	No	0.899	3.04	3
Ethyl Alcohol	1	1	55	—	3.28	19	799	No	0.79	1.59	3

Note A: Water discharged from spray nozzles behaves differently from water discharged from hose streams or from sprinklers discharging relatively large drops. The finely divided drops from a spray nozzle absorb much more heat than an equal weight of water from a hose stream or an equal weight of large drops from a sprinkler. In general, water spray nozzles are suitable for use on fires in flammable liquids having a flash point over 150° F.; but, before purchasing new equipment, consult your insurance Company or the Factory Mutual Engineering Division. In many cases, water from automatic sprinklers will control fire in flammable liquids.

If water is applied to a tank of material such as tempering oil or asphalt, the body of which is at a temperature above 250° F., the steam formed under the surface will cause foaming, resulting in a rapid increase in the volume of the liquid. Under fire conditions, the tank may be overflowed and, consequently, the fire spread. Foaming-over may also result from the application of foam, since foam is largely water. To avoid foaming-over, specially arranged fixed-piping foam extinguishers are available for use on open tanks containing materials heated above 250° F. Dry chemical extinguishers may also be used and will not cause foaming-over.

Note B: While carbon dioxide, dry chemical, and in some instances water spray may be used to extinguish small gas fires, the extinguishment of gas fires by those agents is not generally recommended since the discharge of gas or volatile liquid will continue unless shut off promptly and may well create a more serious explosion hazard. Generally the best procedure is to use water to keep the surroundings cool until the leak can be shut off or until the volatile liquid has completely vaporized.

Abbreviations and Symbols

o - ortho	p - para	sym - symmetrical
m - meta	prim - primary	ter - tertiary
n - normal	sec - secondary	d - decomposes
		> — greater than
		sub - sublimes
		< - less than

PROPERTIES OF INDUSTRIAL LIQUIDS, GASES AND SOLIDS (continued)

Name	Effect On Skin	Relative Toxicity	Flash Point °F. Closed Cup	Flash Point °F. Open Cup	Explosive Limits % by Vol. in Air Lower	Explosive Limits % by Vol. in Air Upper	Auto-ignition Temp. °F.	Susceptibility to Spontaneous Heating	Specific Gravity (Water = 1.00)	Vapor Density (Air = 1.00)	Suitable Extinguishing Agents
Ethylene	1,2,4	—	gas	—	3.02	34	1009	No	—	0.975	4
Ethylene Diamine	—	2	69% 160; 100% 93	175; 110	—	—	715	No	0.890	2.07	3
Ethylene Dichloride	1,2	2	56	65	6.2	15.9	775	—	1.258	3.42	1,2,3
Ethylene Glycol	1	1	232	240	3.2	—	775	No	1.113	2.14	3
Ethylene Oxide	—	—	<0	—	3	80	804	No	0.887	1.52	3
Ethyl Silicate	—	—	—	125	—	—	806	—	0.936	7.22	3
Formaldehyde (gas)	—	—	—	—	7	73	817	—	—	1.075	4
(Sol'n, 37% gas in water)	—	—	130	200	—	—	—	No	—	1.03	3
Formic Acid	—	—	156	—	—	—	1114	—	1.218	1.59	1,3
Fuel Oil No. 1	—	—	110-165	—	—	—	490	No	<1	—	2,3
Fuel Oil No. 2	—	—	110-190	—	—	—	494	No	<1	—	2,3
Fuel Oil No. 3	—	—	125-200	—	—	—	498	No	<1	—	2,3
Fuel Oil No. 4	—	—	150+	250	—	—	505	No	<1	—	1,2,3
Fuel Oil No. 5	—	—	150+	320	—	—	—	No	<1	—	1,2,3
Fuel Oil No. 6	—	—	150+	—	—	—	765	No	—	—	1,2,3
Furfural	1,2,4	2	140	155	2.1	—	739	No	1.159	3.31	1,2,3
Gas, Illuminating	—	—	—	—	5.3	31	1094	No	—	—	4
Gas, Natural	—	—	—	—	4.8	13.5	—	No	—	—	4
Gas, Water	—	—	—	—	9.0	55.0	—	No	—	—	4
Gasoline	1	1	-50	—	1.3	6	495	No	0.75	3-4	2,3
Hexylene Glycol	1	1	—	205	—	—	—	No	0.922	4.07	1,2,3
Hydrogen Sulfide	—	—	gas	—	4.3	45.5	500	No	—	1.18	4
Isoprene	—	—	-65.2	—	—	—	428	—	0.679	2.35	3
Kerosene	1	1	110-165	—	1.16	6.0	490	No	<1	4.5	2,3
Lard Oil (commercial)	—	—	395	—	—	—	833	Yes	<1	—	1,2,3
Linseed Oil	—	—	435	535	—	—	820	Yes	0.93	—	1,2,3
Lubricating Oil, Mineral	—	—	—	300-450	—	—	500-700	No	<1	—	1,2,3
Magnesium (Powder or Chips)	—	—	—	—	—	—	—	—	—	—	5
Methane	—	—	gas	—	5.3	13.9	999	No	—	0.554	4
Methyl Acetate	1	3	15	20	4.1	13.9	935	No	0.925	2.56	3

18

Material											
Methyl Alcohol	1	3	54	60	6.0	36.5	878	No	0.792	1.11	3
Methyl Bromide	—	—	practically non-flammable	—	13.5	14.5	998	No	1.732	3.27	—
Methyl Iso-Butyl Ketone	1,2	1	73	—	—	—	—	No	0.803	3.45	2,3
Methyl Carbitol	—	—	—	200	—	—	—	No	1.035	4.14	1,3
Methyl Chloride	—	—	gas	—	8.1	17.2	1170	No	0.92	1.78	4
Methyl Chloroform	1,2	1	non-flammable	—	15.5 in O2	66.9 in O2	—	No	1.33	4.6	—
Methylene Chloride	1	2	practically non-flammable	—	1.81	11.5	—	No	1.336	2.93	1,2,3
Methyl Ethyl Ketone	1,2	1	30	—	—	—	960	No	0.805	2.48	3
Methyl-Iso Propyl Carbinol	—	—	103	—	—	—	—	—	—	3.03	3
Mineral Oil	—	—	—	380	—	—	—	—	0.80	—	1,2,3
Mineral Spirits	1,2,3,4	2	85	110	0.77 @ 212° F.	—	475	—	—	3.9	2,3
Morpholine	1	1	—	100	—	—	—	No	1.001	3.00	3
Naphtha, V.M. & P.	—	—	20	—	0.92	6.0	450-500	No	0.75	3.75	2,3
Naphthalene	—	—	174	190	0.9	5.9	1053	—	1.145	4.42	1,3
Neatsfoot Oil	—	—	470	—	—	—	828	Yes	0.92	—	1,2,3
Nitrobenzene	—	—	190	—	1.8 @ 200° F.	—	924	—	1.2	4.25	1,2,3
Nitrocellulose (Wet with Solvent)	—	—	40	—	—	—	—	—	—	—	—
Nitroglycerin	—	—	Explodes	—	—	—	518	No	1.601	7.84	—
Octane-n	—	—	56	—	0.84	3.2	450	No	0.706	3.86	2,3
Oleic Acid	—	—	372	—	—	—	685	Yes	0.891	—	1,2,3
Olive Oil	—	2	437	—	—	—	826	Yes	0.910	—	1,2,3
Perchloroethylene	1,2	—	non-flammable	—	—	—	—	No	1.631	5.13	—
Petroleum Ether	—	—	-50	—	1.4	5.9	475	No	0.63-0.66	2.50	2,3
Phenol	3,5	3	175	185	—	—	1319	No	1.07	3.24	1,3
Phosphorus (Red)	—	—	—	—	—	—	500	No	2.30	—	1
Phosphorus (Yellow)	—	—	—	—	—	—	86	No	1.82	—	1
Phthalic Anhydride	—	—	305	330	—	—	1083	Yes	1.527	—	1,3
Pine Oil	—	—	172	175	—	—	—	No	0.86	5.10	1,2,3
Potassium	—	—	—	—	—	—	—	No	0.862	—	5
Propane	1,2	2	gas	—	2.3	7.3	874	No	—	1.56	4
Propyl Alcohol-iso	—	—	53	60	2.5	14.5	852	No	0.789	2.07	3
Propylene Dichloride	1	1	59	65	3.4	12.55	1035	No	1.15	3.89	2,3
Propylene Glycol	—	—	210	225	2.62	—	790	No	1.040	2.62	1,3
Propylene Oxide	—	—	-35	—	2.1	21.5	—	No	0.859	2.00	3

PROPERTIES OF INDUSTRIAL LIQUIDS, GASES AND SOLIDS (concluded)

Name	Effect On Skin	Relative Toxicity	Flash Point °F.		Explosive Limits % by Vol. in Air		Auto-ignition Temp. °F.	Susceptibility to Spontaneous Heating	Specific Gravity (Water = 1.00)	Vapor Density (Air = 1.00)	Suitable Extinguishing Agents
			Closed Cup	Open Cup	Lower	Upper					
Pyridine	1,2,4,5	3	68	—	1.8	12.4	1065	No	0.982	2.73	3
Rubber Cement	—	—	50 or less	—	—	—	—	—	—	—	1,2,3
Sodium	—	—	—	—	—	—	—	No	0.97	—	5
Stearic Acid	—	2	385	425	—	—	743	Yes	0.847	9.80	1,3
Styrene	1,4	2	90	—	1.1	6.1	914	—	0.907	3.60	2,3
Sulfur	—	—	405	440	—	—	450	No	2.046	—	1
Tallow	—	—	509	—	—	—	—	Yes	0.895	—	1,3
Toluene	1,2	2	40	45	1.27	7.0	1026	No	0.866	3.14	2,3
Tributyl Phosphate	—	—	—	295	—	—	—	No	0.973	9.20	1,2,3
Trichloroethylene	1,2	2	practically non-flammable		—	—	—	No	1.47	4.53	—
Tricresyl Phosphate	—	—	460	504	—	—	—	No	—	—	1,2,3
Triethanolamine	—	—	355	365	—	—	—	No	1.13	5.14	1,3
Triethylene Glycol	—	—	350	385	0.89	9.20	700	No	1.125	5.17	1,3
Tung Oil	—	—	552	—	—	—	855	Yes	0.94	—	1,3
Turpentine	1,2	2	95	—	0.8	—	488	Yes	<1	4.84	2,3
Varnish	—	—	<80	—	—	—	—	—	—	—	2,3
Whiskey	—	—	82	—	—	—	—	—	—	—	3
Xylene	1,2	2	63	75	1.0	6.0	924	No	0.88	3.66	2,3
Zinc (dust or powder)	—	—	—	—	—	—	—	No	—	—	5

TOXICITY OF SOLVENTS*

All solvents are poisonous. All, if inhaled in sufficiently large amounts, will kill. Since they are heavier than air, all may displace the oygen required for life if they are used in small confined areas.

The following arbitrary classes of relative toxicity have been established, and are shown in the table. Classification is omitted for those materials about which there is insufficient information.

Class 1:

These materials have a relatively low order of toxicity or produce such a small amount of vapor that the danger accompanying their use is slight in normal room temperature applications.

Class 2:

These materials are moderately toxic. Short exposure to very high concentrations or prolonged exposure to lower concentrations may cause physical disability or even death. In using these materials, local exhaust ventilation and measurement of atmospheric concentrations should be considered. The actual need for both of these steps will depend on the amount and conditions of use.

Class 3:

These materials are definitely toxic. As soon as their use is contemplated, provision should be made for ventilation to remove all of the fumes, for periodic atmospheric monitoring, and for periodic physical examinations. The use of these materials should be brought to the attention of the Medical and Safety Sections.

Class 4:

These materials are dangerous and have been proved so by years of experience and numerous deaths. Safety and Medical Sections should be consulted before these materials are put in use so that adequate safeguards may be established.

SKIN EFFECTS:
Class 1:

All of the materials in this list will defat the skin on prolonged and repeated exposure. This defatting action removes the protective film

* *Courtesy of General Electric Co.*

21

from the skin and leaves it open to attack by the weather, bacteria, or chemical agents. Drying, cracking, and infection frequently follow.

Class 2:

Some of these materials will cause effects similar to those described in Class 1, but on a much shorter period of exposure. It appears that a definite irritating action accompanies the defatting action.

Class 3:

A few materials are actually corrosive to the skin, producing chemical burns, as in this group. It should be remembered that any solvent will produce a burn if held in intimate contact with the skin for sufficient length of time.

Class 4:

Many materials may produce a sensitization reaction even in normal individuals. When this occurs, only a slight contact, or even inhalation of very small amounts of vapor is required to produce severe skin reaction. The solvents most apt to produce this sensitizing action are listed in this group.

Class 5:

A few materials may be absorbed through the skin in sufficient amounts to be dangerous in a relatively short period of time. Solvents appearing in this group should not be used unless this potential danger is understood by all concerned and unless suitable measures for protection against splashes and spill have been taken.

It should be understood that any accurate classification of solvent toxicity and skin effects depends entirely on conditions of use, and that it is impossible to cover all the possible uses in this bulletin. For detailed information on specific problems, contact Industrial Hygiene, Plant Hospital.

FIRST-AID FOR POISONING ACCIDENTS

I. Inhaled Poisons
1. Carry patient (do not let him walk) to fresh air immediately.
2. Open all doors and windows.
3. Loosen all tight clothing.
4. Apply artificial respiration if breathing has stopped or is irregular.
5. Prevent chilling (wrap patient in blankets).
6. Keep patient as quiet as possible.
7. If patient is convulsing, keep him in bed in a semi-dark room; avoid jarring or noise.
8. Do not give alcohol in any form.

II. Skin Contamination
1. Drench skin with water (shower, hose, faucet).
2. Apply stream of water on skin while removing clothing.
3. Cleanse skin thoroughly with water; rapidity in washing is most important in reducing extent of injury.

III. Eye Contamination
1. Hold eyelids open, wash eyes with gentle stream of running water *immediately*. Delay of few seconds greatly increases extent of injury.
2. Continue washing until physician arrives.
3. *Do not use chemicals;* they may increase extent of injury.

IV. Injected Poisons (scorpion and snake bites):
1. Make patient lie down as soon as possible.
2. Do not give alcohol in any form.
3. Apply tourniquet above injection site (e.g., between arm or leg and heart). The pulse in vessels below the tourniquet should not disappear, nor should the tourniquet produce a throbbing sensation. Tourniquet should be loosened for 1 minute every 15 minutes.
4. Apply ice-pack to the site of the bite.
5. Carry patient to physician or hospital; DO NOT LET HIM WALK.

V. Chemical Burns
1. Wash with large quantities of running water (except those caused by phosphorus).

23

2. Immediately cover with loosely applied clean cloth.
3. Avoid use of ointments, greases, powders, and other drugs in first-aid treatment of burns.
4. Treat shock by keeping patient flat, keeping him warm, and reassuring him until arrival of physician.

Measures to Prevent Poisoning Accidents

A. Keep all drugs, poisonous substances, and household chemicals out of the reach of children.
B. Do not store non-edible products on shelves used for storing food.
C. Keep all poisonous substances in their original containers; do not transfer to unlabeled containers.
D. When medicines are discarded, destroy them. Do not throw them where they might be reached by children or pets.
E. When giving flavored and/or brightly colored medicine to children, *always* refer to it as medicine — *never* as candy.
F. Do not take or give medicine in the dark.
G. READ LABELS before using chemical products.

From *The Journal of the American Medical Association*, Oct. 12, 1957, Vol. 165, Copyright 1957, by American Medical Association.

FIRST-AID TREATMENT FOR POISONS SWALLOWED

Poisoning caused by swallowing a poisonous substance is one of the three big emergencies which requires immediate first aid to save life. Every moment's delay means that more of the poison is being absorbed into the system. Prompt action is necessary. Call a physician at once, and then take steps to get rid of the poison.

The signs and symptoms of poisoning vary with the poison taken, Nausea, vomiting, pain in the stomach, cramps, diarrhea, collapse, and convulsions are some of the possible immediate effects.

General First-Aid Treatment

Do not waste time trying to find out what poison was taken. Dilute the poison and wash out the stomach by inducing vomiting *unless the lips, mouth, and tongue are stained or burned,* which indicates that a strong acid of caustic alkali has been swallowed. Both of these measures are accomplished by giving an emetic — a substance that causes vomiting. *Emetics* which can readily be prepared are:

1. Warm salt water — 1 tablespoon of table salt to 1 glass of warm water.

POISONING ACCIDENTS

2. Soapy water — a piece of mild soap shaken up in warm water to make good suds.

If these substances do not cause vomiting, a cup of warm water containing 1 teaspoonful of dry mustard may be given.

Vomiting should be induced repeatedly until the fluid coming from the stomach is clear. If it is necessary to induce vomiting after the person has had several glassfuls of the emetic, tickle the back of his throat.

Strong Acids or Caustic Alkalis: Do not induce vomiting. Follow directions on page 24.

Other Measures: It is most important to keep the victim warm and quiet while giving first aid. If he stops breathing, give artificial respiration at once.

After everything possible has been done to dilute and remove the poison, a soothing drink, such as the raw whites of two or three eggs in a little water, one or two glasses of milk, or a thin paste of starch or flour and water should be given if the victim can swallow. A stimulating drink such as hot coffee may be helpful, except for strychnine poisoning.

Specific First-Aid Treatment for Common Types of Poisoning

If the poison taken is known, specific first-aid treatment should be given, if possible. The nature of the poison may usually be learned from an examination of the surroundings or from what the patient tells you. Specific treatment includes giving an antidote—that is, a substance which neutralizes the poison. For example, alkalis combine with acids to form a new substance which has none of the harmful effects of the acid or alkali. Hence, the antidote for an acid is an alkali, and the antidote for an alkali is an acid. The antidotes for many poisonous household preparations are given on the labels.

If the nature of the poison is unknown, give the universal antidote.

Universal Antidote	or	Substitute
(If a drugstore is handy)		Burned toast
2 Parts—Pulverized charcoal		Milk of magnesia
1 Part —Magnesium oxide		Strong tea
1 Part —Tannic acid		

Always call the doctor, even if you have given the proper antidote.

ANTIDOTES FOR COMMON POISONS .

Acids, Strong—Hydrochloric, nitric, sulphuric, etc.

Alkalis, Caustic—Ammonia, caustic lime (quicklime), caustic soda, caustic potash, lye, etc.
When a strong acid or caustic alkali in a concentrated form has been swallowed, the victim's lips, mouth, and tongue are stained and burned. Usually it is unwise to force vomiting if the poison was taken in concentrated form, for fear of rupturing the corroded walls of the esophagus and stomach. After diluting and neutralizing the poison as described below, give a soothing drink such as a wineglassful of olive oil, a glass of milk, or flour and water.
Acids: To dilute and neutralize an acid swallowed, give two glassfuls of diluted milk of magnesia, or two tablespoonfuls of baking soda in a pint of water, or finely divided chalk in water, or lime in water.
Alkalis: To dilute and neutralize a caustic alkali swallowed, give a wineglassful of vinegar or the juice of four lemons in a pint of water.

Arsenic and Preparations Containing Arsenic* (insect poisons, rat poisons, Paris green, etc.)
Induce vomiting repeatedly by giving several glassfuls of an emetic. In the meantime, send to the drugstore for freshly prepared hydrated oxide of iron and magnesia, the official arsenic antidote. When it comes, give the victim a wineglassful and induce vomiting again.

Barbiturates (sleep-inducing drugs—allonal, amytal, barbital, phenobarbital, etc.)
If the victim is conscious, induce vomiting by giving several glassfuls of an emetic. If the victim is unconscious (in a coma or stupor), keep him warm until the doctor arrives. Give artificial respiration if breathing stops. Injections of picrotoxin or metrazol may be helpful early in the coma stage, but they can be administered only by a physician.

Bichloride of Mercury* (corrosive sublimate)
Give the whites of from three to five eggs immediately, and then induce vomiting repeatedly by giving an emetic.

Carbolic Acid (phenol and preparations containing it)
Immediately give soapsuds or two tablespoonfuls of Epsom salts in a pint of water, and follow with enough lukewarm water to induce vomiting. Then give flour and water to soothe the injured tissues. Do not give oils or fats. Burns on the skin caused by carbolic acid should be washed with large amounts of running water.

Iodine
Give several glassfuls of a thin paste of starch in water or flour in water and induce vomiting until the vomited material no longer has a blue color.

Kerosene
Do not induce vomiting. Use a stomach pump. If the stomach is emptied immediately, no serious complications are likely to occur. If kerosene is breathed into lungs, the results may be serious. It is extremely important to warn the victim to inhale as little as pos-

* "BAL," a chemical compound developed as an antidote to a "war gas" (arsenical Lewisite), has proved to be an effective antidote in both arsenic and bichloride of mercury poisoning. It must be given by hypodermic injection. The quicker the physician gets to the patient, the greater will be the chance of successful treatment with "BAL."

sible if vomiting occurs.

Opium and Its Preparations (codeine, laudanum, morphine, paregoric, soothing sirups, etc.)
If the victim is conscious, induce vomiting by giving several glassfuls of an emetic. Do everything possible to keep him awake. Wash his face with cold water, keep him moving but not to the point of exhaustion, and give quantities of strong black coffee. If the victim is unconscious, keep him warm until the physician arrives. Give artificial respiration if breathing stops.

Phosphorus (rat poisons which contain phosphorus)
Induce vomiting by giving several glassfuls of warm salt water or warm soapsuds. If copper sulphate is on hand or can be obtained quickly from a drugstore, a weak solution consisting of a scant penknife-pointful of copper sulphate (3 grains) in a tumbler of water should be given every 15 minutes until vomiting occurs. The copper sulphate forms a coating over the phosphorus so that it cannot be absorbed. Then give lukewarm water and induce vomiting

again to get the coated phosphorus out of the stomach. Do not give oils or fats.

Salts of fluorides, barium carbonate, or thallium sulphate (rat poisons which contain any of these substances)
Induce vomiting by giving an emetic. Call a doctor at once. No specific antidote is known.

Strychnine (nux vomica, medicines and vermin-killers containing strychnine)
The prevention of convulsions is the main object of first-aid treatment. If it is possible to obtain powdered active charcoal (bone black) from a drug store, give 1 tablespoonful stirred into water. Keep the victim very quiet in a dark room. Do not give an emetic or a stimulant because doing this is apt to bring on convulsions.

Wood and Denatured Alcohol
Induce vomiting by giving an emetic. Follow with bicarbonate of soda (2 teaspoonsfuls in 1 pint of warm water). Continue to induce vomiting until there is no odor of alcohol on the breath. Then place the patient in a dark room and give a glass of milk to which 1 teaspoonful of bicarbonate of soda has been added.

ARTIFICIAL RESPIRATION*

Mouth-to-Mouth (Mouth-to-Nose Method)

If there is foreign matter visible in the mouth, wipe it out quickly with your fingers or a cloth wrapped around your fingers.

1. Tilt the head back so the chin is pointing upward (Fig. 1). Pull or push the jaw into a jutting-out position (Figs. 2, 3).

These maneuvers should relieve obstruction of the airway by moving the base of the tongue away from the back of the throat.

2. Open your mouth wide and place it tightly over the victim's mouth. At the same time pinch the victim's nostrils shut (Fig. 4) or close the nostrils with your cheek (Fig. 5). Or close the victim's mouth and place your mouth over the nose (Fig. 6). Blow into the victim's mouth or nose. (Air may be blown through the victim's teeth, even though they may be clenched.)

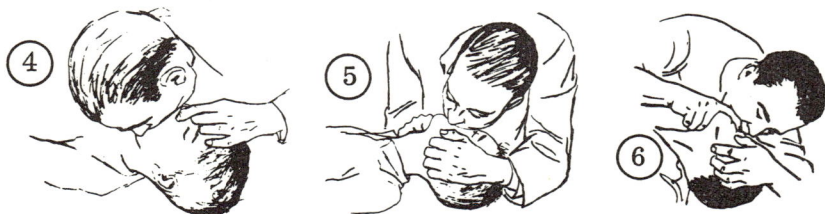

The first blowing efforts should determine whether or not obstruction exists.

3. Remove your mouth, turn your head to the side, and listen for the return rush of air that indicates air exchange. Repeat the blowing effort.

For an adult, blow vigorously at the rate of about 12 breaths per minute. For a child, take relatively shallow breaths appropriate for the child's size, at the rate of about 20 per minute.

4. If you are not getting air exchange, recheck the head and jaw position (Fig. 1 or Figs. 2 and 3). If you still do not get air exchange, quickly turn the victim on his side and administer several sharp blows

*Courtesy American Red Cross

28

ARTIFICIAL RESPIRATION

between the shoulder blades in the hope of dislodging foreign matter (Fig. 7). Again sweep your fingers through the victim's mouth to remove foreign matter.

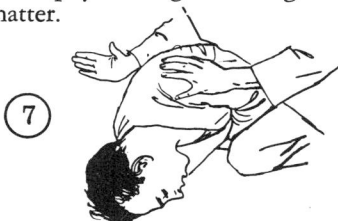

Those who do not wish to come in contact with the person may hold a cloth over the victim's mouth or nose and breathe through it. The cloth does not greatly affect the exchange of air.

Manual Methods of Artificial Respiration

Rescuers who cannot, or will not, use mouth-to-mouth or mouth-to-nose techniques, should use a manual method. The rescuer should not be limited to the use of a single manual method for all cases, since the nature of the injury in any given case may prevent the use of one method, while favoring another.

It has already been pointed out that the base of the tongue tends to press against and block the air passage when a person is unconscious and not breathing. *This action of the tongue can occur whether the victim is in a face-down position or face-up position.*

The Chest-Pressure Arm-Lift (Silvester) Method

If there is foreign matter visible in the mouth, wipe it out quickly with your fingers or a cloth wrapped around your fingers.

1. Place the victim in a face-up position and put something under his shoulders to raise them and allow the head to drop backward (Fig. 8).

2. Kneel at the victim's head, grab his arms at the wrists, cross them, and press them over the lower chest (Fig. 9). This should cause air to flow out.

ARTIFICIAL RESPIRATION

3. Immediately release this pressure and pull the arms outward and upward over his head and backwards as far as possible. This should cause air to rush in (Fig. 10).

4. Repeat this cycle about 12 times per minute, checking the mouth frequently for obstructions.

When the victim is in a face-up position, there is always danger of aspiration of vomitus, blood, or blood clots. This hazard can be reduced by keeping the head extended and turned to one side. If possible, the head should be a little lower than the trunk.

If a second rescuer is available, have him hold the victim's head so that the jaw is jutting out (Fig. 11). The helper should be alert to detect the presence of any stomach contents in the mouth and keep the mouth as clean as possible at all times.

The Back-Pressure Arm-Lift (Holger-Nielsen) Method

If there is foreign matter visible in the mouth, wipe it out quickly with your fingers or a cloth wrapped around your fingers.

1. Place the victim face-down, bend his elbows and place his hands one upon the other, turn his head slightly to one side and extend it as far as possible, making sure the chin is jutting out (Fig. 12).

2. Kneel at the head of the victim. Place your hands on the flat of the victim's back so that the palms lie just below an imaginary line running between the armpits (Fig. 13).

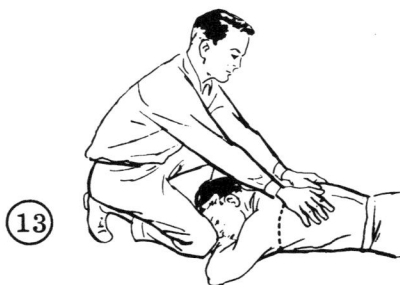

ARTIFICIAL RESPIRATION

3. Rock forward until the arms are approximately vertical and allow the weight of the upper part of your body to exert steady, even pressure downward upon the hands (Fig. 14).

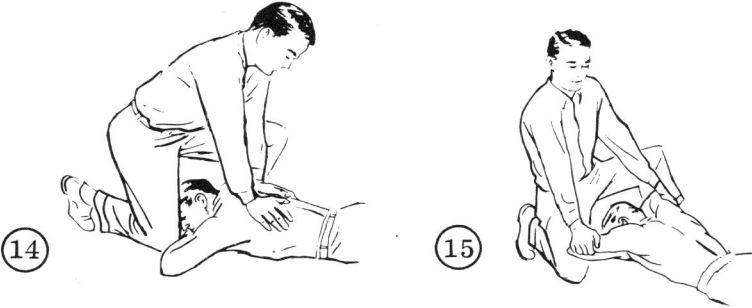

4. Immediately draw his arms upward and toward you, applying enough lift to feel resistance and tension at his shoulders (Fig. 15). Then lower the arms to the ground. Repeat this cycle about 12 times per minute, checking the mouth frequently for obstruction.

If a second rescuer is available, have him hold the victim's head so that the jaw continues to jut out (Fig. 16). The helper should be alert to detect any stomach contents in the mouth and keep the mouth as clean as possible at all times.

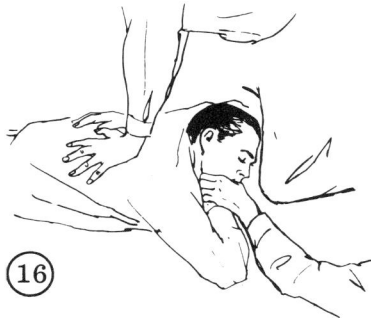

CORRECT LIFTING
PROCEDURE

1. Deep crouch: feet apart, hands grasping opposite corners of the load.

2. The load is held close to the body. Leg muscles are doing the heavy work.

3. The completed lift.

Courtesy National Safety Council.

THRESHOLD LIMIT VALUES FOR 1968

Adopted at the Annual Meeting of the American Conference of Governmental Industrial Hygienists.

Threshold limits should be used as guides in the control of health hazards and should not be regarded as fine lines between safe and dangerous concentrations. They represent conditions under which it is believed that nearly all workers may be repeatedly exposed day after day, without adverse effect. The values listed refer to time-weighted average concentrations for a normal workday. The amount by which these figures may be exceeded for short periods without injury to health depends upon a number of factors, such as the nature of the contaminant, whether very high concentrations even for short periods produce acute poisoning, whether the effects are cumulative, the frequency with which high concentrations occur, and the duration of such periods. All must be taken into consideration in arriving at a decision as to whether a hazardous situation exists. Special consideration should be given to the application of these values in the evaluation of the health hazards which may be associated with exposure to combinations of two or more substances.

Threshold limits are based on the best available information from industrial experience, from experimental studies, and, when possible, from a combination of the two. These values are based on various criteria of toxic effects or on pronounced discomfort; thus, they should not be used as common denominators of toxicity, nor should they be considered as sole criteria in proving or disproving diagnosis of suspected occupational disease.

These limits are intended for use in the field of industrial hygiene and should be employed by persons trained in this field. They are not intended for use, or for modification for use, in the evaluation or control of community air pollution or air-pollution nuisances.

These values are reviewed annually by the Committee on Threshold Limits for changes, revisions, or additions as further information becomes available. The Committee welcomes the suggestion of substances to be added to the list and also comments, references, or reports of experience with these materials.

RECOMMENDED VALUES

RECOMMENDED VALUES
(In Alphabetical Order)

Substance	a) ppm	b) Mg/M³
Acetaldehyde	200	360
Acetic acid	10	25
Acetic anhydride	5	20
Acetone	1,000	2,400
Acetonitrile	40	70
Acetylene dichloride, see 1,2 Dicloro-ethylene		
Acetylene tetrabromide	1	14
Acrolein	0.1	0.25
Acrylamide-Skin	−	0.3
Acrylonitrile-Skin	20	45
Aldrin-Skin	−	0.25
Allyl alcohol-Skin	2	5
Allyl chloride	1	3
Allyl glycidyl ether (AGE)	10	45

Substance	ppm	Mg/M³
Allyl propyl disulfide	2	12
2-Aminoethanol, see Ethanolamine		
2-Aminopyridine	0.5	2
Ammonia	50	35
Ammonium sulfamate (Ammate)	−	15
n-Amyl acetate	100	525
sec-Amyl acetate	125	650
Aniline-Skin	5	19
Anisidine (o, p-isomers)-Skin	−	0.5
Antimony & compounds (as Sb)	−	0.5
ANTU (alpha naphthyl thiourea)	−	0.3
Arsenic & Compounds (as As)	−	0.5
Arsine	0.05	0.2
Azinphos-methyl-Skin	−	0.2
Barium (soluble compounds)	−	0.5
Benzene (benzol)-Skin	25	80
Benzidine-Skin	−	A'
p-Benzoquinone, see Quinone		
Benzoyl peroxide	−	5
Benzyl chloride	1	5

Substance	ppm [a]	Mg/M³ [b]
Beryllium	–	0.002
Biphenyl, see Diphenyl		
Boron oxide	–	15
Boron trifluoride	1	3
Bromine	0.1	0.7
Bromoform-Skin	0.5	5
Butadiene (1, 3-butadiene)	1,000	2,200
Butanethiol, see Butyl mercaptan		
2-Butanone	200	590
2-Butoxy ethanol (Butyl Cellosolve)-Skin	50	240
Butyl acetate (n-butyl acetate)	150	710
n-Butyl acetate	150	710
sec-Butyl acetate	200	950
tert-Butyl acetate	200	950
Butyl alcohol	100	300
* sec–Butyl alcohol	150	450
tert. Butyl alcohol	100	300
Butylamine-Skin	5	15
tert. Butyl chromate (as CrO3)-Skin	–	0.1
n-Butyl glycidyl ether (BGE)	50	270
** Butyl mercaptan	10	35
p–tert. Butyltoluene	10	60
Cadmium (Metal dust and soluble salts)	–	0.2
** Cadmium oxide fume	–	0.1
Calcium arsenate	–	1
Calcium oxide	–	5
** Camphor	–	2
Carbaryl (Sevin) (R)	–	5
Carbon black	–	3.5
Carbon dioxide	5,000	9,000
Carbon disulfide-Skin	20	60
Carbon monoxide	50	55
Carbon tetrachloride-Skin	10	65
Chlordane-Skin	–	0.5
Chlorinated camphene, -Skin	–	0.5
Chlorinated diphenyl oxide	–	0.5
** Chlorine	1	3
Chlorine dioxide	0.1	0.3
Chlorine trifluoride	0.1	0.4
Chloroacetaldehyde	1	3
* α-Chloroacetophenone (phenacylchloride)	0.05	0.3
Chlorobenzene (monochlorobenzene)	75	350
o-Chlorobenzylidene malononitrile (OCBM)	0.05	0.4
Chlorobromomethane	200	1,050
2-Chloro-1,3 butadiene, see Chloroprene		
Chlorodiphenyl (42% chlorine)-Skin	–	1
Chlorodiphenyl (54% chlorine)-Skin	–	0.5
1, Chloro, 2, 3 epoxypropane, see Epichlorhydrin		
2, Chloroethanol, see Ethylene chlorohydrin		
Chloroethylene, see Vinyl chloride		
Chloroform (trichloromethane)	50	240
1-Chloro-1-nitropropane	20	100
Chloropicrin	0.1	0.7
Chloroprene (2-chloro-1, 3-butadiene)-Skin	25	90
Chromic acid and chromates (as CrO3)	–	0.1
* Chromium, sol. chromic, chromous salts as Cr	–	0.5
Metal & insol. salts	–	1
Coal tar pitch volatiles (benzene soluble fraction) (anthracene, BaP, phenanthrene, acridine, chrysene, pyrene)	–	0.2
* Cobalt, metal fume & dust	–	0.1
Copper fume	–	0.1
Dusts and Mists	–	1.0
Cotton dust (raw)	–	1
Crag (R) herbicide	–	15
Cresol (all isomers)-Skin	5	22
Crotonaldehyde	2	6
Cumene -Skin	50	245
Cyanide (as CN)-Skin	–	5
Cyclohexane	300	1,050
Cyclohexanol	50	200
Cyclohexanone	50	200
Cyclohexene	300	1,015
Cyclopentadiene	75	200
2, 4-D	–	10
DDT-Skin	–	1
DDVP-Skin	–	1
Decaborane-Skin	0.05	0.3
Demeton (R)-Skin	–	0.1
Diacetone alcohol (4-hydroxy-4-methyl-2-pentanone)	50	240
1,2 Diaminoethane, see Ethylenediamine		
Diazomethane	0.2	0.4
Diborane	0.1	0.1
1,2-Dibromoethane (ethylene dibromide)-Skin	25	190

Substance	ppm [a]	Mg/M³ [b]
* Dibutyl phosphate	1	5
* Dibutylphthalate	–	5
o- Dichlorobenzene	50	300
p-Dichlorobenzene	75	450
Dichlorodifluoromethane	1,000	4,950
1,3-Dichloro-5, 5-dimethyl hydantoin	–	0.2
1,1,-Dichloroethane	100	400
1,2-Dichloroethane	50	200
1,2-Dichloroethylene	200	790
Dichloroethyl ether-Skin	15	90
Dichloromethane, see Methylenechloride		
Dichloromonofluoromethane	1,000	4,200
1,1-Dichloro-1-nitroethane	10	60
1,2-Dichloropropane, see Propylenedichloride		
Dichlorotetrafluoroethane	1,000	7,000
Dieldrin-Skin	–	0.25
Diethylamine	25	75
Diethylamino ethanol-Skin	10	50
Diethylether, see Ethyl ether		
Difluorodibromomethane	100	860
Diglycidyl ether (DGE)	0.5	2.8
Dihydroxybenzene, see Hydroquinone		
Diisobutyl ketone	50	290
* Diisopropylamine – Skin	5	20
Dimethoxymethane, see Methylal		
Dimethyl acetamide-Skin	10	35
Dimethylamine	10	18
Dimethylaminobenzene, see Xylidene		
Dimethylaniline (N-dimethylaniline)-Skin	5	25
Dimethylbenzene, see Xylene		
Dimethyl 1, 2-dibromo-2, 2-dichloroethyl phosphate, (Dibrom) ⊛	–	3
Dimethylformamide-Skin	10	30
2,6 Dimethylheptanone, see Diisobutyl ketone		
1,1-Dimethylhydrazine-Skin	0.5	1
* Dimethylphthalate	–	5
Dimethylsulfate -Skin	1	5
Dinitrobenzene (all isomers)-Skin	–	1
Dinitro-o-cresol-Skin	–	0.2
Dinitrotoluene	–	1.5
Dioxane (Diethylene dioxide)-Skin	100	360
* Diphenyl	0.2	1
Diphenylmethane diisocyanate (See Methylene bisphenyl isocyanate (MDI)		
Dipropylene glycol methyl ether-Skin	100	600
Di-sec, octyl phthalate (Di-2-ethylhexyl-phthalate	–	5
Endrin-Skin	–	0.1
Epichlorhydrin-Skin	5	19
EPN-Skin	–	0.5
1,2-Epoxypropane, see Propyleneoxide		
2,3-Epoxy-1-propanol see Glycidol		
Ethanethiol, see Ethylmercaptan		
Ethanolamine	3	6
2 Ethoxyethanol-Skin	200	740
2 Ethoxyethylacetate (Cellosolve acetate)-Skin	100	540
Ethyl acetate	400	1,400
Ethyl acrylate-Skin	25	100
Ethyl alcohol (ethanol)	1,000	1,900
Ethylamine	10	18
Ethyl sec-amyl ketone (5-methyl-3-heptanone)	25	130
Ethyl benzene	100	435
Ethyl bromide	200	890
Ethyl butyl ketone (3-Heptanone)	50	230
Ethyl chloride	1,000	2,600
Ethyl ether	400	1,200
Ethyl formate	100	300
** Ethyl mercaptan	10	25
Ethyl silicate	100	850
Ethylene chlorohydrin-Skin	5	16
Ethylenediamine	10	25
Ethylene dibromide, see 1,2-Dibromoethane		
Ethylene dichloride, see 1,2-Dichloroethane		
*i Ethylene glycol dinitrate and or Nitroglycerin – Skin	0.2 [d]	1
Ethylene glycol monomethyl ether acetate, see Methyl cellosolve acetate		
Ethylene imine-Skin	0.5	1
Ethylene oxide	50	90
Ethylidine chloride, see 1,1-Dichloroethane		
N-Ethylmorpholine-Skin	20	94
Ferbam	–	15
Ferrovanadium dust	–	1

34

Substance	a) ppm	b) Mg M³
Fluoride (as F)	–	2.5
Fluorine	0.1	0.2
Fluorotrichloromethane	1,000	5,600
Formaldehyde	5	6
Formic acid	5	9
Furfural Skin	5	20
Furfuryl alcohol	50	200
Gasoline	–	A6
Glycidol (2,3-Epoxy-1-propanol)	50	150
Glycol monoethyl ether, see 2-Ethoxyethanol		
Guthion, ✕ see Azinphosmethyl		
Hafnium	–	0.5
Heptachlor-Skin	–	0.5
** Heptane (n-heptane)	500	2,000
Hexachloroethane-Skin	1	10
* Hexachloronaphthalene – Skin	–	0.2
Hexane (n-hexane)	500	1,800
2-Hexanone	100	410
Hexone	100	410
sec-Hexyl acetate	50	300
Hydrazine-Skin	1	1.3
Hydrogen bromide	3	10
Hydrogen chloride	5	7
Hydrogen cyanide-Skin	10	11
Hydrogen fluoride	3	2
Hydrogen peroxide, 90%	1	1.4
Hydrogen selenide	0.05	0.2
Hydrogen sulfide	10	15
Hydroquinone	–	2
Iodine	0.1	1
Iron oxide fume	–	10
Isoamyl acetate	100	525
Isoamyl alcohol	100	360
Isobutyl acetate	150	700
* Isobutyl alcohol	100	300
Isophorone	25	140
Isopropyl acetate	250	950
Isopropyl alcohol	400	980
Isopropylamine	5	12
Isopropylether	500	2,100
Isopropyl glycidyl ether (IGE)	50	240
Ketene	0.5	0.9
Lead	–	0.2
Lead arsenate	–	0.15
Lindane-Skin	–	0.5
Lithium hydride	–	0.025
L.P.G. (Liquified petroleum gas)	1,000	1,800
Magnesium oxide fume	–	15
Malathion-Skin	–	15
* Maleic anhydride	0.25	1
Manganese	–	5
Mercury-Skin	–	0.1
Mercury (organic compounds)-Skin	–	0.01
Mesityl oxide	25	100
Methanethiol, see Methyl mercaptan		
Methoxychlor	–	15
2-Methoxyethanol, see Methyl cellosolve		
Methyl acetate	200	610
Methyl acetylene (propyne)	1,000	1,650
Methyl acetylene-propadiene mixture (MAPP)	1,000	1,800
Methyl acrylate-Skin	10	35
Methylal (dimethoxymethane)	1,000	3,100
Methyl alcohol (methanol)	200	260
Methylamine	10	12
Methyl amyl alcohol, see Methyl isobutyl carbinol		
Methyl (n-amyl) ketone (2-Heptanone)	100	465
Methyl bromide-Skin	20	80
Methyl butyl ketone, see 2-Hexanone		
Methyl cellosolve-Skin	25	80
Methyl cellosolve acetate-Skin	25	120
Methyl chloride	100	210
Methyl chloroform	350	1,900
Methylcyclohexane	500	2,000
Methylcyclohexanol	100	470
o-Methylcyclohexanone-Skin	100	460
Methyl ethyl ketone (MEK), see 2-Butanone		
Methyl formate	100	250
Methyl iodide - Skin	5	28
Methyl isobutyl carbinol-Skin	25	100
Methyl isobutyl ketone, see Hexone		
Methyl isocyanate - Skin	0.02	0.05
Methyl mercaptan	10	20
Methyl methacrylate	100	410
Methyl propyl ketone, see 2-Pentanone		
αMethyl styrene	100	480
Methylene bisphenyl isocyanate (MDI)	0.02	0.2
Methylene chloride (dichloromethane)	500	1,740
Molybdenum (soluble compounds)	–	5
(insoluble compounds)	–	15
Monomethyl aniline-Skin	2	9
Monomethyl hydrazine-Skin	0.2	0.35
Morpholine-Skin	20	70
* Naphtha (coal tar)	100	400
Napthalene	10	50
β-Naphthylamine	–	A²
Nickel carbonyl	0.001	0.007
Nickel, metal and soluble compounds	–	1
Nicotine-Skin	–	0.5
Nitric acid	2	5
* Nitric oxide	25	30
p-Nitroaniline-Skin	1	6
Nitrobenzene-Skin	1	5
p-Nitrochloro-benzene-Skin	–	1
Nitroethane	100	310
C Nitrogen dioxide	5	9
Nitrogen trifluoride	10	29
C Nitroglycerin-Skin	0.2	2
Nitromethane	100	250
1-Nitropropane	25	90
2-Nitropropane	25	90
N-Nitrosodimethyl-amine (Di-methyl-nitrosoamine)-Skin	–	A³
Nitrotoluene-Skin	5	30
Nitrotrichloromethane, see Chloropicrin		
Octachloronaphthalene – Skin	–	0.1
** Octane	500	2,350
** Oil mist (mineral)	–	5
Osmium tetroxide	–	0.002
Oxalic acid	–	1.
Oxygen difluoride	0.05	0.1
Ozone	0.1	0.2
* Paraquat – Skin	–	0.5
Parathion-Skin	–	0.1
Pentaborane	0.005	0.01
Pentachloronaphthalene-Skin	–	0.5
Pentachlorophenol-Skin	–	0.5
* Pentane	1,000	2,950
2-Pentanone	200	700
Perchloroethylene	100	670
Perchloromethyl mercaptan	0.1	0.8
Perchloryl fluoride	3	13.5
** Petroleum Distillates (naphtha)	500	2,000
Phenol-Skin	5	19
p-Phenylene diamine-Skin	–	0.1
Phenyl ether (vapor)	1	7
Phenyl ether-Biphenyl mixture (vapor)	1	7
Phenylethylene, see Styrene		
* Phenyl glycidyl ether (PGE)	10	60
Phenylhydrazine-Skin	5	22
Phosdrin (Mevinphos) ✕ -Skin	–	0.1
Phosgene (carbonyl chloride)	0.1	0.4
Phosphine	0.3	0.4
Phosphoric acid	–	1
Phosphorus (yellow)	–	0.1
Phosphorus pentachloride	–	1
Phosphorus pentasulfide	–	1
Phosphorus trichloride	0.5	3
Phthalic anhydride	2	12
Picric acid-Skin	–	0.1
Pival® (2-Pivalyl-1, 3-indandione)	–	0.1
Platinum (Soluble Salts)	–	0.002
Polytetrafluoroethylene decomposition products	–	A⁴
products.	–	A
Propane	1,000	1,800
βPropiolactone	–	A⁵
n-Propyl acetate	200	840
* Propyl alcohol	200	500
n-Propyl nitrate	25	110
Propylene dichloride	75	350
Propylene imine - Skin	2	5
Propylene oxide	100	240
Propyne, see Methylacetylene		
Pyrethrum	–	5
Pyridine	5	15
Quinone	0.1	0.4
Rhodium, Metal fume and dusts	–	0.1
Soluble salts	–	0.001
* Ronnel	–	15
Rotenone (commercial)	–	5
Selenium compounds (as Se)	–	0.2
Selenium hexafluoride	0.05	0.4
Silver, metal and soluble compounds	–	0.01
Sodium fluoroacetate (1080) - Skin	–	0.05
Sodium hydroxide	–	2
Stibine	0.1	0.5
** Stoddard solvent	500	2,900

Substance	ppm a)	Mg/M³ b)
Strychnine	–	0.15
** Styrene monomer (phenylethylene)	100	420
Sulfur dioxide	5	13
Sulfur hexafluoride	1,000	6,000
Sulfuric acid	–	1
Sulfur monochloride	1	6
Sulfur pentafluoride	0.025	0.25
Sulfuryl fluoride	5	20
Systox, see Demeton ⊗		
2,4,5 T	–	10
Tantalum	–	5
TEDP - Skin	–	0.2
Teflon ⊗ decomposition products	–	A⁴
Tellurium	–	0.1
Tellurium hexafluoride	0.02	0.2
TEPP - Skin	–	0.05
* Terphenyls	1	9
1,1,1,2-Tetrachloro-2,2-difluoroethane	500	4,170
1,1,2,2-Tetrachloro-1,2-difluoroethane	500	4,170
1,1,2,2-Tetrachloroethane-Skin	5	35
Tetrachloroethylene, see Perchloroethylene		
Tetrachloromethane, see Carbon tetrachloride		
* Tetrachloronaphthalene – Skin	–	2
** Tetraethyl lead (as Pb)-Skin	–	0.075
Tetrahydrofuran	200	590
** Tetramethyl lead (TML) (as Pb) - Skin	–	0.075
* Tetramethyl succinonitrile - Skin	0.5	3
Tetranitromethane	1	8
Tetryl (2,4,6-trinitrophenylmethylnitramine) - Skin	–	1.5
Thallium (soluble compounds) - Skin	–	0.1
Thiram	–	5
Tin (inorganic cmpds, except oxide)	–	2
Tin (organic cmpds)	–	0.1
Titanium dioxide	–	15
Toluene (toluol)	200	750
Toluene-2,4-diisocyanate	0.02	0.14
o-Toluidine - Skin	5	22
Toxaphene, see Chlorinated camphene		
* Tributyl phosphate	–	5
1,1,1-Trichloroethane, see Methyl chloroform		
1,1,2-Trichloroethane - Skin	10	45
Trichloroethylene	100	535
Trichloromethane, see Chloroform		
Trichloronaphthalene - Skin	–	5
1,2,3-Trichloropropane	50	300
1,1,2-Trichloro 1,2,2-trifluoroethane	1,000	7,600
Triethylamine	25	100
Trifluoromonobromomethane	1,000	6,100
2,4,6-Trinitrophenol see Picric acid		
2,4,6-Trinitrophenylmethylnitramine, see Tetryl		
Trinitrotoluene - Skin	–	1.5
Triorthocresyl phosphate	–	0.1
Triphenyl phosphate	–	3
Turpentine	100	560
** Uranium (soluble compounds)	–	0.05
(insoluble compounds)	–	0.25
Vanadium (V₂O₅ dust)	–	0.5
(V₂O₅ fume)	–	0.1
Vinyl benzene, see Styrene		
Vinyl chloride	500	1,300
Vinylcyanide, see Acrylonitrile		
Vinyl toluene	100	480
Warfarin	–	0.1
Xylene (xylol)	100	435
Xylidine - Skin	5	25
Yttrium	–	1
Zinc chloride fume	–	1
Zinc oxide fume	–	5
Zirconium compounds (as Zr)	–	5

Radioactivity: For permissible concentrations of radioisotopes in air, see U.S. Department of Commerce, National Bureau of Standards, Handbook 69, "Maximum Permissible Body Burdens and Maximum Permissible Concentrations of Radionuclides in Air and in Water for Occupational Exposure," June 5, 1959. Also, see U.S. Department of Commerce National Bureau of Standards, Handbook 59, "Permissible Dose from External Sources of Ionizing Radiation," September 24, 1954, and addendum of April 15, 1958.

* 1968 Addition
** See Notice of Intended Changes

Substance	e) m.p.p.c.f.
SILICA	
Crystalline	
** Quartz, Threshold Limit calculated from the formula	$\dfrac{250 \ f)}{\%SiO_2 + 5}$
** Cristobalite " " "	
Amorphous, including natural diatomaceous earth	20
Tremolite	5
SILICATES (less than 1% crystalline silica)	
** Asbestos	5
Mica	20
Soapstone	20
Talc	20
Portland Cement	50
GRAPHITE (natural)	15
"Inert" or Nuisance Particulates	50 (or 15 mg/m³ whichever is the smaller)

Conversion factors
mppcf x 35.3 = million particles per cubic meter
particles per c.c.

NOTICE OF INTENDED CHANGES

These substances, with their corresponding values, comprise those for which either a limit has been proposed for the first time, or for which a change in the "Recommended" listing has been proposed. In both cases, the proposed limits should be considered trial limits that will remain in this listing for a period of at least two years. During this time, the previously Recommended Limit will remain in effect. If, after two years no evidence comes to light that questions the appropriateness of the values herein, the values will be placed in the "Recommended" list. Documentation is available for each of these substances.

Substance	ppm a)	Mg/M³ b)
Abate	–	15
Boron tribromide	1.0	–
Bromine pentafluoride	0.1	–
Butyl mercaptan	0.5	–
+ Cadmium oxide fume (as Cd)	–	0.1
Camphor	2	–
Chlorine	1	–
Cyanogen	10	–
++ Dichloroacetylene	0.1	–
Diethylene triamine – Skin	10	–
Diphenyl amine	–	10
+ Endosulfan (Thiodan ⊗) – Skin	–	0.1
+ Ethyl mercaptan	0.5	–
Fibrous glass	–	5
+ Heptane	500	2,000
++ Indene	10	–
Indium and compounds, as In	–	0.1
Iron salts, soluble, as Fe	–	1
++ Methyl isoamyl ketone	100	475
+ Methyl mercaptan	0.5	–
Methyl silicate	5	–
+ Octane	400	1,900
+ Oil mist (particulate)	–	5 g)
+ Oil vapors	h) A 6	
++ Pentaerythritol (tetramethylomethane)	–	15
Pentane	500	1,500
+ Petroleum distillates	h) A 6	
Propargyl alcohol – Skin	1	–
RDX – Skin	–	1.5
+ Stoddard Solvent	200	–
Styrene	50	–
+ Tetraethyl lead (as Pb) – Skin	–	0.100 i)
+ Tetramethyl lead (as Pb) – Skin	–	0.150 i)
++ Trimethyl benzene	25	–
Tungsten & compounds, as W		
Soluble	–	1
Insoluble	–	5
Uranium, sol. & insol. compounds as U	–	0.2

36

Substance

+ **Asbestos**   12 fibers ml $> 5\mu$ in length [j] , or 2 mppcf [k]
+ **Cristobalite** Use one-half the value calculated from the count
or mass formulae for quartz.

+ **Quartz**   (1) TLV for respirable dust in mg m³ :

$$\text{[m]}$$
$$\frac{10 \text{ mg m}^\cdot}{\% \text{ Respirable Quartz} + 2}$$

(2) "Total dust" respirable and nonrespirable:

$$\frac{30 \text{ mg m}^3}{\% \text{ Quartz} + 2}$$

+ **Tridymite**   Use one-half the value calculated
from formulae for quartz.

a) Parts of vapor or gas per million parts of contaminated
air by volume at 25° C and 760 mm. Hg pressure.
b) Approximate milligrams of particulate per cubic
meter of air.

d) An atmospheric concentration of not more than
0.02 ppm, or personal protection may be
necessary to avoid headache.

e) Millions of particles per cubic foot of air, based on
impinger samples counted by light-field technics.

f) The percentage of crystalline silica in the formula
is the amount determined from air-borne samples,
except in those instances in which other methods
have been shown to be applicable.

g) As sampled by method that does not collect vapors.

h) According to analytically determined composition.

i) For control of general room air; biologic monitoring
is essential for personnel control.

j) As determined by the membrane filter method at 430 X
phase contrast magnification.

k) As counted by the standard impinger, light-field
count technique.

m) Both concentration and per cent quartz for the
application of this limit are to be determined from the
fraction passing a size-selector with the following
characteristics:

Aerodynamic Diameter 'μ' (unit density sphere)	% passing selector
≤ 2	90
2.5	75
3.5	50
5.0	25
10	0

+ 1968 Revision
++ 1968 Addition

PART TWO

MATHEMATICAL TABLES AND CONVERSION FACTORS

TABLES OF WEIGHTS, MEASURES AND VALUES

LONG MEASURE

United States Standard

12 inches	1 foot
3 feet	1 yard
5½ yards, or 16½ feet	1 rod
320 rods, or 5,280 feet	1 mile
1,760 yards	1 mile
40 rods	1 furlong
8 furlongs	1 statute mile
3 miles	1 league

SQUARE MEASURE

United States Standard

144 square inches	1 square foot
9 square feet	1 square yard
30¼ square yards	1 square rod
272¼ square feet	1 square rod
40 square rods	1 rood
4 roods	1 acre
160 square rods	1 acre
640 acres	1 square mile
43,560 square feet	1 acre
4,840 square yards	1 acre

SOLID OR CUBIC MEASURE (VOLUME)

United States Standard

1,728 cubic inches	1 cubic foot
27 cubic feet	1 cubic yard
128 cubic feet	1 cord of wood
24¾ cubic feet	1 perch of stone
2,150.42 cubic inches	1 standard bushel
231 cubic inches	1 standard gallon
40 cubic feet	1 ton (shipping)

DRY MEASURE

United States Standard

2 pints	1 quart
8 quarts	1 peck
4 pecks	1 bushel
2,150.42 cubic inches	1 bushel
1.2445 cubic feet	1 bushel

LIQUID MEASURE (CAPACITY)

United States Standard

4 gills	1 pint
2 pints	1 quart
4 quarts	1 gallon
31½ gallons	1 barrel
2 barrels	1 hogshead
1 gallon	231 cubic inches
7.4805 gallons	1 cubic foot
16 fluid ounces	1 pint
1 fluid ounce	1.805 cubic inches
1 fluid ounce	29.59 cubic centimeters

AVOIRDUPOIS MEASURE (WEIGHT)

(Used for weighing all ordinary substances except precious metals, jewels, and drugs)

United States Standard

27¹¹⁄₃₂ grains	1 dram
16 drams	1 ounce
16 ounces	1 pound
25 pounds	1 quarter
4 quarters	1 hundredweight
100 pounds	1 hundredweight
20 hundredweight	1 ton
2,000 pounds	1 short ton
2,240 pounds	1 long ton

TROY MEASURE WEIGHT)

(Used for weighing gold, silver, and jewels)

24 grains	1 pennyweight
20 pennyweights	1 ounce
12 ounces	1 pound

Comparison of Avoirdupois and Troy Measures

1 pound troy	5,760 grains
1 pound avoirdupois	7,000 grains
1 ounce troy	480 grains
1 ounce avoirdupois	437½ grains
1 karat, or carat	3.2 troy grains
24 karats	pure gold

APOTHECARIES' MEASURE (WEIGHT)

(Used for weighing drugs)

20 grains	1 scruple
3 scruples	1 dram
8 drams	1 ounce
12 ounces	1 pound

APOTHECARIES' FLUID MEASURE (CAPACITY)

60 minims	1 fluid dram
8 fluid drams	1 fluid ounce
16 fluid ounces	1 pint
8 pints	1 gallon

Comparisons (Approximate Liquid Measure)

Apothecaries'	Common	Metric
1 minim	1 to 2 drops	0.06 cu. cm.
60 minims, or		
1 fluid dram	1 teaspoonful	3.75 cu. cm.
2 fluid drams	1 dessertspoonful	7.50 cu. cm.
4 fluid drams	1 tablespoonful	15.00 cu. cm.
8 fluid drams	1 fluid ounce	28.39 cu. cm.
2 fluid ounces	1 wineglassful	59.20 cu. cm.
4 fluid ounces	1 teacupful	118.40 cu. cm.
16 fluid ounces	1 pint	473.11 cu. cm.

Note: Drops are not accurate measures, but for practical purposes it may be considered that one minim equals one drop of watery liquids and fixed oils, but two drops of volatile oils and alcoholic liquids, such as tinctures and fluid extracts.

SURVEYORS' LONG MEASURE

7.92 inches	1 link
25 links	1 rod
4 rods, or 100 links	1 chain
80 chains	1 mile

SURVEYORS' SQUARE MEASURE

625 square links	1 square rod
16 square rods	1 square chain
10 square chains	1 acre
640 acres	1 square mile
36 square miles	1 township

RECIPE CONVERSIONS

Dry Equivalents

	Common	Cubic Inches	Metric
1 Teaspoon	—	.35	5.7 cc
1 Tablespoon	3 Teaspoons	1.05	17.2 cc
1 Cup	16 Tablespoons	16.80	275.3 cc
1 Pint	2 Cups	33.60	550.6 cc
1 Quart	2 Pints	67.20	1.10 liters
1 Peck	8 Quarts	537.61	8.8 liters
1 Bushel	4 Pecks	2150.42	35.24 liters

Liquid Equivalents

		Cubic Inches	Metric
1 Teaspoon	—	.301	4.93 ml
1 Tablespoon	3 Teaspoons	.903	14.80 ml
1 Cup	16 Tablespoons	14.43	236.6 ml
1 Pint	2 Cups	28.875	473.2 ml
1 Quart	2 Pints	57.75	946.4 ml
1 Gallon	4 Quarts	231.00	3.7853 liters

MARINERS' MEASURE

6 feet	1 fathom
100 fathoms	1 cable's length as applied to distances or intervals between ships
120 fathoms	1 cable's length as applied to marine wire cable
7½ cable lengths	1 mile
5,280 feet	1 statute mile
6,080 feet	1 nautical mile
1.152⅔ statute miles	1 nautical or geographical mile
3 geographical miles	1 league
60 geographical miles, or 69.16 statute miles	1 degree of longitude on the equator, or 1 degree of meridian
360 degrees	1 circumference

Note: A knot is not a measure of distance but a measure of speed Current usage makes a knot equivalent to a marine mile per hour (properly it is 1/120 of a marine mile). Hence, when the speed of vessels at sea is being measured, a knot is equal to a nautical mile, or 6,080 feet, or 2,026.66 yards, *per hour.*

CIRCULAR OR ANGULAR MEASURE

60 seconds (60″)	....	1 minute (1′)
60 minutes (60′)	....	1 degree (1°)
30 degrees	....	1 sign
90 degrees	....	1 right angle or quadrant
360 degrees	....	1 circumference

Note: One degree at the equator is approximately 60 nautical miles.

PAPER MEASURE

24 sheets	....	1 quire
20 quires	....	1 ream
2 reams	....	1 bundle
5 bundles	....	1 bale

Note: Although a ream contains 480 sheets, 500 sheets are usually sold as a ream.

UNITED STATES AND BRITISH WEIGHTS AND MEASURES COMPARED

1 British Imperial bushel	1.03205 United States (Winchester) bushels
1 United States bushel	.96895 British Imperial bushel
1 British quart	1.03205 United States dry quarts
1 United States dry quart	.96895 British quart
1 British quart (or gallon)	1.20094 United States liquid quarts (or gallons)
1 United States liquid quart (or gallon)	.83268 British quart (or gallon)

DECIMAL AND METRIC EQUIVALENTS OF COMMON FRACTIONS OF AN INCH

U.S. Inch Frac.	Deci-mal	Mm	U.S. Inch Frac.	Deci-mal	Mm	U.S. Inch Frac.	Deci-mal	Mm	U.S. Inch Frac.	Deci-mal	Mm
1/64	0.01562	0.397	33/64	0.51562	13.097	17/64	0.26562	6.747	49/64	0.76562	19.447
1/32	0.03125	0.794	17/32	0.53125	13.494	9/32	0.28125	7.144	25/32	0.78125	19.844
3/64	0.04688	1.191	35/64	0.54688	13.891	19/64	0.29688	7.541	51/64	0.79688	20.241
1/16	0.06250	1.588	9/16	0.56250	14.288	5/16	0.31250	7.938	13/16	0.81250	20.638
5/64	0.07812	1.984	37/64	0.57812	14.684	21/64	0.32812	8.334	53/64	0.82812	21.034
3/32	0.09375	2.381	19/32	0.59375	15.081	11/32	0.34375	8.731	27/32	0.84375	21.431
7/64	0.10938	2.778	39/64	0.60938	15.478	23/64	0.35938	9.128	55/64	0.85938	21.828
1/8	0.12500	3.175	5/8	0.62500	15.875	3/8	0.37500	9.525	7/8	0.87500	22.225
9/64	0.14062	3.572	41/64	0.64062	16.272	25/64	0.39062	9.922	57/64	0.89062	22.622
5/32	0.15625	3.969	21/32	0.65625	16.669	13/32	0.40625	10.319	29/32	0.90625	23.019
11/64	0.17188	4.366	43/64	0.67188	17.066	27/64	0.42188	10.716	59/64	0.92188	23.416
3/16	0.18750	4.763	11/16	0.68750	17.463	7/16	0.43750	11.113	15/16	0.93750	23.813
13/64	0.20312	5.159	45/64	0.70312	17.859	29/64	0.45312	11.509	61/64	0.95312	24.209
7/32	0.21875	5.556	23/32	0.71875	18.256	15/32	0.46875	11.906	31/32	0.96875	24.606
15/64	0.23438	5.953	47/64	0.73438	18.653	31/64	0.48438	12.303	63/64	0.98438	25.003
1/4	0.25000	6.350	3/4	0.75000	19.050	1/2	0.50000	12.700	1/1	1.00000	25.400

Courtesy Texaco, Inc.

CONVERSIONS: LENGTH, AREA, VOLUME, WEIGHT

L	Inches	×	.0833	= feet
E	Inches	×	.0278	= yards
N	Inches	×	.00001578	= miles
G	Feet	×	.3333	= yards
T	Feet	×	.0001894	= miles
H	Yards	×	36.00	= inches
	Yards	×	3.00	= feet
	Yards	×	.0005681	= miles
	Miles	×	63360	= inches
	Miles	×	5280	= feet
	Miles	×	1760	= yards
	Circumference of circle	×	.31831	= diameter
	Diameter of circle	×	3.1416	= circumference

A	Square inches	×	.00694	= square feet
R	" "	×	.007716	= square yards
E	" feet	×	144.00	= square inches
A	" "	×	11111	= square yards
	" yards	×	1296.00	= square inches
	" "	×	9.00	= square feet
	Dia. of circle squared	×	.7854	= area
	Dia. of sphere squared	×	3.1416	= surface
	Acre	×	43560	= square feet

V	Cubic inches	×	.0005787	= cubic feet
O	Cubic inches	×	.00002143	= cubic yards
L	" "	×	.004329	= U.S. gallons
U	" "	×	0.16387	= litres
M	" feet	×	1728.00	= cubic inches
E	" "	×	.03704	= cubic yards
	" "	×	7.4805	= U.S. gallons
	" "	×	6.2288	= imperial gallons
	" yards	×	46656.00	= cubic inches
	" "	×	27.00	= cubic feet
	" meters	×	264.17	= U.S. gallons
	Litres	×	61.026	= cubic inches
	U.S. gallons	×	231	= cubic inches
	" "	×	0.83268	= imperial gallons
	Imperial gallons	×	1.20094	= U.S. gallons
	" "	×	4.54596	= litres
	" "	×	277.42	= cubic inches
	Litres	×	0.264178	= U.S. gallons
	"	×	0.219905	= imperial gallons
	Dia. of sphere cubed	×	.5236	= volume

W	Grain (avoirdupois)	×	.002288	= ounces
E	Ounces "	×	.0625	= pounds
I	" "	×	.00003125	= tons
G	Pounds "	×	16.00	= ounces
H	" "	×	.01	= hundredweight
T	" "	×	.0005	= tons
	Tons "	×	32000.00	= ounces
	" "	×	2000.00	= pounds
	Long Tons	×	2240	= pounds
	Metric tons	×	0.98421	= long tons
	Long tons	×	1.01605	= metric tons
	Kilograms	×	2.20462	= pounds
	Long tons	×	1016.047	= kilograms
	Metric tons	×	2204.6223	= pounds
	Metric tons	×	1000	= kilograms
	Specific gravity	×	62.3	= lbs. per cubic foot approximately
	" "	×	0.0278115	= tons per cubic foot approximately
	35.96 ÷ specific gravity			= cubic foot per ton approximately

CONVERSION FACTORS

To convert from a unit in the column at the left to a related unit in a shaded horizontal line, multiply by factor at intersection.

VOLUME	cu. in.	ml.	liters	drams (U.S.fl.)	ounces (U.S.fl.)	ounces (Br.fl.)
Cubic inches		16.3868	.0163868	4.4332	0.5541	0.57651
Milliliters	0.061024		0.001	0.27052	0.03381	0.03520
Liters	61.024	1000		270.5179	33.8147	35.196
Drams (U.S.fl. or apoth.)	0.22559	3.6966	3.6966×10^{-3}		0.125	0.13011
Ounces (U.S.fl.)	1.80469	29.5729	0.029573	8		1.0409
Ounces (Br.fl.)	1.73457	28.4121	2.84121×10^{-2}	7.6860	0.9607	
Gallons (U.S.)*	231	3785.3	3.7853	1024	128	133.23
Gallons (Br.)**	277.4	4545.96	4.54596	1230	153.72	160
Barrels (U.S.)	7276.5	1.1924×10^{5}	119.2369	32256	4032.0	41967
Minims (U.S.)	3.7597×10^{-3}	0.061610	6.161×10^{-5}	0.016667	2.0833×10^{-3}	2.1684×10^{-3}
Minims (Br.)	3.6122×10^{-3}	.059192	5.9192×10^{-5}	0.016013	2.00154×10^{-3}	2.0833×10^{-3}
Cubic feet	1728	2.8316×10^{4}	28.316	7660.60	957.568	997.37

* 1 U.S. gallon of water at 16.7°C (62°F) weighs 3.780 kg. or 8.337 pounds (avoir.)
** 1 British Imperial or Canadian gallon at 16.7°C (62°F) has a mass of 10 pounds (avoir.)

MASS	grams	kilograms	ounces (avoir.)	pounds (avoir.)	ounces (troy) ap	pounds (troy) ap
Grams		0.001	3.527×10^{-2}	2.205×10^{-3}	3.215×10^{-2}	2.679×10^{-3}
Kilograms	1000		35.274	2.2046	32.151	2.6792
Ounces (avoir.)	28.350	0.028350		0.0625	0.91146	0.075955
Pounds (avoir.)*	453.59	0.45359	16.0		14.583	1.2153
Ounces (troy or apoth.)	31.103	0.03110	1.0971	0.068571		0.08333
Pounds (troy)	373.24	0.37324	13.166	0.82286	12	
Grains	0.06480	6.480×10^{-5}	2.286×10^{-3}	1.429×10^{-4}	2.083×10^{-3}	1.736×10^{-4}
Drams (troy)**	3.8879	3.888×10^{-3}	0.13714	8.571×10^{-3}	0.1250	1.042×10^{-2}
Drams (avoir.)	1.7718	1.772×10^{-3}	0.0625	3.906×10^{-3}	0.056966	4.747×10^{-3}
Tons (short)	9.072×10^{5}	907.19	3.200x10⁴	2000	2.917×10^{4}	2430.6
Tons (long)	1.016×10^{6}	1016.0	3.584×10^{4}	2240	3.267×10^{4}	2722.2
Milligrams	0.001	1×10^{-6}	3.527×10^{-5}	2.205×10^{-6}	3.215×10^{-5}	2.679×10^{-6}

* Mass of 27.692 cubic inches water weighed in air at 4.0°C, 760 mm mercury pressure.
** Same as British drachm

POWER	watts	KW	ft.lb./sec	ft.lb./min.	erg/sec	BTU/min
Watts		0.001	0.73756	44.254	1×10^{7}	0.056884
Kilowatts	1000		737.56	4.4254×10^{4}	1×10^{10}	56.884
Foot pounds per second	1.35582	1.3558×10^{-3}		60	1.3558×10^{7}	0.077124
Foot pounds per minute	0.2259	2.2597×10^{-5}	0.016667		2.2597×10^{5}	1.2854×10^{-3}
Ergs per second	1×10^{-7}	1×10^{-10}	7.3756×10^{-8}	4.4254×10^{-6}		5.688×10^{-9}
BTU* per minute	17.580	0.017580	12.9600	777.980	1.7580×10^{8}	
Gram Centimeters per sec.	9.8067×10^{-5}	9.8067×10^{-8}	7.2330×10^{-5}	4.3397×10^{-3}	980.665	5.5783×10^{-6}
Kilogram calories per minute	69.767	.069767	51.457	3087.4	6.9770×10^{8}	3.9685
Horsepower (U.S.)	745.7	0.7457	550	33,000	7.457×10^{9}	42.4176
Lumens	1.496×10^{-3}	1.496×10^{-6}	1.0034×10^{-3}	6.6204×10^{-2}	1.496×10^{4}	8.5096×10^{-5}
Joules per second	1	0.001	0.73756	44.254	1×10^{7}	0.056884
BTU*per hour	0.29299	9.2299×10^{-4}	0.21610	12.9668	2.9299×10^{6}	0.01667

* British Thermal Units (Mean)

WORK AND ENERGY	g.cal.	kg.cal.	ergs	Joules	BTU	ft. lb.
Gram Calories (mean)		0.001	4.186×10^{7}	4.186	3.9680×10^{-3}	3.0874
Kilogram Calories	1000		4.186×10^{10}	4186	3.9680	3087.4
Ergs	2.3889×10^{-8}	2.3889×10^{-11}		1×10^{-7}	9.4805×10^{-11}	7.3756×10^{-8}
Joules	0.23889	2.3889×10^{-4}	1×10^{7}		9.4805×10^{-4}	0.73756
BTU (mean)	251.98	0.25198	1.0548×10^{10}	1054.8		777.98
Foot Pounds	0.32389	3.2389×10^{-4}	1.35582×10^{7}	1.3558	1.2854×10^{-3}	
Kilogram meters	2.3427	2.3427×10^{-3}	9.8066×10^{7}	9.8066	9.2967×10^{-3}	7.2330
Liter Atmospheres (normal)	24.206	2.4206×10^{-2}	1.0133×10^{9}	101.328	0.09606	74.735
Horsepower Hours	6.4130×10^{5}	641.30	2.6845×10^{13}	2.6845×10^{6}	2454.0	1.9800×10^{6}
Foot poundals	0.010067	10.067×10^{-6}	4.21402×10^{5}	.04214	3.9952×10^{-5}	0.031081
Kilowatt Hours	8.6001×10^{5}	860.01	3.6000×10^{13}	3.6000×10^{6}	3413.0	2.6552×10^{6}
Watt Hours	860.01	0.86001	3.6000×10^{10}	3600	3.4130	2655.3

FOR THE LABORATORY

To convert from a unit in the column at the right to a related unit in a shaded horizontal line, multiply by factor at intersection.

gallons (U.S.)	gallons (Br.)	barrels (U.S.)	minims (U.S.)	minims (Br.)	cu. ft.	VOLUME
4.3290×10^{-3}	3.606×10^{-3}	1.37429×10^{-4}	256.976	276.842	5.78704×10^{-4}	Cubic inches
2.6418×10^{-4}	2.199×10^{-4}	8.387×10^{-6}	16.231	16.894	3.5316×10^{-5}	Milliliters
0.26418	0.21998	8.387×10^{-3}	16231	16894	0.035316	Liters
9.7656×10^{-4}	8.13165×10^{-4}	3.1×10^{-5}	60	62.451	1.3054×10^{-4}	Drams (U.S.fl. or apoth.)
7.8125×10^{-3}	6.5053×10^{-3}	2.48×10^{-4}	480	499.61	1.0443×10^{-3}	Ounces (U.S.fl.)
0.07506	6.250×10^{-3}	2.3828×10^{-4}	461.160	480	1.0033×10^{-3}	Ounces (Br.fl.)
....	0.83268	0.031746	6.1440×10^{4}	6.3950×10^{4}	0.13368	Gallons (U.S.)*
1.20094	....	3.8125×10^{-2}	7.3783×10^{4}	7.9620×10^{4}	0.16053	Gallons (Br.)**
31.5	26.23	....	1.9354×10^{6}	2.01442×10^{6}	4.2109	Barrels (U.S.)
1.6276×10^{-5}	1.3553×10^{-5}	5.1669×10^{-7}	....	1.04085	2.176×10^{-6}	Minims (U.S.)
1.5637×10^{-5}	1.30208×10^{-5}	4.7882×10^{-7}	0.96075	....	2.0904×10^{-6}	Minims (Br.)
7.481	6.229	0.23743	4.5961×10^{5}	4.7838×10^{5}	....	Cubic feet

* 1 U.S. gallon of water at 16.7°C (62°F) weighs 3.780 kg or 8.337 pounds (avoir.)
** 1 British Imperial or Canadian gallon at 16.7°C (62°F) has a mass of 10 pounds (avoir.)

grains	drams (troy) ap	drams (avoir)	tons (short)	tons (long)	milligrams	MASS
15.432	0.25721	0.5644	1.102×10^{-6}	9.842×10^{-7}	1000	Grams
15432	257.21	564.38	1.102×10^{-3}	9.842×10^{-4}	1×10^{6}	Kilograms
437.5	7.2917	16.000	3.125×10^{-5}	2.790×10^{-5}	2.8350×10^{4}	Ounces (avoir.)
7000	116.67	256.00	5.0×10^{-4}	4.464×10^{-4}	4.5359×10^{5}	Pounds (avoir.)*
480	8	17.554	3.061×10^{-5}	3.061×10^{-5}	3.1104×10^{4}	Ounces (troy or apoth.)
5760	96	210.65	4.114×10^{-4}	3.674×10^{-4}	3.7324×10^{5}	Pounds (troy)
....	0.01667	0.03657	7.142×10^{-8}	6.377×10^{-8}	64.799	Grains
60	....	2.1943	4.284×10^{-6}	3.826×10^{-6}	3.888×10^{3}	Drams (troy)**
27.344	0.45573	....	1.953×10^{-6}	1.744×10^{-6}	1.7718×10^{3}	Drams (avoir.)
1.4×10^{7}	2.334×10^{5}	5.120×10^{5}	....	0.89286	9.0718×10^{8}	Tons (short)
1.568×10^{7}	2.613×10^{5}	5.734×10^{5}	1.1200	....	1.0160×10^{9}	Tons (long)
0.015432	2.5721×10^{-4}	5.644×10^{-4}	1.102×10^{-9}	9.842×10^{-10}	....	Milligrams

* Mass of 27.692 cubic inches water weighed in air at 4.0°C, 760 mm mercury pressure.
** Same as British drachm

g.cm/sec	kg.cal/min	HP	Lumens	Joules/sec	BTU/hr.	POWER
1.0197×10^{4}	0.01433	1.341×10^{-3}	668	1	3.41304	Watts
1.0197×10^{7}	14.3334	1.3410	6.68×10^{5}	1000	3413.04	Kilowatts
1.3826×10^{4}	.019433	1.8182×10^{-3}	906.28	1.3558	4.6274	Foot pounds per second
2.3043×10^{2}	3.2389×10^{-4}	3.0303×10^{-5}	13.3456	0.02260	0.07712	Foot pounds per minute
1.0197×10^{-3}	1.4333×10^{-9}	1.3410×10^{-10}	6.6845×10^{-6}	1×10^{-7}	3.4130×10^{-7}	Ergs per second
1.7926×10^{5}	0.2520	0.023575	11751	17.580	60	BTU* per minute.
....	1.4056×10^{-6}	1.3151×10^{-7}	0.065552	9.8067×10^{-5}	3.3470×10^{-4}	Gram Centimeters per sec.
7.1146×10^{5}	....	0.093557	46636	69.769	238.11	Kilogram calories per minute
7.6042×10^{6}	10.688	....	498129	745.7	2545.1	Horsepower (U.S.)
15.254	2.1437×10^{-5}	2.0061×10^{-6}	....	1.496×10^{-3}	5.1069×10^{-3}	Lumens
1.0197×10^{4}	0.01433	1.341×10^{-3}	668	....	3.41304	Joules per second
2.9878×10^{3}	4.1997×10^{-3}	3.9291×10^{-4}	195.80	0.29299	....	BTU* per hour

* British Thermal Units (Mean)

kg.meters	L-Atm	H.P.hours	ft.poundals	KWH	WH	WORK AND ENERGY
0.42585	0.041311	1.5593×10^{-6}	99.334	1.1628×10^{-6}	1.1628×10^{-3}	Gram Calories (mean)
426.85	41.311	1.5593×10^{-3}	99334	1.1628×10^{-3}	1.1628	Kilogram Calories
1.0197×10^{-8}	9.8689×10^{-10}	3.7251×10^{-14}	2.3730×10^{-6}	2.7778×10^{-14}	2.7778×10^{-11}	Ergs
0.10197	9.8689×10^{-3}	3.7251×10^{-7}	23.730	2.7778×10^{-7}	2.7778×10^{-4}	Joules
107.56	10.409	3.9292×10^{-4}	2.5030×10^{4}	2.930×10^{-4}	0.2930	BTU (mean)
0.13825	0.013381	5.0505×10^{-7}	32.174	3.7662×10^{-7}	3.7662×10^{-4}	Foot pounds
....	0.096781	3.6529×10^{-6}	232.71	2.7241×10^{-6}	2.7241×10^{-3}	Kilogram Meters
10.333	....	3.7745×10^{-5}	2404.5	2.8164×10^{-5}	2.8164×10^{-2}	Liter Atmospheres (normal)
2.7374×10^{6}	26494	....	6.3705×10^{7}	0.7457	745.7	Horsepower Hours
4.2972×10^{-4}	4.1588×10^{-4}	1.5697×10^{-9}	....	1.17055×10^{-8}	1.17055×10^{-5}	Foot poundals
3.6705×10^{6}	3.5529×10^{6}	1.3410	8.5430×10^{7}	....	1000	Kilowatt Hours
367.09	3.5529×10^{3}	1.3410×10^{-3}	8.5430×10^{4}	0.001	....	Watt Hours

Compiled by Fisher Scientific Compan

FOUR-PLACE TABLE OF COMMON LOGARITHMS

N	0	1	2	3	4	5	6	7	8	9
10	0000	0043	0086	0128	0170	0212	0253	0294	0334	0374
11	0414	0453	0492	0531	0569	0607	0645	0682	0719	0755
12	0792	0828	0864	0899	0934	0969	1004	1038	1072	1106
13	1139	1173	1206	1239	1271	1303	1335	1367	1399	1430
14	1461	1492	1523	1553	1584	1614	1644	1673	1703	1732
15	1761	1790	1818	1847	1875	1903	1931	1959	1987	2014
16	2041	2068	2095	2122	2148	2175	2201	2227	2253	2279
17	2304	2330	2355	2380	2405	2430	2455	2480	2504	2529
18	2553	2577	2601	2625	2648	2672	2695	2718	2742	2765
19	2788	2810	2833	2856	2878	2900	2923	2945	2967	2989
20	3010	3032	3054	3075	3096	3118	3139	3160	3181	3201
21	3222	3243	3263	3284	3304	3324	3345	3365	3385	3404
22	3424	3444	3464	3483	3502	3522	3541	3560	3579	3598
23	3617	3636	3655	3674	3692	3711	3729	3747	3766	3784
24	3802	3820	3838	3856	3874	3892	3909	3927	3945	3962
25	3979	3997	4014	4031	4048	4065	4082	4099	4116	4133
26	4150	4166	4183	4200	4216	4232	4249	4265	4281	4298
27	4314	4330	4346	4362	4378	4393	4409	4425	4440	4456
28	4472	4487	4502	4518	4533	4548	4564	4579	4594	4609
29	4624	4639	4654	4669	4683	4698	4713	4728	4742	4757
30	4771	4786	4800	4814	4829	4843	4857	4871	4886	4900
31	4914	4928	4942	4955	4969	4983	4997	5011	5024	5038
32	5051	5065	5079	5092	5105	5119	5132	5145	5159	5172
33	5185	5198	5211	5224	5237	5250	5263	5276	5289	5302
34	5315	5328	5340	5353	5366	5378	5391	5403	5416	5428
35	5441	5453	5465	5478	5490	5502	5514	5527	5539	5551
36	5563	5575	5587	5599	5611	5623	5635	5647	5658	5670
37	5682	5694	5705	5717	5729	5740	5752	5763	5775	5786
38	5798	5809	5821	5832	5843	5855	5866	5877	5888	5899
39	5911	5922	5933	5944	5955	5966	5977	5988	5999	6010
40	6021	6031	6042	6053	6064	6075	6085	6096	6107	6117
41	6128	6138	6149	6160	6170	6180	6191	6201	6212	6222
42	6232	6243	6253	6263	6274	6284	6294	6304	6314	6325
43	6335	6345	6355	6365	6375	6385	6395	6405	6415	6425
44	6435	6444	6454	6464	6474	6484	6493	6503	6513	6522
45	6532	6542	6551	6561	6571	6580	6590	6599	6609	6618
46	6628	6637	6646	6656	6665	6675	6684	6693	6702	6712
47	6721	6730	6739	6749	6758	6767	6776	6785	6794	6803
48	6812	6821	6830	6839	6848	6857	6866	6875	6884	6893
49	6902	6911	6920	6928	6937	6946	6955	6964	6972	6981
50	6990	6998	7007	7016	7024	7033	7042	7050	7059	7067
51	7076	7084	7093	7101	7110	7118	7126	7135	7143	7152
52	7160	7168	7177	7185	7193	7202	7210	7218	7226	7235
53	7243	7251	7259	7267	7275	7284	7292	7300	7308	7316
54	7324	7332	7340	7348	7356	7364	7372	7380	7388	7396
N	0	1	2	3	4	5	6	7	8	9

FOUR-PLACE TABLE OF COMMON LOGARITHMS

N	0	1	2	3	4	5	6	7	8	9
55	7404	7412	7419	7427	7435	7443	7451	7459	7466	7474
56	7482	7490	7497	7505	7513	7520	7528	7536	7543	7551
57	7559	7566	7574	7582	7589	7597	7604	7612	7619	7627
58	7634	7642	7649	7657	7664	7672	7679	7686	7694	7701
59	7709	7716	7723	7731	7738	7745	7752	7760	7767	7774
60	7782	7789	7796	7803	7810	7818	7825	7832	7839	7846
61	7853	7860	7868	7875	7882	7889	7896	7903	7910	7917
62	7924	7931	7938	7945	7952	7959	7966	7973	7980	7987
63	7993	8000	8007	8014	8021	8028	8035	8041	8048	8055
64	8062	8069	8075	8082	8089	8096	8102	8109	8116	8122
65	8129	8136	8142	8149	8156	8162	8169	8176	8182	8189
66	8195	8202	8209	8215	8222	8228	8235	8241	8248	8254
67	8261	8267	8274	8280	8287	8293	8299	8306	8312	8319
68	8325	8331	8338	8344	8351	8357	8363	8370	8376	8382
69	8388	8395	8401	8407	8414	8420	8426	8432	8439	8445
70	8451	8457	8463	8470	8476	8482	8488	8494	8500	8506
71	8513	8519	8525	8531	8537	8543	8549	8555	8561	8567
72	8573	8579	8585	8591	8597	8603	8609	8615	8621	8627
73	8633	8639	8645	8651	8657	8663	8669	8675	8681	8686
74	8692	8698	8704	8710	8716	8722	8727	8733	8739	8745
75	8751	8756	8762	8768	8774	8779	8785	8791	8797	8802
76	8808	8814	8820	8825	8831	8837	8842	8848	8854	8859
77	8865	8871	8876	8882	8887	8893	8899	8904	8910	8915
78	8921	8927	8932	8938	8943	8949	8954	8960	8965	8971
79	8976	8982	8987	8993	8998	9004	9009	9015	9020	9025
80	9031	9036	9042	9047	9053	9058	9063	9069	9074	9079
81	9085	9090	9096	9101	9106	9112	9117	9122	9128	9133
82	9138	9143	9149	9154	9159	9165	9170	9175	9180	9186
83	9191	9196	9201	9206	9212	9217	9222	9227	9232	9238
84	9243	9248	9253	9258	9263	9269	9274	9279	9284	9289
85	9294	9299	9304	9309	9315	9320	9325	9330	9335	9340
86	9345	9350	9355	9360	9365	9370	9375	9380	9385	9390
87	9395	9400	9405	9410	9415	9420	9425	9430	9435	9440
88	9445	9450	9455	9460	9465	9469	9474	9479	9484	9489
89	9494	9499	9504	9509	9513	9518	9523	9528	9533	9538
90	9542	9547	9552	9557	9562	9566	9571	9576	9581	9586
91	9590	9595	9600	9605	9609	9614	9619	9624	9628	9633
92	9638	9643	9647	9652	9657	9661	9666	9671	9675	9680
93	9685	9689	9694	9699	9703	9708	9713	9717	9722	9727
94	9731	9736	9741	9745	9750	9754	9759	9763	9768	9773
95	9777	9782	9786	9791	9795	9800	9805	9089	9814	9818
96	9823	9827	9832	9836	9841	9845	9850	9854	9859	9863
97	9868	9872	9877	9881	9886	9890	9894	9899	9903	9908
98	9912	9917	9921	9926	9930	9934	9939	9943	9948	9952
99	9956	9961	9965	9969	9974	9978	9983	9987	9991	9996
N	0	1	2	3	4	5	6	7	8	9

CONVERSION FACTORS

The metric system is used by chemists and scientists generally because of the ease with which calculations may be made and data compared. These tables show the relationship between some of the more common units in the Metric and U. S. Systems.

	METRIC UNITS	To	U.S. EQUIVALENTS	
Lengths	1 millimeter		0.03937	inch
	1 centimeter		0.3937	inch
	1 meter		39.37	inches or 1.0936 yards
	1 kilometer		1093.61	yards or 0.6214 mile
Areas	1 square millimeter		0.00155	square inch
	1 square centimeter		0.155	square inch
	1 square meter		10.764	square feet or
			1.196	square yards
	1 square kilometer		0.3861	square mile
Volumes	1 cubic millimeter		0.000061	cubic inch
	1 cubic centimeter		0.061	cubic inch
	1 liter		61.025	cubic inches
	1 cubic meter		35.314	cubic feet or
			1.3079	cubic yards
Capacities	1 milliliter (0.001 liter)		0.0338	U.S. fluid ounce
	1 liter		2.1134	U.S. liquid pints
	1 liter		1.0567	U.S. liquid quarts
	1 liter		0.2642	U.S. gallon
Weights	1 gram		0.03527	avoir. ounce or
			15.4324	grains
	1 kilogram (1000 grams)		2.2046	avoir. pounds

	U.S. SYSTEM UNITS	To	METRIC EQUIVALENTS	
Lengths	1 inch		25.4	millimeters or
			2.54	centimeters
	1 foot		0.3048	meter
	1 yard		0.9144	meter
	1 mile		1.6093	kilometers
Areas	1 square inch		645.16	square millimeters or
			6.452	square centimeters
	1 square foot		0.0929	square meter
	1 square yard		0.8361	square meter
	1 square mile		2.59	square kilometers
Volumes	1 cubic inch		16,387.2	cubic millimeters or
			16.3872	cubic centimeters
	1 cubic foot		0.02832	cubic meter
	1 cubic yard		0.7646	cubic meter
Capacities	1 U.S. fluid ounce		29.573	milliliters
	1 U.S. liquid pint		0.47317	liter
	1 U.S. liquid quart		0.94633	liter
	1 U.S. gallon		3.78533	liters
Weights	1 grain		0.0648	gram
	1 avoir. ounce		28.35	grams
	1 avoir. pound		0.4536	kilogram
	1 Troy ounce		31.1035	grams

The cubic millimeter, cubic centimeter and cubic meter are units of volume derived from basic units of length. The liter, however, is defined as the volume occupied by a kilogram of water at 4° C. and at standard atmospheric pressure. Consequently the cubic centimeter (c.c.) and the milliliter (ml.) are not exactly similar. (1 ml. = 1.000027 c.c.) The milliliter, by common consent, is now recognized as the preferable unit for the measurement of volume in chemical laboratory practice.

Courtesy Allied Chemical

NATURAL FUNCTIONS OF ANGLES

Deg.	Sine	Cosine	Tangent	Cotangent	Deg.
0	0.0000	1.0000	0.0000	∞	90
1	0.0175	0.9998	0.0175	57.2900	89
2	0.0349	0.9994	0.0349	28.6363	88
3	0.0523	0.9986	0.0524	19.0811	87
4	0.0698	0.9976	0.0699	14.3007	86
5	0.0872	0.9962	0.0875	11.4301	85
6	0.1045	0.9945	0.1051	9.5144	84
7	0.1219	0.9925	0.1228	8.1443	83
8	0.1392	0.9903	0.1405	7.1154	82
9	0.1564	0.9877	0.1584	6.3138	81
10	0.1736	0.9848	0.1763	5.6713	80
11	0.1908	0.9816	0.1944	5.1446	79
12	0.2079	0.9781	0.2126	4.7046	78
13	0.2250	0.9744	0.2309	4.3315	77
14	0.2419	0.9703	0.2493	4.0108	76
15	0.2588	0.9659	0.2679	3.7321	75
16	0.2756	0.9613	0.2867	3.4874	74
17	0.2924	0.9563	0.3057	3.2709	73
18	0.3090	0.9511	0.3249	3.0777	72
19	0.3256	0.9455	0.3443	2.9042	71
20	0.3420	0.9397	0.3640	2.7475	70
21	0.3584	0.9336	0.3839	2.6051	69
22	0.3746	0.9272	0.4040	2.4751	68
23	0.3907	0.9205	0.4245	2.3559	67
24	0.4067	0.9135	0.4452	2.2460	66
25	0.4226	0.9063	0.4663	2.1445	65
26	0.4388	0.8988	0.4877	2.0503	64
27	0.4540	0.8910	0.5095	1.9626	63
28	0.4695	0.8829	0.5317	1.8807	62
29	0.4848	0.8746	0.5543	1.8040	61
30	0.5000	0.8660	0.5774	1.7321	60
31	0.5150	0.8572	0.6009	1.6643	59
32	0.5299	0.8480	0.6249	1.6003	58
33	0.5446	0.8387	0.6494	1.5399	57
34	0.5592	0.8290	0.6745	1.4826	56
35	0.5736	0.8192	0.7002	1.4281	55
36	0.5878	0.8090	0.7265	1.3764	54
37	0.6018	0.7986	0.7536	1.3270	53
38	0.6157	0.7880	0.7813	1.2799	52
39	0.6293	0.7771	0.8098	1.2349	51
40	0.6428	0.7660	0.8391	1.1918	50
41	0.6561	0.7547	0.8693	1.1504	49
42	0.6691	0.7431	0.9004	1.1106	48
43	0.6820	0.7314	0.9325	1.0724	47
44	0.6947	0.7193	0.9657	1.0355	46
45	0.7071	0.7071	1.0000	1.0000	45
Deg.	Cosine	Sine	Cotangent	Tangent	Deg.

Courtesy New Departure Division of General Motors

U. S., ENGLISH AND METRIC CONVERSIONS

Pounds per Imperial Gallon $= $ Lbs. per U.S. Gal. $\times$ 1.20094

Kilos per U.S. Gallon $= \dfrac{\text{Pounds per U.S. Gallon}}{\text{Pounds per Kilo (2.20462)}}$

U.S. Gallons per 100 Kilos $= \dfrac{\text{Pounds per 100 Kilos (220.462)}}{\text{Pounds per U.S. Gallon}}$

Kilos per Imperial Gallon $= \dfrac{\text{Pounds per Imperial Gallon}}{\text{Pounds per Kilo}}$

Imperial Gallons per 100 Kilos $= \dfrac{\text{Pounds per 100 Kilos}}{\text{Pounds per Imperial Gallon}}$

Cu. Feet per Ton of 2240 Pounds $= \dfrac{2240}{\text{Pounds per U.S. Gallon} \times \text{U.S. Gallons per Cu. Foot (7.4805)}}$

U.S. Gallons per Ton of 2240 Pounds $= \dfrac{2240}{\text{Pounds per U.S. Gallon}}$

Imperial Gals. per Ton of 2240 lbs. $= \dfrac{2240}{\text{Pounds per Imperial Gallon}}$

Liters per Ton of 2240 Pounds $= \dfrac{2240}{\text{Pounds per Liter (Pounds per U.S. Gallon} \quad 0.264178}$

42 Gal. Barrels per Ton of 2240 pounds $= \dfrac{\text{U.S. Gals. per Ton of 2240 Pounds}}{42}$

Kilos per liter $= \dfrac{\text{Pounds per Kilo}}{\text{Pounds per Liter}}$

Liters per Kilo $= \dfrac{\text{Pounds per Liter}}{\text{Pounds per Kilo}}$

U.K. 9-lb. Gallon per U.S. Gallon $= \dfrac{\text{Pounds per U.S. Gallon}}{9}$

U.S. Gallons per U.K. 9 lb. Gallon $= \dfrac{9}{\text{Pounds per U.S. Gallon}}$

Liters per U.K. 9-lb. Gallon $= \dfrac{9}{\text{Pounds per Liter}}$

U.K. 9-lb. Gallons per Liter $= \dfrac{\text{Pounds per Liter}}{9}$

Courtesy Texaco, Inc.

MARINE WEIGHTS AND MEASURES

5280	feet	=	1	mile	
16½	feet	=	1	rod	
2	yards	=	1	fathom	
1.15156	miles	=	1	knot	
1000	millimeters	=	1	meter	
100	centimeters	=	1	meter	
1000	meters	=	1	kilometer	
0.3937	inch	=	1	centimeter	
39.37	inches	=	1	meter	
25.4	millimeters	=	1	inch	
.6214	mile	=	1	kilometer	
144	sq. in.	=	1	sq. ft.	
4840	sq. yds.	=	1	acre	
231	cu. in.	=	1	gallon	
32	ounces (volume)	=	1	quart	
42	gallons	=	1	bbl.	
1.2	U.S. gallons	=	1	Imperial gallon	
1000	cubic centimeters	=	1	liter	
3785	cubic centimeters	=	1	gallon	
61.023	cubic inches	=	1	liter	
1.0567	quarts	=	1	liter	
16	ounces (weight)	=	1	pound	

2000	pounds	=	1	ton — net	
2240	pounds	=	1	ton — gross	
2204.6	pounds	=	1	metric ton	
1000	milligrams	=	1	gram	
1000	grams	=	1	kilogram	
453.6	grams	=	1	pound	
8,328	pounds water	=	1	U.S. gallon	
10	pounds water	=	1	Imperial gallon	
62.4	pounds water	=	1	cu. ft.	
.433	lbs. per sq. in.	=	1	foot water	
491	lbs. per sq in.	=	1	inch mercury	
13.61	inches water	=	1	inch mercury	
14.7	lbs. per sq. in.	=	1	atmosphere	
0.0335	kgs. per sq. in.	=	1	atmosphere	
.0703	kgs. per sq. in.	=	1	lb. per sq. in.	
.0807	lbs. air at 32°F.	=	1	cu. ft.	
550	ft. lbs. per sec.	=	1	Horsepower	
745.7	Watts	=	1	Horsepower	
1.34	Horsepower	=	1	Kilowatt	
778	ft. lbs.	=	1	B.T.U.	
2546.5	B.T.U.	=	1	H.P. Hour	
1.8	B.T.U. per lb.	=	1	calorie per kg.	

53

FUNCTIONS OF NUMBERS

No.	Square	Cube	Sq. Rt.	Cu. Rt.	Reciprocal	Circum.	Area
1	1	1	1.0000	1.0000	1.000000000	3.1416	0.7854
2	4	8	1.4142	1.2599	.500000000	6.2832	3.1416
3	9	27	1.7321	1.4422	.333333333	9.4248	7.0686
4	16	64	2.0000	1.5874	.250000000	12.5664	12.5664
5	25	125	2.2361	1.7100	.200000000	15.7080	19.635
6	36	216	2.4495	1.8171	.166666667	18.850	28.274
7	49	343	2.6458	1.9129	.142857143	21.991	38.485
8	64	512	2.8284	2.0000	.125000000	25.133	50.266
9	81	729	3.0000	2.0801	.111111111	28.274	63.617
10	100	1,000	3.1623	2.1544	.100000000	31.416	78.540
11	121	1,331	3.3166	2.2240	.090909091	34.558	95.033
12	144	1,728	3.4641	2.2894	.083333333	37.699	113.10
13	169	2,197	3.6056	2.3513	.076923077	40.841	132.73
14	196	2,744	3.7417	2.4101	.071428571	43.982	153.94
15	225	3,375	3.8730	2.4662	.066666667	47.124	176.71
16	256	4,096	4.0000	2.5198	.062500000	50.265	201.06
17	289	4,913	4.1231	2.5713	.058823529	53.407	226.98
18	324	5,832	4.2426	2.6207	.055555556	56.549	254.47
19	361	6,859	4.3589	2.6684	.052631579	59.690	283.53
20	400	8,000	4.4721	2.7144	.050000000	62.832	314.16
21	441	9,261	4.5826	2.7589	.047619048	65.973	346.36
22	484	10,648	4.6904	2.8020	.045454545	69.115	380.13
23	529	12,167	4.7958	2.8439	.043478261	72.257	415.48
24	576	13,824	4.8990	2.8845	.041666667	75.398	452.39
25	625	15,625	5.0000	2.9240	.040000000	78.540	490.87
26	676	17,576	5.0990	2.9625	.038461538	81.681	530.93
27	729	19,683	5.1962	3.0000	.037037037	84.823	572.56
28	784	21,952	5.2915	3.0366	.035714286	87.965	615.75
29	841	24,389	5.3852	3.0723	.034482759	91.106	660.52
30	900	27,000	5.4772	3.1072	.033333333	94.248	706.86
31	961	29,791	5.5678	3.1414	.032258065	97.389	754.77
32	1,024	32,768	5.6569	3.1748	.031250000	100.53	804.25
33	1,089	35,937	5.7446	3.2075	.030303030	103.67	855.30
34	1,156	39,304	5.8310	3.2396	.029411765	106.81	907.92
35	1,225	42,875	5.9161	3.2717	.028571429	109.96	962.11
36	1,296	46,656	6.0000	3.3019	.027777778	113.10	1,017.88
37	1,369	50,653	6.0828	3.3322	.027027027	116.24	1,075.21
38	1,444	54,872	6.1644	3.3620	.026315789	119.38	1,134.11
39	1,521	59,319	6.2450	3.3912	.025641026	122.52	1,194.59
40	1,600	64,000	6.3246	3.4200	.025000000	125.66	1,256.64
41	1,681	68,921	6.4031	3.4482	.024390244	128.81	1,320.25
42	1,764	74,088	6.4807	3.4760	.023809524	131.95	1,385.44
43	1,849	79,507	6.5574	3.5034	.023255814	135.09	1,452.20
44	1,936	85,184	6.6332	3.5303	.022727273	138.23	1,520.53
45	2,025	91,125	6.7082	3.5569	.022222222	141.37	1,590.43
46	2,116	97,336	6.7823	3.5830	.021739130	144.51	1,661.90
47	2,209	103,823	6.8557	3.6088	.021276600	147.65	1,734.94
48	2,304	110,592	6.9282	3.6342	.020833333	150.80	1,809.56
49	2,401	117,649	7.0000	3.6593	.020408163	153.94	1,885.74
50	2,500	125,000	7.0711	3.6840	.020000000	157.08	1,963.50

FUNCTIONS OF NUMBERS

No.	Square	Cube	Sq. Rt.	Cu. Rt.	Reciprocal	Circum.	Area
51	2,601	132,651	7.1414	3.7084	.019607843	160.22	2,042.82
52	2,704	140,608	7.2111	3.7325	.019230769	163.36	2,123.72
53	2,809	148,877	7.2801	3.7563	.018867925	166.50	2,206.18
54	2,916	157,464	7.3485	3.7798	.018518519	169.65	2,290.22
55	3,025	166,375	7.4162	3.8030	.018181818	172.79	2,375.83
56	3,136	175,616	7.4833	3.8259	.017857143	175.93	2,463.01
57	3,249	185,193	7.5498	3.8485	.017543860	179.07	2,551.76
58	3,364	195,112	7.6158	3.8709	.017241379	182.21	2,642.08
59	3,481	205,379	7.6811	3.8930	.016949153	185.35	2,733.97
60	3,600	216,000	7.7460	3.9149	.016666667	188.50	2,827.43
61	3,721	226,981	7.8102	3.9365	.016393443	191.64	2,922.47
62	3,844	238,328	7.8740	3.9579	.016129032	194.78	3,019.07
63	3,969	250,047	7.9373	3.9791	.015873016	197.92	3,117.25
64	4,096	262,144	8.0000	4.0000	.015625000	201.06	3,216.99
65	4,225	274,625	8.0623	4.0207	.015384615	204.20	3,318.31
66	4,356	287,496	8.1240	4.0412	.015151515	207.34	3,421.19
67	4,489	300,763	8.1854	4.0615	.014925373	210.49	3,525.65
68	4,624	314,432	8.2462	4.0817	.014705882	213.63	3,631.68
69	4,761	328,509	8.3066	4.1016	.014492754	216.77	3,739.28
70	4,900	343,000	8.3666	4.1213	.014285714	219.91	3,848.45
71	5,041	357,911	8.4261	4.1408	.014084517	223.05	3,959.19
72	5,184	373,248	8.4853	4.1602	.013888889	226.19	4,071.50
73	5,329	389,017	8.5440	4.1793	.013698630	229.34	4,185.39
74	5,476	405,224	8.6023	4.1983	.013513514	232.48	4,300.84
75	5,625	421,875	8.6603	4.2172	.013333333	235.62	4,417.86
76	5,776	438,976	8.7178	4.2358	.013157895	238.76	4,536.46
77	5,929	456,533	8.7750	4.2543	.012987013	241.90	4,656.63
78	6,084	474,552	8.8318	4.2727	.012820513	245.04	4,778.36
79	6,241	493,039	8.8882	4.2908	.012658228	248.19	4,901.67
80	6,400	512,000	8.9443	4.3089	.012500000	251.33	5,026.55
81	6,561	531,441	9.0000	4.3267	.012345679	254.47	5,153.00
82	6,724	551,368	9.0554	4.3445	.012195122	257.61	5,281.02
83	6,889	571,787	9.1104	4.3621	.012048193	260.75	5,410.61
84	7,056	592,704	9.1652	4.3795	.011904762	263.89	5,541.77
85	7,225	614,125	9.2195	4.3968	.011764706	267.04	5,674.50
86	7,396	636,056	9.2736	4.4140	.011627907	270.18	5,808.80
87	7,569	658,503	9.3274	4.4310	.011494253	273.32	5,944.68
88	7,744	681,472	9.3808	4.4480	.011363636	276.46	6,082.12
89	7,921	704,969	9.4340	4.4647	.011235955	279.60	6,221.14
90	8,100	729,000	9.4868	4.4814	.011111111	282.74	6,361.73
91	8,281	753,571	9.5394	4.4979	.010989011	285.88	6,503.88
92	8,464	778,688	9.5917	4.5144	.010869565	289.03	6,647.61
93	8,649	804,357	9.6437	4.5307	.010752688	292.17	6,792.91
94	8,836	830,584	9.6954	4.5468	.010638298	295.31	6,939.78
95	9,025	857,375	9.7468	4.5629	.010526316	298.45	7,088.22
96	9,216	884,736	9.7980	4.5789	.010416667	301.59	7,238.23
97	9,409	912,673	9.8489	4.5947	.010309278	304.73	7,389.81
98	9,604	941,192	9.8995	4.6104	.010204082	307.88	7,542.96
99	9,801	970,299	9.9499	4.6261	.010101010	311.02	7,697.69
100	10,000	1,000,000	10.0000	4.6416	.010000000	314.16	7,853.98

Courtesy New Departure Division of General Motors

GEOMETRIC FORMULAS

To Obtain:	Multiply:	by:
Annulus		
Area of	Diff. of sq. of diam	0.78540
"	Diff. of sq. of radii	3.1416
Circle		
Area of	Circum. . . . . :	½ × radius
"	Circum.	¼ × diameter
"	Circum.².	0.079577
"	Diameter²	0.78540
"	Radius².	3.1416
Circum. of	Diameter	3.1416
"	Radius	6.2832
Diam. of	Circum.	0.31831
Radius of	Circum.	0.15915
Side of equal square of . . .	Circum. of circle	0.28207
" . . .	Diam. of circle	0.88614
Side of inscribed equal.		
triangle of.	Diam. of circle	0.86603
Side of inscribed square of	Circum. of circle.	0.22508
"	Diam. of circle	0.70711
Cone, Regular		
Volume of	Area of base	⅓ × altitude
Cone, Right Circular		
Lateral area of.	Radius of base	3.1416 × slant height
Volume of	(Radius of base)²	1.0472 × altitude
Cube		
Diagonal of.	Length of one side	1.7321
Total surface area of. . . .	Area of one side	6
Volume of	Area of one side	Length of one side
"	(Length of one side)³	1
Cycloid		
Area of	(Radius of circle)²	9.4248
Length of arc of	Radius of circle	8
Cylinder, Hollow		
External surface area of .	External radius	6.2832 × height
Internal surface area of . .	Internal radius	6.2832 × height
Volume of	Sq. of radius	3.1416 × height
Cylinder, Truncated Right Circular		
Lateral area of.	Perimeter of base	Average height
Volume of	Area of base	Average height
Ellipse		
Area of	Product of axes	0.78540
"	Product of semi-axes . . .	3.1416
Circum. of	Sum of 2 diameters.	½ × 3.1416

GEOMETRIC FORMULAS

To Obtain:	Multiply:	by:
Fillet		
Area of	(Radius of circle)^2	0.21460
Parabola		
Area of section of	Max. width of section. . . .	$\frac{2}{3}$ × length of cord
Parallelogram		
Area of	Length of base	Altitude
Prism, Rectangular		
Volume of	Area of base	Altitude
Prism, Regular		
Lateral area of	Perimeter of base	Altitude
Volume of	Area of base	Altitude
Pyramid, Regular		
Lateral area of	Perimeter of base	$\frac{1}{2}$ × slant height
Volume of	Area of base	$\frac{1}{3}$ × altitude
Rectangle		
Area of	Length of base	Altitude
Rhombus		
Area of	Product of diagonals	$\frac{1}{2}$
Sector		
Area of	Length of arc.	$\frac{1}{2}$ × radius
Sphere		
Side of inscribed cube of. .	Radius	1.1547
Surface of	Circum.	Diameter
"	Diameter^2	3.1416
Volume of	Circum.^{3}.	0.016887
"	Diameter^3	0.52360
"	Radius^3.	4.1888
"	Surface.	$\frac{1}{6}$ × diameter
Volume of inscribed cube of	Radius^3.	1.5395
Spheroid		
Area of	Product of revolving and fixed axis	3.1416
Volume of	Square of revolving axis .	Fixed axis × .5236
Trapezoid		
Area of	Sum of parallel sides . . .	$\frac{1}{2}$ × altitude
Triangle		
Area of	Length of base	$\frac{1}{2}$ × altitude

RIGHT-ANGLED TRIANGLE
To find the perpendicular height when the base and the sum of the perpendicular and hypotenuse are known

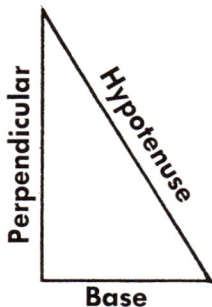

RULE:—From the square of the sum of perpendicular and hypotenuse subtract the square of the base and divide the difference by twice the sum of perpendicular and hypotenuse.

Or, divide the square of the base by the combined length of perpendicular and hypotenuse; one-half of the difference between the quotient and the combined length is the perpendicular.

EXAMPLE:—A 90-foot flagpole is broken so that its top reaches the ground 30 feet from the stump, forming a right-angled triangle. How high up is the flagpole broken?

SOLUTION:—(90 ft. $\times$ 90 ft.) — (30 ft. $\times$ 3 ft.) = 7200 ft.^{2}
7200 ft.^{2} $\div$ 2 $\times$ 90 ft. = 40 ft.
Or: (30 ft. $\times$ 30 ft.) $\div$ 90 ft. = 10 ft.
(90 ft. — 10 ft.) $\div$ 2 = 40 ft.

58

PART THREE
PHYSICAL PROPERTIES OF MATTER

STEAM TEMPERATURE — PRESSURE DATA FOR CONDENSERS

Temp. deg. fahr.	Vacuum in inches of mercury referred to a 30 in. bar. (Mercury at 58.4 deg. fahr.)	Pressure, lb. per sq. in. absolute	Pressure, inches of mercury, with mercury at 32 deg. fahr.	Temp. deg. fahr.	Vacuum in inches of mercury referred to a 30 in. bar. (Mercury at 58.4 deg. fahr.)	Pressure, lb. per sq. in. absolute	Pressure, inches of mercury, with mercury at 32 deg. fahr.
50	29.637	0.1780	0.363	90	28.580	0.696	1.417
52	29.609	0.1917	0.390	92	28.489	0.741	1.508
54	29.579	0.2063	0.420	94	28.392	0.789	1.605
56	29.547	0.2219	0.452	96	28.290	0.838	1.706
58	29.513	0.2385	0.486	98	28.183	0.891	1.813
				100	28.070	0.946	1.926
60	29.477	0.2562	0.522	102	27.951	1.005	2.045
62	29.439	0.2749	0.560	104	27.825	1.066	2.171
64	29.398	0.2949	0.601	106	27.692	1.131	2.303
66	29.354	0.3161	0.644	108	27.550	1.199	2.443
68	29.308	0.3386	0.690	110	27.404	1.271	2.589
70	29.259	0.3626	0.739	112	27.250	1.346	2.740
72	29.208	0.3880	0.790	114	27.088	1.426	2.904
74	29.153	0.4148	0.845	116	26.919	1.509	3.073
76	29.095	0.4432	0.903	118	26.739	1.597	3.252
78	29.034	0.4735	0.964	120	26.553	1.689	3.438
				122	26.355	1.785	3.635
80	28.968	0.505	1.029	124	26.149	1.886	3.841
82	28.899	0.539	1.098	126	25.931	1.992	4.057
84	28.826	0.575	1.171	128	25.706	2.103	4.282
86	28.749	0.613	1.248	130	25.48	2.219	4.52
88	28.666	0.654	1.331				

TANK SOUNDINGS CORRECTION

To determine the correct fuel or water sounding in a given double bottom tank, when the vessel's draft is greater aft than foreward (called drag).

D = Drag of vessel in feet
LS = Length of vessel in feet
LT = Length of double bottom tank in feet
X = D × LT ÷ LS

Example: $\dfrac{D7' \times LT100'}{LS700'} = 1$ ft. to be deducted from actual sounding.

CONVERSION TABLE: FRESH WATER AND SEA WATER

The following conversion table is for fresh water and sea water at 16.7°C (62°F). Specific gravity of sea water at 15°C is 1.025; at 16.7°C, 1.0247.

FRESH WATER		SALT WATER	
8.337 lb.	1 gal. (U. S.)	8.543 lb.	1 gal.
62.43 lb.	1 cubic foot	64 to 64.4 lbs.	1 cubic foot
268.68 gal.	1 long ton	266.22 gal.	1 long ton
35.915 cu. ft.	1 long ton	35.586 cu. ft.	1 long ton
35.88 cu. ft.	1 ton		
7.481 gal.	1 cubic foot	7.481 gal.	1 cubic foot

HEAT OF COMBUSTION OF CRUDE OILS, FUEL OILS AND KEROSENE

(National Bureau of Standards)*

GRAVITY DEGREES A. P. I.	TOTAL HEAT OF COMBUSTION	
	BTU -LB.	BTU.-GAL.
1	17,740**	157,800**
2	17,840**	157,500**
3	17,940**	157,200**
4	18,040**	156,900**
5	18,250	157,700
6	18,330	157,300
7	18,390	156,600
8	18,440	155,900
9	18,490	155,330
10	18,540	154,600
11	18,590	153,900
12	18,640	153,300
13	18,690	152,600
14	18,740	152,000
15	18,790	151,300
16	18,840	150,700
17	18,890	150,000
18	18,930	149,400
19	18,980	148,800
20	19,020	148,100
21	19,060	147,500
22	19,110	146,800
23	19,150	146,200
24	19,190	145,600
25	19,230	145,000
26	19,270	144,300
27	19,310	143,700
28	19,350	143,100
29	19,380	142,500
30	19,420	141,800
31	19,450	141,200
32	19,490	140,600
33	19,520	140,000
34	19,560	139,400
35	19,590	138,800
36	19,620	138,200
37	19,650	137,600
38	19,680	137,000
39	19,720	136,400
40	19,750	135,800
41	19,780	135,200
42	19,810	134,700
43	19,830	134,100
44	19,860	133,500
45	19,890	132,900
46	19,920	132,400
47	19,940	131,900
48	19,970	131,200
49	20,000	130,700

*From Miscellaneous Publication M97 "Thermal Properties of Petroleum Products"— Published by permission of the Director National Bureau of Standards.
**Based on limited data for Arabian crude, corrected for Sulfur content.

USEFUL CONVERSION FACTORS

Weight, Area, Volume

1 cu ft water = 62.4 lb @ 60 F
1 US gal = 8.34 lb water @ 60 F
1 US gal = 231 cu in = 0.134 cu ft = 0.833 Imp gal
1 Imp gal = 277.4 cu in = 1.2 US gal
1 lb = 453.6 grams (g) = 0.454 kilograms (kg)
1 kg = 1000 g = 2.2 lb
1 cu ft = 1728 cu in = 7.48 US gal = 6.23 Imp gal
1 slug = 32.2 lb

Work and Power

1 hp = 0.745 kw = 42.4 Btu/min = 2544 Btu/hr = 33,000 ft lb/min
1 boiler hp (bhp) = 33,475 Btu/hr
1 kw = 1000 watts (w) = 1.341 hp = 56.88 Btu/min = 3412 Btu/hr
1 kw hr = 1000 w hr = 3412 Btu
1 Btu = 0.029 kw hr = 778 ft lb = 0.555 pcu (lb C unit)

Pressure and Flow

1 normal atmosphere = 1.0332 kg per sq cm.
$\qquad\qquad\qquad\qquad$ = 1.0133 bars = 14.696 lb per sq in
1 lb/sq in = 2.04 in Hg @ 62 F = 2.31 ft water @ 62 F
1 lb per sq in = 0.0703 kg per sq cm
1 psia = psig + 14.7
1 kg per sq cm = 14.223 lb per sq in
1 kg per sq m = 0.2048 lb per sq ft
1 lb per sq ft = 4.8824 kg per sq m
1 kg per sq cm = 0.9678 normal atmosphere
g/cm^3 = sp gr
sp gr × 62.4 = lb/cu ft
1 gpm = 0.134 cu ft/min = 500 lb/hr × sp gr
1 cu ft/min (cfm) = 448.8 gal/hr (gph)
1 centipoise = 2.42 lb/ft hr
1 lb/ft sec = 1488 centipoises = 3600 lb/ft hr

Heat Transfer

1 Btu/hr ft^2 F = 0.0001355 g-cal sec cm^2 C
1 g-cal/sec cm^2 C = 7380 Btu/hr ft^2 F

Thermal Conductivity

1 Btu/hr ft^2 F = 0.00413 g-cal/sec cm^2 C cm
1 g-cal/sec cm^2 C cm = 242 Btu/hr ft^2 F ft

PHYSICAL PROPERTIES — SOLIDS*

	lbs./cu. ft.	sp. gr. @ 60°F	sp. ht. @ 600F	k	mp
Aluminum	165	2.64	0.23	117.0	1216
Asbestos board	55	.88	0.19	0.096	250
Asphalt, solid	81	1.1 to 1.5	0.22 to 0.4	0.43	
Brickwork & Masonry	112	1.6 to 2.0	0.22	0.4	
Calcium silicate	11	0.177		0.027	
Celotex	16			0.027	
Clay, dry	137 avg.	1.9 to 2.4	0.224	0.072	3160
Coal	90 avg.	1.2 to 1.8	0.26 to 0.37		
Coal tars	75 avg.	1.2	0.35 @ 40C		
Coke, solid	75 avg.	1.0 to 1.4	0.265	3.4	
Copper	556	8.92	0.1	220.0	1981
Cork	15	.25	0.48	0.025	
Cotton cloth	93	1.5	0.32	0.03	
Glass, pyrex	140	2.25	0.2	0.63	
Glass, wool	4.5	0.072	0.157	0.0225	
Ice	56	.9	0.5	1.41	32
Lead	710	11.34	0.031	20.0	621
Leather	59 avg.	0.86 to 1.02	0.36	0.092	
Magnesia 85%	13	.208	0.27	0.034	
Nickel	537	8.9	0.11	36.0	2651
Paper	58 avg.	0.7 to 1.15	0.45	0.075	
Paraffin	54 to 57	0.86 to 0.91	.62	0.14	100 to 140
Rubber, vulcanized	69	1.1	0.415	0.1	
Sand	90 to 105	1.4 to 1.70	0.19	0.19	
Silk	97	1.25 to 1.35	0.33	0.03	
Steel, mild @ 70F	490	7.9	0.11	26.0	2507
Steel, mild @ 1600F			0.16	18.0	2550
Steel, stainless, 300 series	501	8.04	0.12	9.4	
Styrofoam	1.3 to 2.0			0.02	
Sulfur	125	2.0	0.203	0.1	230
Titanium (commercial)	282	4.5	0.13	11.0	3135
Woods, vary from	28 to 49	0.35 to 0.9	0.45 to 0.65	0.1	
Wool	82	1.32	0.325	0.02	
Zinc	440	7.05	0.095	65.0	787

*Reproduced by permission of Platecoil Division, Tranter Manufacturing, Inc., Lansing, Michigan

	mol. wt	sp. gr 60-70F	sp ht 60F	mp F	bp F	LH	k	Visc. cp 40F (4.4C)	cp 80F (26.7C)	cp 120F (49C)	cp 160F (71C)	SSU 40F (4.4C)	SSU 80F (26.7C)	SSU 120F (49C)	SSU 160F (71C)
Acids															
Acetic acid, 100%	60	1.05	.48	62	245	175[1]	.095	1.65	1.18	0.85	0.65				
Acetic acid, 10%		1.01													
Fatty acid — oleic	282	0.89	.6	13	547		.092								
Fatty acid — palmitic	336	0.847	.75	146	520		.083								
Fatty acid — stearic	284	0.847	.44	157	721		.078								
Hydrochloric acid 31.5% (muriatic)		1.15		-53				2.5	1.85	1.42	1.1				
Hydrochloric acid 10% (muriatic)		1.05													
Nitric acid, 95%		1.50		-44	187			1.45	1.05	.8	.61				
Nitric acid, 60%		1.37		-9.4				3.4	2.2	1.5	1.05				
Nitric acid, 10%		1.05													
Phenol (carbolic acid)	94	1.07	.76	106	360			14.5	7.3	3.9	2.1				
Phosphoric acid, 20%		1.11	.56												
Phosphoric acid, 10%		1.05													
Sulfuric acid, 110%			.35	51	625	219[1]	.15	82.0	41.0	22.0	12.2	280	100	55	
Sulfuric acid, 98%		1.84		48	554			46.0	23.0	11.5	6.4	118	68	46	37
Sulfuric acid, 60%		1.50	.58				.24	8.9	5.8	3.9	2.7				
Sulfuric acid, 20%		1.14													
Water solutions															
Brine — calcium chloride, 25%		1.23	.689	-21			.28	4.5	2.1	0.95	0.52				
Brine — sodium chloride, 25%		1.19	.786	+16	221		.24	3.3	2.1	1.3	.92				
Sea water		1.03	.94												
Sodium hydroxide, 50% (caustic soda)		1.53	.78					250.0	77.0	26.0	9.5	950	240	84	46
Sodium hydroxide, 30%		1.33	.84						9.6	4.5	4.5				
Water	18	1.0	1.0	32	212	144	.34	1.55	0.86	0.56	0.4				
Food Products*															
Dextrose, corn syrup 40° Baume			.76			101						170000	11000	1700	430
Dextrose, corn syrup 45° Baume						120							2×10^6	120000	12000
Fish, fresh, avg.			.88			30									
Fruit, fresh, avg.						144									
Honey			.34			96						10000	450	155	88
Ice		.9	.5			22									
Ice cream			.70			52									
Lard		.92	.64			90									
Maple syrup			.48			124									
Meat, fresh, avg.			.70												
Milk, 3.5%			.90												
Molasses, primary A			.6										10000	2600	
Molasses, secondary B													70000	10000	
Molasses, blackstrap (final) C													300000	25000	
Starch		1.53	.3												
Sucrose, 60% sugar syrup		1.29						156	41.0	14.0	7.0	500	150	68	
Sucrose, 40% sugar syrup		1.18						120	5.0	2.5	1.6				
Sugar, cane & beet		1.66	.92												
Vegetables, fresh, avg.			.90			72									
Wines, table and dessert, avg.		1.03		7 to 22		130									

Properties of Petroleum Products and Miscellaneous Liquids (Courtesy Platecoil Division, Tranter Manufacturing, Inc.)

The table below has been reconstructed from the rotated original. The four right‑hand viscosity columns are Saybolt Universal (SSU) values at four test temperatures; the columns headed 86, 34, 17 (plus the adjacent un‑labelled column) are absolute‑viscosity values.

Product	mol wt	sp gr	sp ht	mp, °F	bp, °F	LH	k
Petroleum Products							
Asphalt, RS-1, MS-1, SS-1, emulsion		1.0					
Asphalt, RC-0, MC-0, SC-0, cut back							
Asphalt, RC-3, MC-3, SC-3, cut back							
Asphalt, RC-5, MC-5, SC-5, cut back							
Asphalt, 100-120 penetration		1.0					
Asphalt, 40-50 penetration		1.01					
Benzene	78	.844	.41	42	176	170[1]	0.087
Gasoline		.6	.53			140[1]	
No. 1 Fuel Oil (Kerosene)		.811	.47			110[1]	0.078
No. 2 Fuel Oil, —PS100		.865	.44				0.084
No. 3 Fuel Oil, —PS200		.887	.43				0.08
No. 4 Fuel Oil		.901	.42				0.078
No. 5 Fuel Oil, —PS300		.937	.41				0.075
No. 6 Fuel Oil, Bunker C—PS400		.956	.40				0.072
Transformer oil, light		.898	.42				0.070
Transformer oil, medium		.91	.42				0.075
34° API Mid-continent crude		.855	.44				0.08
28° API gas oil		.887	.42				0.078
Quench and tempering oil		.91					
SAE—5W (#8 machine lube oil)		.88					
SAE—10W (#10 machine lube oil)							
SAE—20 (# 20 machine lube oil)							
SAE—30 (# 30 machine lube oil)							
SAE—40							
SAE—50							
Paraffin, melted	92	.9	.69	100-133	660-800	70	0.14
Toluene	92	.862	.42	-139	231	157[1]	0.084
Miscellaneous							
Acetone, 100%	58	.789	.514	-137	133	225[1]	.096
Alcohol, ethyl, 95%		.81	.6			370[1]	.11
Alcohol, methyl, 90%		.82	.65	-106	-27		.13
Ammonia, 100%	17	.77	1.1				.29
Cotton seed oil		.905	1.0				.26
Creosote	(See coal tars)	.95	.47			123	.1
Dowtherm A	166	.995	.63	54	500		.08
Dowtherm C	231	1.10	.35-.65	70-220	600		.08
Ethylene glycol	62	1.11	.58	12.5	387	346[1]	.153
Glue, 2 parts water, 1 part dry glue		1.09	.89				
Glycerol, 100% (glycerin)	92	1.26	.58	62.5	554	340[1]	.164
Glycerol, 50%		1.13		-6.5	552		.24
Linseed oil		.93	.44	-5.0	544		
Phthalic anhydride	148	1.53		267			
Soybean oil		.92		239			
Sulfur, melted	32	1.8	.215	239	832	90	.074
Trichloroethylene	166	1.62		-99	189	184[1]	
Turpentine, spirits of	136	.86	.42	-14	320		.074
Carbon tetrachloride	154	1.58	.21	-95	170	841[1]	.095

Viscosity (absolute viscosity columns, then Saybolt Universal, SSU):

Product	.8 col	86	34	17	SSU (a)	SSU (b)	SSU (c)	SSU (d)
Asphalt, RS-1, MS-1, SS-1, emulsion					40	400	160	85
Asphalt, RC-0, MC-0, SC-0, cut back					43	950	340	150
Asphalt, RC-3, MC-3, SC-3, cut back					84	40000	7000	1600
Asphalt, RC-5, MC-5, SC-5, cut back					480	500000	45000	8000
Asphalt, 100-120 penetration						3500 at 250F		
Asphalt, 40-50 penetration						8000 at 250F		
Benzene	.8	.62	.46	.30				
Gasoline	.7	.55	.44	.35		36	33	32
No. 1 Fuel Oil (Kerosene)	3.3	2.1	1.4	.95		36	41	37
No. 2 Fuel Oil	4.6	2.6	1.6	1.15		52	62	42
No. 3 Fuel Oil	15.0	7.0	4.0	2.9		125	370	125
No. 4 Fuel Oil	92.0	24.0	9.6	5.0		1600	680	180
No. 5 Fuel Oil		390.0	75.0	25.0		4500	49	40
No. 6 Fuel Oil, Bunker C		1000.0	155.0	40.0			70	50
Transformer oil, light	34.2	12.1	6.3	3.9	170	72	37	34
Transformer oil, medium	89.0	28.2	11.9	6.7	460	145	48	41
34° API Mid-continent crude	15	6.5	3.0	2.0	88	51		
28° API gas oil	25	9.0	6.0	4.0	135	59		
Quench and tempering oil	170	50	22	11	550	160	74	51
SAE—5W		200	60	25	1500	265	120	64
SAE—10W		400	100	45	2900	500	170	80
SAE—20					5000	870	260	110
SAE—30					8500	1400	380	150
SAE—40					23000	3600	720	225
SAE—50								
Paraffin, melted	1200		.57	.36				
Toluene	.75		.45					
Acetone, 100%	.4	.32	.26	.21				
Alcohol, ethyl, 95%	2.0	1.3	.8	.53				
Alcohol, methyl, 90%	1.0	.73	.53	.43				
Ammonia, 100%	.14	.1	.08	.06				
Cotton seed oil	1.8	1.2						
Dowtherm A	44.0	19.0	9.0	4.5	185	86	53	39
Dowtherm C	11.0	5.4	2.8	1.5				
Ethylene glycol	72	37	20	11				
Glycerol, 100% (glycerin)		490.0	130.0	56.0	25000	3100	700	230
Phthalic anhydride		45.0						
Sulfur, melted	.7	.58	.46	.4				
Trichloroethylene	1.9	1.35	.95	.7				
Carbon tetrachloride	1.3	.95	.72	.56				

[1] This figure is latent heat of vaporization
mol wt — molecular weight
sp ht — Btu/lb F
mp — Melting point, F
bp — Boiling point, F
LH — Latent heat of fusion, Btu
k — Thermal conductivity, Btu/sq ft hr F ft
*sp ht of food products are for above freezing. Below freezing the values are approx. 60% of those given.

DENSITY EQUIVALENTS FOR LIQUIDS
AT 60°F. (15.56°C.)

Degrees A. P. I.	Specific Gravity	Pounds per U.S. Gallon	Pounds per Imp. Gallon	Kilos per U.S. Gallon	U. S. Gal. per 100 Kilos	Kilos per Imperial Gallon	Imp. Gal. per 100 Kilos
0	1.0760	8.962	10.76	4.065	24.60	4.882	20.48
1	1.0679	8.895	10.68	4.035	24.78	4.845	20.64
2	1.0599	8.828	10.60	4.004	24.97	4.809	20.79
3	1.0520	8.762	10.52	3.974	25.16	4.773	20.95
4	1.0443	8.698	10.45	3.945	25.35	4.738	21.11
5	1.0366	8.634	10.37	3.916	25.53	4.703	21.26
6	1.0291	8.571	10.29	3.888	25.72	4.669	21.42
7	1.0217	8.509	10.22	3.860	25.91	4.635	21.57
8	1.0143	8.448	10.15	3.832	26.10	4.602	21.73
9	1.0071	8.388	10.07	3.804	26.28	4.569	21.89
10	1.0000	8.328	10.00	3.778	26.47	4.537	22.04
11	.9930	8.270	9.93	3.751	26.66	4.505	22.20
12	.9861	8.212	9.86	3.725	26.85	4.473	22.35
13	.9792	8.155	9.79	3.699	27.03	4.442	22.51
14	.9725	8.099	9.73	3.674	27.22	4.412	22.67
15	.9659	8.044	9.66	3.649	27.41	4.382	22.82
16	.9593	7.989	9.59	3.624	27.60	4.352	22.98
17	.9529	7.935	9.53	3.599	27.78	4.322	23.13
18	.9465	7.882	9.47	3.575	27.97	4.294	23.29
19	.9402	7.830	9.40	3.552	28.16	4.265	23.45
20	.9340	7.778	9.34	3.528	28.34	4.237	23.60
21	.9279	7.727	9.28	3.505	28.53	4.209	23.76
22	.9218	7.676	9.22	3.482	28.72	4.181	23.92
23	.9159	7.627	9.16	3.460	28.91	4.155	24.07
24	.9100	7.578	9.10	3.437	29.09	4.128	24.22
25	.9042	7.529	9.04	3.415	29.28	4.101	24.38
26	.8984	7.481	8.98	3.393	29.47	4.075	24.54
27	.8927	7.434	8.93	3.372	29.66	4.050	24.69
28	.8871	7.387	8.87	3.351	29.84	4.024	24.85
29	.8816	7.341	8.82	3.330	30.03	3.999	25.01
30	.8762	7.296	8.76	3.309	30.22	3.974	25.16
31	.8708	7.251	8.71	3.289	30.40	3.950	25.32
32	.8654	7.206	8.65	3.269	30.59	3.925	25.48
33	.8602	7.163	8.60	3.249	30.78	3.902	25.63
34	.8550	7.119	8.55	3.229	30.97	3.878	25.79
35	.8498	7.076	8.50	3.210	31.16	3.855	25.94
36	.8448	7.034	8.45	3.191	31.34	3.832	26.10
37	.8398	6.993	8.40	3.172	31.53	3.809	26.25
38	.8348	6.951	8.35	3.153	31.72	3.786	26.41
39	.8299	6.910	8.30	3.134	31.90	3.764	26.57
40	.8251	6.870	8.25	3.116	32.09	3.742	26.72
41	.8203	6.830	8.20	3.098	32.28	3.721	26.88
42	.8155	6.790	8.15	3.080	32.47	3.699	27.04
43	.8109	6.752	8.11	3.063	32.65	3.678	27.19
44	.8063	6.713	8.06	3.045	32.84	3.657	27.35
45	.8017	6.675	8.02	3.028	33.03	3.636	27.50
46	.7972	6.637	7.97	3.011	33.22	3.615	27.66
47	.7927	6.600	7.93	2.994	33.40	3.595	27.81
48	.7883	6.563	7.88	2.977	33.59	3.575	27.97
49	.7839	6.526	7.84	2.960	33.78	3.555	28.13
50	.7796	6.490	7.79	2.944	33.97	3.535	28.29
51	.7753	6.455	7.75	2.928	34.15	3.516	28.44
52	.7711	6.420	7.71	2.912	34.34	3.497	28.59
53	.7669	6.385	7.67	2.896	34.53	3.478	28.75
54	.7628	6.350	7.63	2.880	34.72	3.459	28.91
55	.7587	6.316	7.59	2.865	34.91	3.441	29.07
56	.7547	6.283	7.55	2.850	35.09	3.423	29.22
57	.7507	6.249	7.51	2.835	35.28	3.404	29.38
58	.7467	6.216	7.47	2.820	35.47	3.386	29.53
59	.7428	6.184	7.43	2.805	35.65	3.369	29.69
60	.7389	6.151	7.39	2.790	35.84	3.351	29.84
61	.7351	6.119	7.35	2.776	36.03	3.333	30.00
62	.7313	6.087	7.31	2.761	36.22	3.316	30.16
63	.7275	6.056	7.27	2.747	36.40	3.299	30.31
64	.7238	6.025	7.24	2.733	36.59	3.282	30.47
65	.7201	5.994	7.20	2.719	36.78	3.265	30.63
66	.7165	5.964	7.16	2.705	36.97	3.249	30.78
67	.7128	5.934	7.13	2.692	37.15	3.232	30.94
68	.7093	5.904	7.09	2.678	37.34	3.216	31.09
69	.7057	5.874	7.05	2.664	37.53	3.200	31.25
70	.7022	5.845	7.02	2.651	37.72	3.184	31.41
71	.6988	5.817	6.99	2.639	37.90	3.169	31.56
72	.6953	5.788	6.95	2.625	38.09	3.153	31.72
73	.6919	5.759	6.92	2.612	38.28	3.137	31.88
74	.6886	5.731	6.88	2.600	38.47	3.122	32.03
75	.6852	5.703	6.85	2.587	38.66	3.107	32.10

Courtesy Texaco, Inc.

66

NOMOGRAPHIC CHART
SPECIFIC GRAVITY — POUNDS — GALLONS

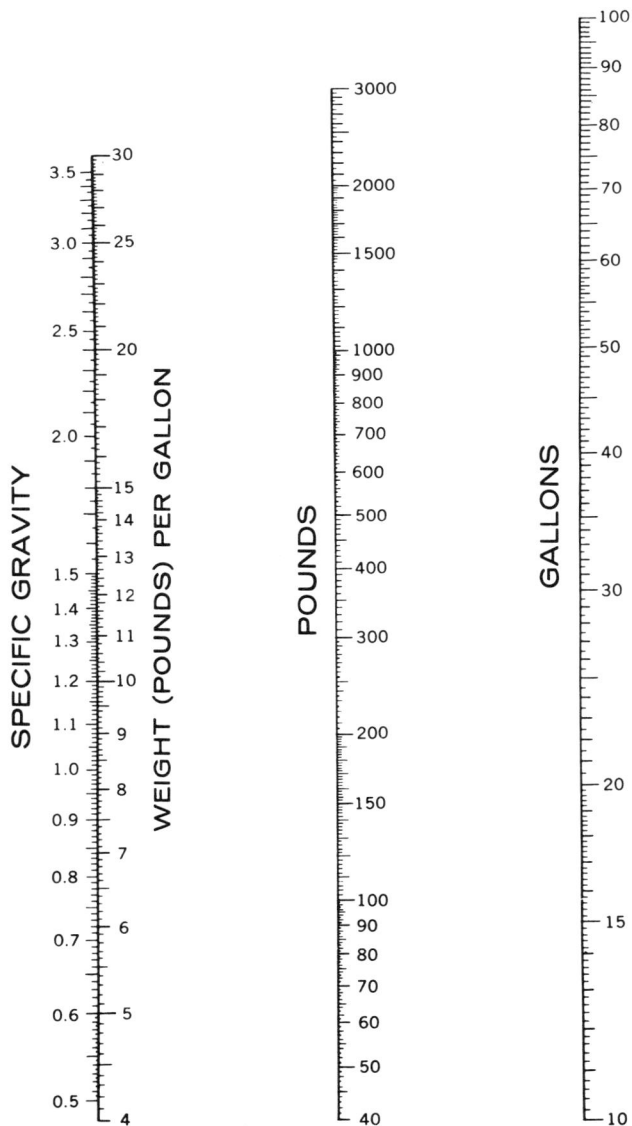

SPECIFIC GRAVITY

3.5
3.0
2.5

2.0

1.5
1.4
1.3
1.2
1.1
1.0
0.9

0.8

0.7

0.6

0.5

WEIGHT (POUNDS) PER GALLON

30

25

20

15
14
13
12
11
10
9
8

7

6

5

4

POUNDS

3000

2000

1500

1000
900
800
700

600

500

400

300

200

150

100
90
80
70

60

50

40

GALLONS

100
90
80

70

60

50

40

30

20

15

10

SPECIFIC GRAVITY

HYDROMETER CONVERSION TABLE FOR LIQUIDS LIGHTER THAN WATER

Specific Gravity 60/60°F.	Degrees A.P.I. 60°F.	Pounds Per Gal. 60°F.	Gallons Per Pound 60°F.	Degrees Baume 60°F.
1.0000	10	8.33	.1200	10
.9859	12.01	8.21	.1218	12
.9722	14.05	8.10	.1235	14
.9589	16.06	7.99	.1252	16
.9459	18.09	7.88	.1269	18
.9333	20.11	7.78	.1285	20
.9211	22.13	7.67	.1304	22
.9091	24.15	7.57	.1321	24
.8974	26.18	7.48	.1337	26
.8861	28.19	7.38	.1355	28
.8750	30.21	7.29	.1372	30
.8642	32.23	7.20	.1389	32
.8537	34.25	7.11	.1406	34
.8434	36.27	7.03	.1422	36
.8333	38.30	6.94	.1441	38
.8235	40.32	6.86	.1458	40
.8140	42.33	6.78	.1475	42
.8046	44.36	6.70	.1493	44
.7955	46.38	6.63	.1508	46
.7865	48.41	6.55	.1527	48
.7778	50.43	6.48	.1543	50
.7692	52.45	6.41	.1560	52
.7609	54.46	6.34	.1577	54
.7527	56.49	6.27	.1595	56
.7447	58.51	6.20	.1613	58
.7368	60.54	6.14	.1629	60
.7292	62.55	6.07	.1647	62
.7216	64.59	6.01	.1664	64
.7143	66.61	5.95	.1681	66
.7071	68.62	5.89	.1698	68
.7000	70.64	5.83	.1715	70
.6931	72.65	5.78	.1730	72
.6863	74.69	5.72	.1748	74
.6796	76.71	5.66	.1767	76
.6731	78.73	5.60	.1786	78
.6667	80.74	5.55	.1802	80
.6604	82.76	5.50	.1818	82
.6542	84.79	5.45	.1835	84
.6481	86.83	5.40	.1852	86
.6422	88.84	5.36	.1866	88
.6364	90.84	5.30	.1887	90
.6306	92.88	5.25	.1905	92
.6250	94.90	5.21	.1919	94
.6195	96.92	5.16	.1938	96
.6140	98.94	5.11	.1957	98
.6087	100.96	5.07	.1972	100

$$°A.P.I. = \frac{141.5}{Sp.\ Gr.\ 60/60°F.} - 131.5$$

$$Degrees\ Baume = \frac{140}{Sp.\ Gr.\ 60/60°F.} - 130$$

$$At\ 60°F.,\ Degrees\ Baume = 145 - \frac{145}{Sp.\ Gr.\ 60/60°F.}$$

HYDROMETER CONVERSION TABLE FOR LIQUIDS HEAVIER THAN WATER

Specific Gravity 60/60°F.	Pounds Per Gal. 60°F.	Gallons Per Pound 60°F.	Degrees Baume 60°F.
1.000	8.33	.1200	0
1.001	8.34	.1199	
1.004	8.36	.1196	
1.005	8.37	.1195	
1.007	8.38	.1193	1
1.014	8.46	.1182	2
1.021	8.50	.1176	3
1.028	8.56	.1168	4
1.036	8.63	.1159	5
1.043	8.69	.1151	6
1.050	8.75	.1143	7
1.058	8.81	.1135	8
1.066	8.88	.1126	9
1.074	8.94	.1119	10
1.082	9.01	.1110	11
1.090	9.08	.1101	12
1.099	9.15	.1093	13
1.107	9.21	.1086	14
1.115	9.29	.1076	15
1.124	9.36	.1068	16
1.133	9.43	.1060	17
1.142	9.51	.1052	18
1.151	9.59	.1043	19
1.160	9.67	.1034	20
1.169	9.74	.1027	21
1.179	9.81	.1019	22
1.189	9.9	.1010	23
1.198	9.99	.1001	24
1.208	10.07	.0993	25
1.218	10.16	.0984	26
1.229	10.24	.0977	27
1.239	10.32	.0969	28
1.250	10.41	.0961	29
1.261	10.51	.0951	30
1.272	10.59	.0944	31
1.283	10.69	.0935	32
1.295	10.78	.0928	33
1.306	10.84	.0923	34
1.318	10.98	.0911	35
1.330	11.09	.0902	36
1.343	11.18	.0894	37
1.355	11.29	.0886	38
1.368	11.39	.0878	39
1.381	11.51	.0869	40
1.394	11.61	.0861	41
1.408	11.72	.0853	42
1.421	11.84	.0845	43
1.436	11.96	.0836	44
1.450	12.08	.0828	45
1.465	12.21	.0819	46
1.480	12.33	.0811	47
1.495	12.46	.0803	48
1.510	12.58	.0795	49
1.526	12.72	.0786	50
1.543	12.85	.0778	51
1.559	12.99	.0770	52
1.576	13.13	.0762	53
1.593	13.27	.0754	54
1.611	13.42	.0745	55
1.629	13.57	.0737	56
1.648	13.72	.0729	57
1.667	13.87	.0721	58
1.686	14.04	.0712	59
1.706	14.21	.0704	60

STANDARD ATMOSPHERE DATA

Altitude Feet	Mm. Hg. Absolute	Inches Hg. Absolute	PSI Absolute	Millibars	Microns
120,000	3.344	.132	.0646	4.45	.....
124,000	2.848	.112	.0552	3.79	.....
130,000	2.260	.089	.0437	3.01	.....
136,000	1.813	.071	.0352	2.41	.....
140,000	1.575	.062	.0305	2.01	.....
144,000	1.375	.054	.0266	1.83	.....
150,000	1.128	.044	.0218	1.50	.....
160,000	.827	.033	.0160	1.10	827.
170,000	.616	.024	.0119	.822	616.
180,000	.459	.018	.0088	.611	459.
190,000	.343	.014	.00665	.456	343.
200,000	.257	.010	.00498	.342	257.
210,000	.18876	.00743	.00365	.25162	188.
220,000	.13653	.00538	.00264	.18199	136.
230,000	.09722	.00383	.00188	.12959	97.2
240,000	.06723	.00265	.00130	.08962	67.2
250,000	.04551	.00179	.00088	.06066	45.5
260,000	.03062	.00121	.000592	.04082	30.6
270,000	.01970	.00078	.000381	.02626	19.7
280,000	.01319	.00052	.000255	.01758	13.2
290,000	.00910	.00036	.000176	.01213	9.10
300,000	.00646	.00025	.000125	.00861	6.46
310,000	.00465	.00018	.000090	.00620	4.65
320,000	.003455	.000136	.0000668	.004606	3.46
330,000	.002601	.000102	.0000503	.003467	2.60
340,000	.001971	.000078	.0000385	.002654	1.99
350,000	.001536	.000060	.0000297	.002047	1.53
360,000	.001195	.000047	.0000231	.001593	1.19
370,000	.000936	.000037	.0000181	.001248	0.936
380,000	.000719	.000028	.0000139	.000958	0.719
390,000	.000590	.000023	.0000114	.000786	0.590
393,700	.000543	.000021	.0000105	.000724	0.543

Altitude Feet	Mm. Hg. Absolute	Inches Hg. Absolute	PSI Absolute	Millibars	Microns
0	760.	29.92	14.7	1013.1	.....
2,000	706.6	27.82	13.6	940.	.....
4,000	656.3	25.84	12.7	873.	.....
5,000	632.3	24.89	12.2	840.	.....
6,000	609.0	23.98	11.8	810.	.....
8,000	564.4	22.22	10.9	750.	.....
10,000	522.6	20.58	10.1	695.	.....
12,000	483.3	19.03	9.4	642.	.....
14,000	446.4	17.57	8.6	594.	.....
15,000	428.8	16.88	8.4	569.	.....
16,000	411.8	16.21	7.96	548.	.....
18,000	379.4	14.94	7.35	504.	.....
20,000	349.1	13.75	6.76	464.	.....
25,000	281.9	11.00	5.41	374.	.....
30,000	225.6	8.88	4.34	299.	.....
35,000	178.7	7.04	3.46	236.	.....
40,000	140.7	5.54	2.72	187.	.....
45,000	110.8	4.36	2.14	147.	.....
50,000	87.30	3.436	1.68	116.	.....
55,000	68.76	2.707	1.33	91.5	.....
60,000	54.15	2.132	1.04	72.0	.....
65,000	43.06	1.694	.834	57.4	.....
70,000	33.95	1.334	.656	45.1	.....
75,000	26.78	1.054	.517	35.6	.....
80,000	21.13	.833	.408	28.1	.....
85,000	16.67	.656	.322	22.19	.....
90,000	13.15	.518	.254	17.50	.....
95,000	10.37	.408	.201	13.78	.....
100,000	8.19	.322	.159	10.90	.....
104,987	6.47	.254	.125	8.62	.....
110,000	5.135	.202	.0994	6.84	.....
116,000	3.954	.155	.0765	5.26	.....

Bowser Technical Refrigeration, Terryville, Connecticut, Bulletin 754, page 11

VISCOSITY CONVERSION TABLES*

The following table provides a comparison of various viscosity ratings, so that if the viscosity is given in terms other than Saybolt Universal, it can be translated quickly by following horizontally to the Saybolt Universal column.

Seconds Saybolt Universal ssu	Kinematic Viscosity Centistokes *	Seconds Saybolt Furol ssf	Seconds Redwood 1 (Standard)	Seconds Redwood 2 (Admiralty)	Degrees Engler	Degrees Barbey
31	1.00		29		1.00	6200
35	2.56		32.1		1.16	2420
40	4.30		36.2	5.10	1.31	1440
50	7.40		44.3	5.83	1.58	838
60	10.3	12.95	52.3	6.77	1.88	618
70	13.1	13.70	60.9	7.60	2.17	483
80	15.7	14.44	69.2	8.44	2.45	404
90	18.2		77.6	9.30	2.73	348
100	20.6	15.24	85.6	10.12	3.02	307
150	32.1	19.30	128	14.48	4.48	195
200	43.2	23.5	170	18.90	5.92	144
250	54.0	28.0	212	23.45	7.35	114
300	65.0	32.5	254	28.0	8.79	95
400	87.60	41.9	338	37.1	11.70	70.8
500	110.0	51.6	423	46.2	14.60	56.4
600	132	61.4	508	55.4	17.50	47.0
700	154	71.1	592	64.6	20.45	40.3
800	176	81.0	677	73.8	23.35	35.2
900	198	91.0	762	83.0	26.30	31.3
1000	220	100.7	896	92.1	29.20	28.2
1500	330	150	1270	138.2	43.80	18.7
2000	440	200	1690	184.2	58.40	14.1
2500	550	250	2120	230	73.0	11.3
3000	660	300	2540	276	87.60	9.4
4000	880	400	3380	368	117.0	7.05
5000	1100	500	4230	461	146	5.64
6000	1320	600	5080	553	175	4.70
7000	1540	700	5920	645	204.5	4.03
8000	1760	800	6770	737	233.5	3.52
9000	1980	900	7620	829	263	3.13
10000	2200	1000	8460	921	292	2.82
15000	3300	1500	13700		438	2.50
20000	4400	2000	18400		584	1.40

*Kinematic Viscosity (in centistokes) = $\dfrac{\text{Absolute viscosity (in centipoises)}}{\text{Specific Gravity}}$

70

APPROXIMATE VISCOSITY CONVERSION TABLE

KINEMATIC VISCOSITY	SAYBOLT UNIVERSAL	SAYBOLT FUROL	REDWOOD NO. 1	ENGLER DEGREES
Centistokes	SECONDS	SECONDS	SECONDS	
2	32.6		31.2	1.10
3	36.0		33.5	1.21
4	39.1		35.8	1.31
5	42.4		38.4	1.40
6	45.6		41.0	1.48
7	48.8		43.7	1.56
8	52.1		46.3	1.65
9	55.5		49.0	1.75
10	58.9		52.1	1.84
12	66.0		58.2	2.04
15	77.4		68.0	2.30
20	97.8		85	2.87
25	119		103	3.4
30	141		122	4.0
35	164		144	4.6
40	186		163	5.3
50	232	26.1	201	6.6
60	278	30.6	243	7.8
80	371	39.6	323	10.4
100	464	48.6	405	13.0
120	556	57.8	484	15.8
150	695	71.7	610	19.5
200	927	95.0	800	26.0
500	2317	236	2020	65
1000	4800	472	4100	133

Courtesy Texaco, Inc.

TEMPERATURE CONVERSION FORMULAS

To convert from	To	Substitute in formula
Degrees Centigrade	Degrees Fahrenheit	(°C. × 9/5) + 32
Degrees Centigrade	Degrees Kelvin	(°C. + 273.16)
Degrees Centigrade	Degrees Reaumur	(°C. × 4/5)
Degrees Fahrenheit	Degrees Centigrade	(°F. − 32) × 5/9
Degrees Fahrenheit	Degrees Rankin	(°F. + 459.69)
Degrees Fahrenheit	Degrees Reaumur	(°F. − 32) × 4/9
Degrees Reaumur	Degrees Centigrade	(°Reaumur×5/4)
Degrees Reaumur	Degrees Fahrenheit	(°Reaumur × 9/4) + 32

71

TEMPERATURE CONVERSION TABLES

C.		F.	C.		F.
0.56	1	1.8	3.33	6	10.8
1.11	2	3.6	3.89	7	12.6
1.67	3	5.4	4.44	8	14.4
2.22	4	7.2	5.00	9	16.2
2.78	5	9.0	5.56	10	18.0

—100 to 95

C.		F.	C.		F.
−73.3	**−100**	−148	6.11	**43**	109.4
−67.8	**−90**	−130	6.67	**44**	111.2
−62.2	**−80**	−112	7.22	**45**	113.0
−56.7	**−70**	−94	7.78	**46**	114.8
−51.1	**−60**	−76	8.33	**47**	116.6
−45.6	**−50**	−58	8.89	**48**	118.4
−40.0	**−40**	−40	9.44	**49**	120.2
−34.4	**−30**	−22	10.0	**50**	122.0
−28.9	**−20**	−4	10.6	**51**	123.8
−23.3	**−10**	14	11.1	**52**	125.6
−17.8	**0**	32	11.7	**53**	127.4
−17.2	**1**	33.8	12.2	**54**	129.2
−16.7	**2**	35.6	12.8	**55**	131.0
−16.1	**3**	37.4	13.3	**56**	132.8
−15.6	**4**	39.2	13.9	**57**	134.6
−15.0	**5**	41.0	14.4	**58**	136.4
−14.4	**6**	42.8	15.0	**59**	138.2
−13.9	**7**	44.6	15.6	**60**	140.0
−13.3	**8**	46.4	16.1	**61**	141.8
−12.8	**9**	48.2	16.7	**62**	143.6
−12.2	**10**	50.0	17.2	**63**	145.4
−11.7	**11**	51.8	17.8	**64**	147.2
−11.1	**12**	53.6	18.3	**65**	149.0
−10.6	**13**	55.4	18.9	**66**	150.8
−10.0	**14**	57.2	19.4	**67**	152.6
−9.44	**15**	59.0	20.0	**68**	154.4
−8.89	**16**	60.8	20.6	**69**	156.2
−8.33	**17**	62.6	21.1	**70**	158.0
−7.78	**18**	64.4	21.7	**71**	159.8
−7.22	**19**	66.2	22.2	**72**	161.6
−6.67	**20**	68.0	22.8	**73**	163.4
−6.11	**21**	69.8	23.3	**74**	165.2
−5.56	**22**	71.6	23.9	**75**	167.0
−5.00	**23**	73.4	24.4	**76**	168.8
−4.44	**24**	75.2	25.0	**77**	170.6
−3.89	**25**	77.0	25.6	**78**	172.4
−3.33	**26**	78.8	26.1	**79**	174.2
−2.78	**27**	80.6	26.7	**80**	176.0
−2.22	**28**	82.4	27.2	**81**	177.8
−1.67	**29**	84.2	27.8	**82**	179.6
−1.11	**30**	86.0	28.3	**83**	181.4
−0.56	**31**	87.8	28.9	**84**	183.2
−0	**32**	89.6	29.4	**85**	185.0
0.56	**33**	91.4	30.0	**86**	186.8
1.11	**34**	93.2	30.6	**87**	188.6
1.67	**35**	95.0	31.1	**88**	190.4
2.22	**36**	96.8	31.7	**89**	192.2
2.78	**37**	98.6	32.2	**90**	194.0
3.33	**38**	100.4	32.8	**91**	195.8
3.89	**39**	102.2	33.3	**92**	197.6
4.44	**40**	104.0	33.9	**93**	199.4
5.00	**41**	105.8	34.4	**94**	201.2
5.56	**42**	107.6	35.0	**95**	203.0

96 to 1100

C.		F.	C.		F.
35.6	**96**	204.8	304	**580**	1076
36.1	**97**	206.6	310	**590**	1094
36.7	**98**	208.4	316	**600**	1112
37.2	**99**	210.2	321	**610**	1130
37.8	**100**	212.0	327	**620**	1148
38	**100**	212	332	**630**	1166
43	**110**	230	338	**640**	1184
49	**120**	248	343	**650**	1202
54	**130**	266	349	**660**	1220
60	**140**	284	354	**670**	1238
66	**150**	302	360	**680**	1256
71	**160**	320	366	**690**	1274
77	**170**	338	371	**700**	1292
82	**180**	356	377	**710**	1310
88	**190**	374	382	**720**	1328
93	**200**	392	388	**730**	1346
99	**210**	410	393	**740**	1364
100	**212**	413	399	**750**	1382
104	**220**	428	404	**760**	1400
110	**230**	446	410	**770**	1418
116	**240**	464	416	**780**	1436
121	**250**	482	421	**790**	1454
127	**260**	500	427	**800**	1472
132	**270**	518	432	**810**	1490
138	**280**	536	438	**820**	1508
143	**290**	554	443	**830**	1526
149	**300**	572	449	**840**	1544
154	**310**	590	454	**850**	1562
160	**320**	608	460	**860**	1580
166	**330**	626	466	**870**	1598
171	**340**	644	471	**880**	1616
177	**350**	662	477	**890**	1634
182	**360**	680	482	**900**	1652
188	**370**	698	488	**910**	1670
193	**380**	716	493	**920**	1688
199	**390**	734	499	**930**	1706
204	**400**	752	504	**940**	1724
210	**410**	770	510	**950**	1742
216	**420**	788	516	**960**	1760
221	**430**	806	521	**970**	1778
227	**440**	824	527	**980**	1796
232	**450**	842	532	**990**	1814
238	**460**	860	538	**1000**	1832
243	**470**	878	543	**1010**	1850
249	**480**	896	549	**1020**	1868
254	**490**	914	554	**1030**	1886
260	**500**	932	560	**1040**	1904
266	**510**	950	566	**1050**	1922
271	**520**	968	571	**1060**	1940
277	**530**	986	577	**1070**	1958
282	**540**	1004	582	**1080**	1976
288	**550**	1022	588	**1090**	1994
293	**560**	1040	593	**1100**	2012
299	**570**	1058			

NOTE:—The numbers in bold face type refer to the temperature either in degrees Centigrade or Fahrenheit which it is desired to convert into the other scale. If converting from Fahrenheit degrees to Centigrade degrees the equivalent temperature will be found in the left column, while if converting from degrees Centigrade to degrees Fahrenheit, the answer will be found in the column on the right.

HEAT LOSS FROM WATER SURFACE AT VARIOUS WATER TEMPERATURES AND AIR VELOCITIES

Air Temperatures, 60°F., Relative Humidity, 70%

Water Temp F	AIR VELOCITY — FEET PER SECOND HEAT LOSS — Btu/Hr (Sq Ft)							
	0	0.5	1	2	5	10	20	50
60	7	18	21	26	34	56	95	180
70	33	52	60	78	105	170	270	580
80	78	110	125	150	210	315	510	1050
90	130	180	210	240	330	490	780	1600
100	205	270	320	350	480	710	1150	2300
110	290	370	420	480	670	1000	1600	3300
120	400	500	570	660	930	1350	2200	4400
130	550	660	750	890	1240	1800	3000	6000
140	710	870	970	1150	1600	2400	4000	8000
150	950	1130	1260	1510	2100	3200	5300	10500
160	1230	1450	1600	2000	2700	4050	6900	13700
170	1600	1900	2100	2600	3700	5200	9100	18500
180	2050	2600	2900	3550	5000	7200	12500	25000
190	2600	3550	4000	4950	6900	10300	17500	35000
200	3300	5200	5700	7000	9700	14600	25000	50000

From "Heat Losses from Tanks, Vats and Kettles" by Samuel J. Friedman, E. I. DuPont De Nemours and Co., Heating and Ventilating, Apr. 1948.

Elements	Symbol	Density (Specific Gravity)	Weight Per Cubic Foot	Specific Heat	Melting Point Degrees Centigrade	Degrees Fahrenheit
Aluminum	Al	2.7	166.7	0.212	658.7	1217.7
Antimony	Sb	6.69	418.3	0.049	630	1166
Armco Iron		7.9	490.0	0.115	1535	2795
Carbon	C	2.34	219.1	0.113	3600	6512
Chromium	Cr	6.92	431.9	0.104	1615	3034
Columbium	Cb	7.06	452.54		1700	3124
Copper	Cu	8.89	555.6	0.092	1083	1981.4
Gold	Au	19.33	1205.0	0.032	1063	1946
Hydrogen	H	0.070*	0.00533		−259	−434.2
Iridium	Ir	22.42	1400.0	0.032	2300	4172
Iron	Fe	7.865	490.9	0.115	1530	2786
Lead	Pb	11.37	708.5	0.030	327	621
Manganese	Mn	7.4	463.2	0.111	1260	2300
Mercury	Hg	13.55	848.84	0.033	−38.7	−37.6
Nickel	Ni	8.80	555.6	0.109	1452	2645.6
Nitrogen	N	0.97*	.063		−210	−346
Oxygen	O	1.10*	.0866		−218	−360
Phosphorus	P	1.83	146.1	0.19	44	111.2
Platinum	Pt	21.45	1336.0	0.032	1755	3191
Potassium	K	0.87*	54.3	0.170	62.3	144.1
Silicon	Si	2.49	131.1	0.175	1420	2588
Silver	Ag	10.5	655.5	0.055	960.5	1761
Sodium	Na	0.971	60.6	0.253	97.5	207.5
Sulphur	S	1.95	128.0	0.173	119.2	246
Tin	Sn	7.30	455.7	0.054	231.9	449.5
Titanium	Ti	5.3	218.5	0.110	1795	3263
Tungsten	W	17.5	1186.0	0.034	3000	5432
Uranium	U	18.7	1167.0	0.028		
Vanadium	V	6.0	343.3	0.115	1720	3128
Zinc	Zn	7.19	443.2	0.093	419	786.2
Bronze (90 Cu 10 Sn)		8.78	548.0		850–1000	1562–1832
Brass (90 Cu 10 Zn)		8.60	540.0		1020–1030	1868–1886
Brass (70 Cu 30 Zn)		8.44	527.0		900–940	1652–1724
Cast Pig Iron		7.1	443.2		1100–1250	2012–2282
Open Hearth Steel		7.8	486.9		1350–1530	2462–2786
Wrought Iron Bars		7.8	486.9		1530	2786

*Density compared with air.

Courtesy Posey Iron Works, Lancaster, Pa.

FUEL PREHEAT TEMPERATURES vs FUEL VISCOSITY

SSU/ 100°F	Fuel Viscosity SSF/ 122°F*	Redw'd #1/ 100F°	Pumping** Temp., °F	Preheat Temp. °F*** For 70 SSU	100 SSU	200 SSU
200	12	176	—	160	133	100
300	17	264	26	177	153	116
400	22	352	34	189	162	126
500	27	440	42	198	171	135
600	32	528	46	204	176	141
700	36	616	50	208	182	146
800	40	704	53	211	185	150
900	44	792	57	215	188	153
1000	48	880	61	219	192	157
1050	50	924	64	220	194	158
1600	75	1408	73	242	208	172
2200	100	1936	82	246	216	180
3000	125	2639	87	255	225	188
3600	150	3167	91	260	232	193
4400	175	3891	95	266	236	197
5000	200	4399	100	270	240	200
5800	225	5103	102	275	244	204
6500	250	5719	104	277	247	206
7100	275	6247	106	280	250	210
7800	300	6862	109	282	253	211
10,000	350	8798	113	287	257	217
11,500	400	10,118	115	291	261	220
13,000	450	11,438	118	294	265	223

*Approx. Converted from SSU/100°F **5,000 SSU ***Atomizing vis. at nozzle or injector

Courtesy Texaco, Inc.

EXPANSION COEFFICIENTS OF PETROLEUM OILS

Coefficient of Expansion	Degrees API	Gravity Ranges Specific Gravity
at 60°F.	at 60°F.	at 60°F.
0.00035	Below 14.9	Above 0.9665
0.00040	15 to 34.9	0.9659 to 0.8504
0.00050	35 to 50.9	0.8498 to 0.7758
0.00060	51 to 63.9	0.7753 to 0.7242
0.00070	64 to 78.9	0.7238 to 0.6725
0.00080	79 to 88.9	0.6722 to 0.6420
0.00085	89 to 93.9	0.6417 to 0.6278

The coefficient of expansion for a given gravity range may be used for calculating the volume at 60°F. of any oil having a gravity within the given range from its volume at a different temperature by:

1) When the temperature is below 60°F., multiplying the volume by a factor of 1 minus the coefficient of expansion times the difference tween the temperature and 60°F.

Example: What is the volume at 60°F. of 1000 gals. of an oil at 40°F., having a gravity of 25° API?
Factor $= 1 + (0.0004 \times 20) = 1.008$
Vol. at 60°F. $= 1000 \times 1.008 = 1008$ gals.

2) When the temperature is above 60°F., multiplying the volume by a factor of 1 minus the coefficient of expansion times the difference between the temperature and 60°F.

Example: What is the volume at 60°F. of 1000 gals. of an oil at 80°F., having a gravity of 25° API?
Factor $= 1 - (0.0004 \times 20) = 0.992$
Vol. at 60°F. $= 1000 \times 0.992 = 992$ gals.

To determine the weight per gallon of a product from its A.P.I. Gravity, it is necessary first to convert to specific gravity as follows:

$$\text{Sp. Gr.} = \frac{141.5}{131.5 + \text{A.P.I.}}$$

Having the specific gravity, multiply by 8.328 to obtain the weight per gallon.

Petroleum products are usually referred to on the A.P.I. scale of gravity for liquids lighter than water, which figure is reached from the specific gravity as follows:

$$\text{A. P. I. Gravity} = \frac{141.5}{\text{Sp. Gr.}} - 131.5$$

AIR-CONDITIONING DATA

Refrigerant Pressure vs. Temperature

Figures in last four columns are gage pressures in lb. per sq. in.

*Denotes inches vacuum.

Temp. (Deg. F)	"Freon 12"	"Freon 22"	Methyl Chloride	Sulphur Dioxide
—40	11.0*	0.6	15.9*	23.5*
—35	8.3*	2.7	13.9*	22.4*
—30	5.5*	5.0	11.5*	21.1*
—25	2.3*	7.5	8.9*	19.6*
—20	0.6	10.3	6.1*	17.9*
—15	2.5	13.3	3.0*	16.1*
—10	4.5	16.6	0.3	13.9*
— 5	6.7	20.3	2.1	11.5*
0	9.2	24.2	4.2	8.9*
5	11.8	28.4	6.5	5.9*
10	14.7	33.0	8.9	2.6*
15	17.7	37.9	11.6	0.5
20	21.1	43.3	14.5	2.5
25	24.6	49.0	17.5	4.6
30	28.5	53.3	21.0	7.0
35	32.6	61.7	24.6	9.6
40	37.0	69.0	28.6	12.4
45	41.7	76.5	32.8	15.5
50	46.7	84.7	37.3	18.8
55	52.0	93.5	42.1	22.4
60	57.7	102.5	47.3	26.2
65	63.7	112.0	52.8	30.4
70	70.1	122.5	58.7	34.9
75	76.9	133.0	65.0	39.8
80	84.1	145.0	71.6	45.0
85	91.7	156.7	78.5	50.6
90	99.6	170.1	86.0	56.6
95	108.1	183.4	93.8	62.9
100	116.9	197.9	102.0	69.8
105	126.2	212.5	110.7	77.2
110	136.0	228.7	119.8	85.0
115	146.3	245.0	129.5	93.3
120	157.1	262.6	139.5	106.2

Courtesy Texaco, Inc.

PIPELINE AND TANK CAR DOME CAPACITIES

	Contains Gallons	Dome Diam.	Gals. Per In.	Dome Diam.	Gals. Per In.
1 foot 1-in. dia. pipe 1.049 (ID)	.0449	20″	1.36	60″	12.24
1 foot 2-in. dia. pipe 2.067 (ID)	.1743	22	1.65	62	13.07
1 foot 3-in. dia. pipe 3.068 (ID)	.3840	24	1.96	64	13.93
1 foot 4-in. dia. pipe 4.026 (ID)	.6613	26	2.30	66	14.81
1 foot 5-in. dia. pipe 5.047 (ID)	1.0393	28	2.66	68	15.72
1 foot 6-in. dia. pipe 6.065 (ID)	1.5008	30	3.00	70	16.66
1 foot 6-in. dia. pipe 5.761 (ID)	1.3541	32	3.48	72	17.63
1 foot 7-in. dia. pipe 7.023 (ID)	2.0124	34	3.90	74	18.62
1 foot 8-in. dia. pipe 8.071 (ID)	2.6578	36	4.40	76	19.64
1 foot 8-in. dia. pipe 7.625 (ID)	2.3721	38	4.91	78	20.69
1 foot 9-in. dia. pipe 8.941 (ID)	3.2616	40	5.40	80	21.76
1 foot 10-in. dia. pipe 10.192 (ID)	4.2382	42	6.00	82	22.86
1 foot 10-in. dia. pipe 10.020 (ID)	4.0963	44	6.58	84	23.99
1 foot 12-in. dia. pipe 12.090 (ID)	5.9637	46	7.19	86	25.15
1 foot 12-in. dia. pipe 12.000 (ID)	5.8752	48	7.83	88	26.33
1 foot 24-in. dia. pipe 24.000 (ID)	23.5008	50	8.50	90	27.54
1 foot 4-ft. dia. tank	94.0032	52	9.19	92	28.78
1 foot 5-ft. dia. tank	146.8800	54	9.91	94	30.04
1 foot 10-ft. dia. tank	587.5200	56	10.66	96	31.33
1 foot 20-ft. dia. tank	2350.0800	58	11.44	98	32.65
1 foot 50-ft. dia. tank	14688.0000				

Dome Diameter Squared x .0034
Equals U. S. Gallons per Inch

Courtesy E. W. Saybolt & Co.

SHIPPING TONNAGE

40 Cubic Feet of Round or   )
50 Cubic Feet of Hewn Timber) = 1 U.S. Shipping Ton = 32.143 U.S. Bushels.
42   Cubic Feet = 1 British Shipping Ton = 33.75 U.S. Bushels
100   Cubic Feet = 1 Register Ton (assumed for measurement of internal capacity of a vessel).
45.8 Cubic Feet = 1 Ton Lackawana Coal, or 48.89 lb. per cu. ft.
40.5 Cubic Feet = 1 Ton Lehigh Coal,   or 55.32 lb. per cu. ft.
42   Cubic Feet = 1 Ton Average Hard Coal.
46   Cubic Feet = 1 Ton Soft Coal.
88   Cubic Feet = 1 Ton Coke.
   A ton of round timber, when square, is supposed to produce 40 cubic feet; hence, one-fifth is lost by squaring.

WEIGHT PER CUBIC FOOT, MISCELLANEOUS MATERIALS

Aluminum	163 lbs.	Loose earth and sand	95 lbs.
Anthracite coal	50-55	Marble	171
Bituminous coal	45-55	Mercury	849
Brick	125	Oak wood	55
Bronze	552	Red pine	42
Cast iron	450	Rubber	95
Clay	135	Steel	490
Copper	555	Strong soil	127
Common soil	124	Tallow	59
Cork	15	Water	62.5
Granite	165	White pine	30
Lead	710	Wrought iron	486¾

PROPERTIES OF SATURATED STEAM*

Reproduced by permission of Platecoil Division, Tranter Manufacturing, Inc., Lansing, Michigan

Pressure lb Gauge	Pressure lb Absolute	Tempera- ture Deg Fahr	v_g Specific Volume Cu Ft per lb	h_f Heat of Liquid	h_{fg} Latent Heat of Evapora- tion	h_g Total Heat of Steam	s_f Entropy of Water	s_g Entropy of Steam
0	14.7	212.	26.79	180.0	970.4	1150.4	.3118	1.7565
1	15.7	215.3	25.23	183.4	968.2	1151.6	.3168	1.7511
5	19.7	227.2	20.38	195.3	960.6	1155.9	.3343	1.7332
10	24.7	239.4	16.49	207.7	952.5	1160.2	.3522	1.7146
15	29.7	249.7	13.88	218.2	945.5	1163.7	.3672	1.6999
20	34.7	258.8	11.99	227.4	939.3	1166.7	.3801	1.6875
25	39.7	266.9	10.57	235.6	933.7	1169.3	.3914	1.6767
30	44.7	274.1	9.45	243.0	928.5	1171.5	.4015	1.6670
35	49.7	280.6	8.56	249.7	923.8	1173.5	.4108	1.6586
40	54.7	286.7	7.82	255.9	919.4	1175.3	.4191	1.6510
45	59.7	292.4	7.20	261.8	915.1	1176.9	.4268	1.6436
50	64.7	297.7	6.68	267.2	911.2	1178.4	.4340	1.6372
55	69.7	302.6	6.23	272.3	907.4	1179.7	.4407	1.6311
60	74.7	307.3	5.83	277.1	903.9	1181.0	.4471	1.6255
65	79.7	311.8	5.49	281.7	900.5	1182.2	.4531	1.6203
70	84.7	316.0	5.18	286.1	897.2	1183.3	.4587	1.6154
75	89.7	320.1	4.91	290.3	894.0	1184.3	.4641	1.6108
80	94.7	323.9	4.67	294.3	891.0	1185.3	.4691	1.6063
85	99.7	327.6	4.441	298.1	888.2	1186.3	.4740	1.6022
90	104.7	331.2	4.241	301.8	885.3	1187.1	.4786	1.5982
95	109.7	334.6	4.058	305.4	882.6	1188.0	.4831	1.5944
100	114.7	337.9	3.890	308.8	880.0	1188.8	.4875	1.5909

105	119.7	341.1	3.735	312.1	877.4	1189.5	.4917	1.5875
110	124.7	344.2	3.591	315.3	874.9	1190.2	.4957	1.5841
115	129.7	347.2	3.460	318.4	872.5	1190.9	.4996	1.5809
120	134.7	350.1	3.338	321.5	870.1	1191.6	.5033	1.5779
125	139.7	352.9	3.226	324.4	867.8	1192.2	.5070	1.5749
130	144.7	355.7	3.118	327.3	865.5	1192.8	.5105	1.5721
135	149.7	358.3	3.018	330.1	863.3	1193.4	.5140	1.5694
140	154.7	360.9	2.925	332.8	861.1	1193.9	.5173	1.5666
145	159.7	363.4	2.839	335.5	859.0	1194.5	.5206	1.5641
150	164.7	365.9	2.758	338.1	856.9	1195.0	.5237	1.5617
155	169.7	368.4	2.680	340.6	854.8	1195.4	.5267	1.5592
160	174.7	370.7	2.606	343.1	852.8	1195.9	.5297	1.5568
165	179.7	373.0	2.537	345.5	850.9	1196.4	.5326	1.5544
170	184.7	375.3	2.472	347.9	848.9	1196.8	.5355	1.5522
175	189.7	377.5	2.410	350.3	847.0	1197.3	.5382	1.5499
180	194.7	379.7	2.350	352.6	845.1	1197.7	.5409	1.5478
185	199.7	381.8	2.293	354.8	843.3	1198.1	.5435	1.5457
190	204.7	383.9	2.240	357.0	841.5	1198.5	.5462	1.5437
195	209.7	385.9	2.190	359.1	839.7	1198.8	.5487	1.5417
200	214.7	387.9	2.141	361.3	837.9	1199.2	.5512	1.5399
210	224.7	391.7	2.050	366.0	833.9	1199.9	.5550	1.5353
220	234.7	395.4	1.961	369.5	830.9	1200.4	.5596	1.5316
230	244.7	399.9	1.882	374.0	826.9	1200.9	.5642	1.5277
240	254.7	402.6	1.811	377.8	823.5	1201.3	.5684	1.5242
250	264.7	406.0	1.744	381.5	820.2	1201.7	.5726	1.5207
260	274.7	409.3	1.682	385.1	817.0	1202.1	.5766	1.5173
270	284.7	412.6	1.624	388.6	813.8	1202.4	.5806	1.5141
280	294.7	414.8	1.571	392.1	810.6	1202.7	.5844	1.5108
290	304.7	418.8	1.520	395.4	807.4	1202.8	.5882	1.5077
300	314.7	421.7	1.474	398.7	804.6	1203.3	.5917	1.5049

INTERNATIONAL ATOMIC WEIGHTS

Name	Sym-bol	Atomic Number	Atomic Weight	Name	Sym-bol	Atomic Number	Atomic Weight
Actinium	Ac	89	227	Mercury	Hg	80	200.61
Aluminum	Al	13	26.98	Molybdenum	Mo	42	95.95
Americium	Am	95	243*	Neodymium	Nd	60	144.27
Antimony	Sb	51	121.76	Neon	Ne	10	20.183
Argon	Ar	18	39.944	Neptunium	Np	93	237*
Arsenic	As	33	74.91	Nickel	Ni	28	58.69
Astatine	At	85	210*	Niobium	Nb	41	92.91
Barium	Ba	56	137.36	Nitrogen	N	7	14.008
Berkelium	Bk	97	245*	Nobelium	No	102	253*(?)
Beryllium	Be	4	9.013	Osmium	Os	76	190.2
Bismuth	Bi	83	209.00	Oxygen	O	8	16.0000
Boron	B	5	10.82	Palladium	Pd	46	106.7
Bromine	Br	35	79.916	Phosphorus	P	15	30.975
Cadmium	Cd	48	112.41	Platinum	Pt	78	195.23
Calcium	Ca	20	40.08	Plutonium	Pu	94	242*
Californium	Cf	98	248*	Polonium	Po	84	210
Carbon	C	6	12.010	Potassium	K	19	39.100
Cerium	Ce	58	140.13	Praseodymium	Pr	59	140.92
Cesium	Cs	55	132.91	Promethium	Pm	61	145*
Chlorine	Cl	17	35.457	Protactinium	Pa	91	231
Chromium	Cr	24	52.01	Radium	Ra	88	226.05
Cobalt	Co	27	58.94	Radon	Rn	86	222
Copper	Cu	29	63.54	Rhenium	Re	75	186.31
Curium	Cm	96	245*	Rhodium	Rh	45	102.91
Dysprosium	Dy	66	162.46	Rubidium	Rb	37	85.48
Einsteinium	Es	99	247*	Ruthenium	Ru	44	101.1
Erbium	Er	68	167.2	Samarium	Sm	62	150.43
Europium	Eu	63	152.0	Scandium	Sc	21	44.96
Fermium	Fm	100	254*	Selenium	Se	34	78.96
Fluorine	F	9	19.00	Silicon	Si	14	28.09
Francium	Fr	87	223*	Silver	Ag	47	107.880
Gadolinium	Gd	64	156.9	Sodium	Na	11	22.991
Gallium	Ga	31	69.72	Strontium	Sr	38	87.63
Germanium	Ge	32	72.60	Sulfur	S	16	32.066†
Gold	Au	79	197.0	Tantalum	Ta	73	180.95
Hafnium	Hf	72	178.6	Technetium	Tc	43	99*
Helium	He	2	4.003	Tellurium	Te	52	127.61
Holmium	Ho	67	164.94	Terbium	Tb	65	158.93
Hydrogen	H	1	1.0080	Thallium	Tl	81	204.39
Indium	In	49	114.76	Thorium	Th	90	232.05
Iodine	I	53	126.91	Thulium	Tm	69	168.94
Iridium	Ir	77	192.2	Tin	Sn	50	118.70
Iron	Fe	26	55.85	Titanium	Ti	22	47.90
Krypton	Kr	36	83.80	Tungsten	W	74	183.92
Lanthanum	La	57	138.92	Uranium	U	92	238.07
Lead	Pb	82	207.21	Vanadium	V	23	50.95
Lithium	Li	3	6.940	Xenon	Xe	54	131.3
Lutetium	Lu	71	174.99	Ytterbium	Yb	70	173.04
Magnesium	Mg	12	24.32	Yttrium	Y	39	88.92
Manganese	Mn	25	54.94	Zinc	Zn	30	65.38
Mendelevium	Md	101	256*(?)	Zirconium	Zr	40	91.22

* Mass number of the isotope of longest known half-life.

† Because of natural variations in relative abundance of the sulfur isotopes, its atomic weight has a range of ±0.003.

THE DILUTION AND CONCENTRATION
OF LIQUIDS AND MIXTURES

RECTANGLE METHOD

The figures expressing the percentage concentration of two solutions (or those of one solution, and the figure 0 *for water*, where dilution with water is desired) are written in the two left hand corners of a rectangle, and the figure expressing the desired concentration is placed on the intersection of the two diagonals of this rectangle.

Now substract the figures on the diagonals, and write the result at the other end of the respective diagonal. These figures then indicate what quantities of the solutions whose concentration is given on the other end of the respective *horizontal* line, must be taken to obtain a solution of the desired concentration. For example, to make a 12% solution, by mixing an 8% and a 15% solution we prepare Fig. 1, which indicates that we have to take 3 parts by weight of the 8% solution, and 4 parts by weight of the 15% solution to obtain (7 parts by weight of) the 12% solution.

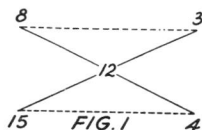

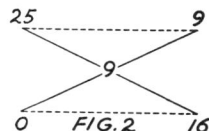

FIG. 1

Again, if we wish to dilute a 25% solution so as to obtain a 9% solution, we place the figure 25 in, for example, the upper left corner of a rectangle and place figure 0 (concentration of the solution in pure water) in the lower left corner, and then place the figure 9 (desired concentration) at the point of intersection of the diagonals, and subtracting across the diagonals, we obtain Fig. 2: 9 parts by weight of the 25% solution, if mixed with 16 parts by weight of water, will give 25 parts by weight of a 9% solution.

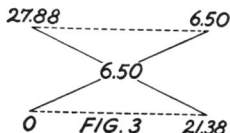

FIG. 2

In diluting to a given Baumé strength or Specific Gravity, the percentage composition, corresponding to the Baumé of Specific Gravity, must be taken from the following tables. For instance; supposing a 32° Baumé chloride of alumina solution is to be diluted to 8° Baumé with water. By reference to table on page 208 a 32° Baumé solution contains 27.88% Al_2Cl_6, and an 8° Baumé solution contains 6.50%

FIG. 3

Al_2Cl_6. These percentages must be used in finding the weights of chloride of alumina and water to be mixed by the above method. According to the scheme as outlined above, the percentages are arranged as in Fig. 3 and the subtractions made along the diagonals, the lower from the higher. Thus when 32° Baumé chloride of alumina is mixed with water in the proportion 6.50 pounds to 21.38 pounds, 27.88 pounds of solution will be obtained at 8° Baumé.

Courtesy Monsanto Chemical Company

ACIDITY AND ALKALINITY

The pH Value

The use of pH values to express the degree of acidity or alkalinity of solutions was at one time merely of theoretical interest. Now, with the availability of rugged industrial-type pH meters, it is one of the most common controls for chemical and processing industries.

A simplified explanation of the meaning of pH may be of interest to those not already familiar with it.

In the pH scale, the figure 7.0 represents an exact neutrality. This is the pH of chemically pure water. If an alkali such as caustic soda is added to pure water, the pH value of the solution is increased and may rise to values as high as 14.0. If, on the other hand, an acid such as hydrochloric acid is added, the pH value decreases as more acid is added.

The pH value, therefore, indicates first of all the condition of a solution with respect to acidity or alkalinity. For example, the fact that a solution has a pH value of 6.0 indicates that it has an acid reaction, while a pH value of 8.0 indicates an alkaline solution. These values, however, have an additional and much more important function in that they are an absolutely accurate measure of the *relative* degree of acidity or alkalinity.

For example, the value pH 6.0 means that a solution has an acidity ten times that of pure water while for pH 5.0 the value is 100 times that of water. The table below shows these and other values graphically:

pH Value	Relative Acidity or Alkalinity in Terms of Pure Water.	
0	X 10,000,000	⎫
1	X 1,000,000	
2	X 100,000	
3	X 10,000	⎬ Acidity
4	X 1,000	
5	X 100	
6	X 10	⎭
7	1	Pure Water
8	X 10	⎫
9	X 100	
10	X 1,000	
11	X 10,000	⎬ Alkalinity
12	X 100,000	
13	X 1,000,000	
14	X 10,000,000	⎭

The following example will illustrate the value of pH in determining the relative degree of acidity of two solutions:

ACIDITY AND ALKALINITY

Two acid solutions are made up, one containing 0.37% of hydrochloric acid, the other 0.60% of acetic acid. Equal quantities of these two solutions require exactly the same quantity of a solution of a caustic soda to neutralize them and, according to this method of evaluation, they are of an equal degree of acidity. Determinations of the pH values of the two solutions, however, would show:

$$0.37\% \text{ hydrochloric acid} = \text{pH } 1.04$$
$$0.60\% \text{ acetic acid} \qquad = \text{pH } 2.89$$

Reference to the table on the preceding page will show that the difference in these two pH values indicates that the hydrochloric acid solution is nearly 100 times more strongly acid than the acetic acid solution. In this instance, it will be noted that pH values bring out clearly the fact that hydrochloric acid is a very strong acid while acetic acid is relatively weak. The general behavior of these two acids readily confirms this fact.

Equipment is now available for making rapid and accurate determinations of pH values either by colorimetric or electrometric methods. No technical training is required to use this equipment.

RELATION BETWEEN HEAT COLORS AND APPROPRIATE TEMPERATURES

Color	Temperature	
	°F	°C
Dazzling..	3450	1900
White..	2200	1200
Light yellow	1975	1080
Yellow...	1825	995
Orange...	1725	940
Salmon..	1650	900
Bright red......................................	1550	845
Cherry or full red	1375	745
Medium cherry	1175	635
Dark red.......................................	1050	565
Red just visible	930	500

PART FOUR

METAL WORKING AND MECHANICAL DATA

HARDNESS CONVERSION TABLE

E = diam. in mm., 3000 Kg. load, 10 mm. ball

D = hardness number

C = 150 Kg. load, 120° Diamond cone

B = 100 Kg. load, 1/16-inch diameter ball

A = Shore Scleroscope number

F = tensile strength 1000 psi.

BRINELL		ROCKWELL			
E	D	C	B	A	F
2.25	745	68	...	100	368
2.30	712	66	...	95	352
2.35	682	64	...	91	337
2.40	653	62	...	87	324
2.45	627	60	...	84	311
2.50	601	58	...	81	298
2.55	578	57	...	78	287
2.60	555	55	120	75	276
2.65	534	53	119	72	266
2.70	514	52	119	70	256
2.75	495	50	117	67	247
2.80	477	49	117	65	238
2.85	461	47	116	63	229
2.90	444	46	115	61	220
2.95	429	45	115	59	212
3.00	415	44	114	57	204
3.05	401	42	113	55	196
3.10	388	41	112	54	189
3.15	375	40	112	52	182
3.20	363	38	110	51	176
3.25	352	37	110	49	170
3.30	341	36	109	48	165
3.35	331	35	109	46	160
3.40	321	34	108	45	155
3.45	311	33	108	44	150
3.50	302	32	107	43	146
3.55	293	31	106	42	142
3.60	285	30	105	40	138
3.65	277	29	104	39	134
3.70	269	28	104	38	131
3.75	262	26	103	37	128
3.80	255	25	102	37	125
3.85	248	24	102	36	122
3.90	241	23	100	35	119
3.95	235	22	99	34	116

BRINELL		ROCKWELL			
E	D	C	B	A	F
4.00	229	21	98	33	113
4.05	223	20	97	32	110
4.10	217	18	96	31	107
4.15	212	17	96	31	104
4.20	207	16	95	30	101
4.25	202	15	94	30	99
4.30	197	13	93	29	97
4.35	192	12	92	28	95
4.40	187	10	91	28	93
4.45	183	9	90	27	91
4.50	179	8	89	27	89
4.55	174	7	88	26	87
4.60	170	6	87	26	85
4.65	166	4	86	25	83
4.70	163	3	85	25	82
4.75	159	2	84	24	80
4.80	156	1	83	24	78
4.85	153	..	82	23	76
4.90	149	..	81	23	75
4.95	146	..	80	22	74
5.00	143	..	79	22	72

Permission of American Society for Metals. (Above is a portion of Hardness Conversion Table from "Metals Handbook.")

SINE BAR

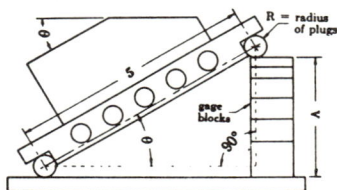

R = radius of plugs

gage blocks

$$A = 5 \sin \theta$$

TAPERED PINS

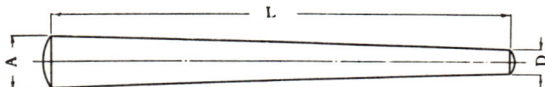

.25 inch taper per foot. D = drill size

Length	.75	1.00	1.25	1.5	1.75	2	2.25	2.5	2.75	3	3.25	3.5	3.75	4	4.5	5	5.5
No. A	D	D	D	D	D	D	D	D	D	D	D	D	D	D	D	D	D
0 .156	.140	.135	.130	.125	.120	.115	.110	.104	.099	.094	.089	.083	.078	.073	.062	.051	.041
1 .172	.156	.151	.146	.141	.136	.130	.125	.120	.115	.110	.104	.099	.094	.089	.078	.068	.057
2 .193	.177	.172	.167	.162	.157	.151	.146	.141	.136	.131	.125	.120	.115	.110	.099	.089	.078
3 .219	.203	.198	.193	.188	.183	.177	.172	.167	.162	.157	.151	.146	.141	.136	.125	.115	.104
4 .250	.234	.229	.224	.219	.214	.208	.203	.198	.193	.188	.183	.177	.172	.167	.156	.146	.135
5 .289	.273	.268	.263	.258	.253	.247	.242	.237	.232	.227	.221	.216	.211	.206	.195	.185	.174
6 .341	.325	.320	.315	.310	.305	.299	.294	.289	.284	.279	.273	.268	.263	.258	.247	.237	.226
7 .409	.393	.388	.383	.378	.373	.367	.362	.357	.352	.347	.341	.336	.331	.326	.315	.305	.294
8 .492	.476	.471	.466	.461	.456	.450	.445	.440	.435	.430	.424	.419	.413	.409	.398	.388	.377
9 .591	.575	.570	.565	.560	.555	.549	.544	.539	.534	.529	.523	.518	.513	.508	.497	.487	.476
10 .706	.690	.685	.680	.675	.670	.664	.659	.654	.649	.644	.638	.633	.628	.623	.612	.602	.591

GAUGES FOR WIRE, SHEET AND TWIST DRILLS

No. of Gauge	Washburn & Moen	American or Brown & Sharpe	Birmingham or Stubbs	U. S. standard for Plate (Iron & Steel)	Stubbs Steel Wire	Imperial Wire Gauge	Morse Twist Drill and Steel Wire	Wood and Machine Screws	American S. & W. Piano & Music Wire
7–0	.....	.....	....	.500	....	.....	.....	....	....
6–0	.....	.....	....	.469	....	.464	.....	....	....
5–0	.....	.....	....	.438	....	.432	.....	....	.005
4–0	.394	.460	.454	.406	....	.400	.....	....	.006
3–0	.362	.410	.425	.375	....	.372	.....	.032	.007
2–0	.331	.365	.380	.344	....	.348	.....	.045	.008
0	.307	.325	.340	.313	....	.324	.....	.058	.009
1	.283	.289	.300	.281	.227	.300	.228	.071	.010
2	.263	.258	.284	.266	.219	.276	.221	.084	.011
3	.244	.229	.259	.250	.212	.252	.213	.097	.012
4	.225	.204	.238	.234	.207	.232	.209	.110	.013
5	.207	.182	.220	.219	.204	.212	.206	.124	.014
6	.192	.162	.203	.203	.201	.192	.204	.137	.016
7	.177	.144	.180	.188	.199	.176	.201	.150	.018
8	.162	.128	.165	.172	.197	.160	.199	.163	.020
9	.148	.114	.148	.156	.194	.144	.196	.176	.022
10	.135	.102	.134	.141	.191	.128	.194	.189	.024
11	.120	.091	.120	.125	.188	.116	.191	.203	.026
12	.105	.081	.109	.109	.185	.104	.189	.216	.029
13	.092	.072	.095	.094	.182	.092	.185	.229	.031
14	.080	.064	.083	.078	.180	.080	.182	.242	.033
15	.072	.057	.072	.070	.178	.072	.180	.255	.035
16	.063	.051	.065	.063	.175	.064	.177	.268	.037
17	.054	.045	.058	.056	.172	.056	.173	.282	.039
18	.047	.040	.049	.050	.168	.048	.170	.295	.041
19	.041	.036	.042	.044	.164	.040	.166	.308	.043
20	.035	.032	.035	.038	.161	.036	.161	.321	.045
21	.032	.028	.032	.034	.157	.032	.159	.334	.047
22	.028	.025	.028	.031	.155	.028	.157	.347	.049
23	.025	.023	.025	.028	.153	.024	.154	.360	.051
24	.023	.020	.022	.025	.151	.022	.152	.374	.055
25	.020	.018	.020	.022	.148	.020	.150	.387	.059
26	.018	.016	.018	.019	.146	.018	.147	.400	.063
27	.0173	.0141	.016	.0171	.143	.0164	.144	.413	.067
28	.0162	.0126	.014	.0156	.139	.0149	.141	.426	.071
29	.015	.0112	.013	.014	.134	.0136	.136	.439	.075
30	.014	.010	.012	.0125	.127	.0124	.129	.453	.080
31	.0132	.0089	.010	.0109	.120	.0116	.120	.466	.085
32	.0128	.0079	.009	.0101	.115	.0108	.116	.479	.090
33	.0118	.007	.008	.0093	.112	.010	.113	.492	.095
34	.0104	.0063	.007	.0085	.110	.0092	.111	.505	.100
35	.0095	.0056	.005	.0078	.108	.0084	.110	.518	.106
36	.009	.005	.004	.007	.106	.0076	.1065	.532	.112
37	.....	.0044	....	.0066	.103	.0068	.104	.545	.118
38	.....	.0039	....	.0062	.101	.006	.1015	.558	.124
39	.....	.0035	....	.....	.099	.0052	.0995	.571	.130
40	.....	.0031	....	.....	.097	.0048	.098	.584	.138
41	.....	.....	....	.....	.095	.....	.096	.597	.146
42	.....	.....	....	.....	.092	.....	.094	.611	.154
43	.....	.....	....	.....	.088	.....	.089	.624	.162
44	.....	.....	....	.....	.085	.....	.086	.637	.170
45	.....	.....	....	.....	.081	.....	.082	.650	.180
46	.....	.....	....	.....	.079	.....	.081	.663	....
47	.....	.....	....	.....	.077	.....	.079	.676	....
48	.....	.....	....	.....	.075	.....	.076	.690	....
49	.....	.....	....	.....	.072	.....	.073	.703	....
50	.....	.....	....	.....	.069	.....	.070	.716	....

CONVERSION TABLES — STEEL AND 5% CLAD STEEL

Gage in Fractions of an Inch	Gage in Decimal Equivalents of an Inch	Gage Equivalents in Pounds per Square Foot for STEEL	Thickness of Cladding in Decimal Equivalents of an Inch on 5% CLAD STEEL
1/64	.0156	.637	.0008*
1/32	.0312	1.275	.0016*
3/64	.0469	1.912	.0023*
1/16	.0625	2.550	.0031*
5/64	.0781	3.187	.0039*
3/32	.0937	3.825	.0047*
7/64	.1093	4.462	.0055*
1/8	.1250	5.100	.0063*
9/64	.1406	5.737	.0070*
5/32	.1562	6.375	.0078*
11/64	.1719	7.012	.0086*
3/16	.1875	7.650	.0093**
13/64	.2031	8.287	.0103**
7/32	.2187	8.925	.0109**
15/64	.2344	9.562	.0117**
1/4	.2500	10.200	.0125**
17/64	.2656	10.837	.0133**
9/32	.2812	11.475	.0141**
19/64	.2969	12.112	.0148**
5/16	.3125	12.750	.0156**
21/64	.3281	13.387	.0164**
11/32	.3437	14.025	.0172**
23/64	.3594	14.662	.0180**
3/8	.3750	15.300	.0187**
25/64	.3906	15.937	.0195**
13/32	.4062	16.575	.0203**
27/64	.4219	17.212	.0211**
7/16	.4375	17.850	.0218**
29/64	.4531	18.487	.0227**
15/32	.4687	19.125	.0234**
31/64	.4844	19.762	.0242**
1/2	.5000	20.400	.0250
33/64	.5156	21.037	.0258
17/32	.5312	21.675	.0266
35/64	.5469	22.312	.0273
9/16	.5625	22.950	.0282
37/64	.5781	23.587	.0289
19/32	.5937	24.225	.0297
39/64	.6094	24.862	.0305
5/8	.6250	25.500	.0312
41/64	.6406	26.137	.0320
21/32	.6562	26.775	.0328
43/64	.6719	27.412	.0336
11/16	.6875	28.050	.0344
45/64	.7031	28.687	.0352
23/32	.7187	29.325	.0359
47/64	.7344	29.962	.0367
3/4	.7500	30.600	.0375
49/64	.7656	31.237	.0383
25/32	.7812	31.875	.0391
51/64	.7969	32.512	.0398
13/16	.8125	33.150	.0406
53/64	.8281	33.787	.0414
27/32	.8437	34.425	.0422
55/64	.8594	35.062	.0430
7/8	.8750	35.700	.0438
57/64	.8906	36.337	.0445
29/32	.9062	36.975	.0453
59/64	.9219	37.612	.0461
15/16	.9375	38.250	.0469
61/64	.9531	38.887	.0477
31/32	.9687	39.525	.0484
63/64	.9844	40.162	.0492
1.0	1.0000	40.800	.0500
2.0	2.0000	81.600	.1000
3.0	3.0000	122.400	.1500
4.0	4.0000	163.200	.2000

*Gages not produced by Lukens.   **5% clad steel is not regularly available in these gages.

Courtesy Lukens Steel Company

GEAR FORMULAS
(ALL DIMENSIONS IN INCHES UNLESS NOTED)

Table of Tangents	
Angle	Tangent
3°	.0524
5°	.0875
8°	.141
10°	.176
13°	.231
15°	.268
18°	.325
20°	.364
25°	.466
30°	.577
35°	.700

$$\text{Ratio} = \frac{\text{Number Gear Teeth}}{\text{Number Pinion Teeth}} = \frac{\text{Pinion RPM}}{\text{Gear RPM}}$$

$$\text{Pinion Pitch Dia.} = \frac{2 \times \text{Center Distance}}{(\text{Ratio} + 1)}$$

$$\text{Diametral Pitch (DP)} = \frac{\text{Number of Teeth}}{\text{Pitch Dia.}} \quad \text{or} \quad \frac{\pi}{\text{CP}}$$

$$\text{Circular Pitch (CP)} = \frac{\text{Pitch Dia.} \times \pi}{\text{Number of Teeth}} \quad \text{or} \quad \frac{\pi}{\text{DP}}$$

$$\text{Tooth Pressure (pounds)} = \frac{126,000 \times HP}{\text{Pitch Dia.} \times RPM}$$

Single Helical Thrust (Pounds) = Tooth Pressure x Tangent Helix Angle

Pitch Line Velocity (ft. per min.) = .262 x Pitch Dia. x RPM

GENERAL FORMULAS

$$\text{Horsepower} = \frac{P(\text{pounds}) \times 2\,\pi \times R(\text{inches}) \times RPM}{33,000 \times 12}$$

$$\text{Horsepower} = \frac{P \times R \times RPM}{63,000} \quad \text{or} \quad \frac{\text{Torque} \times RPM}{63,000}$$

$$\text{Torque (inch pounds)} = \frac{HP \times 63,000}{RPM} \quad \text{or} \quad P \times R$$

$$\text{Shaft Stress (Pounds per sq. inch)} = \frac{HP \times 321,000}{RPM \times \text{Shaft Dia.}^3}$$

$$\text{Journal Velocity (Feet per second)} = \frac{\text{Journal Dia. (Inches)} \times RPM}{229}$$

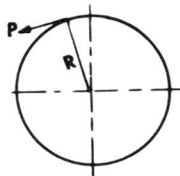

OVERHUNG LOAD (POUNDS) INCLUDING MODIFYING FACTORS

$$\text{Single Sprocket} = \frac{HP \times 63,000}{RPM \times \text{Radius}}$$

$$\text{V-belt Sheaves} = \frac{HP \times 94,500}{RPM \times \text{Radius}}$$

$$\text{Pinions or Multiple Sprocket} = \frac{HP \times 78,750}{RPM \times \text{Radius}}$$

$$\text{Flat Belt Pulleys} = \frac{HP \times 157,500}{RPM \times \text{Radius}}$$

CONVERSION FACTORS

1 HP = 33,000 ft. pounds per min.
1 HP = 0.7457 KW
1 KW = 1.341 HP
1 BTU = 778 ft. pounds
1 HP = 2545 BTU/HR.
1 gal. (water) = 8.336 pounds

Courtesy The Falk Corporation

DRILL SIZES FOR MACHINE SCREWS

Fractional Size Drills Inches	Wire Gauge and Letter Size Drills	Decimal Equiv- alent Inches	Machine Screw				
			No.	O. D.	Threads Per Inch	Tap Drill	Clear. Drill
	80	.0135					
	79	.0145					
1/64		.0156					
	78	.0160					
	77	.0180					
	76	.0200					
	75	.0210					
	74	.0225					
	73	.0240					
	72	.0250					
	71	.0260					
	70	.0280					
	69	.0292					
	68	.0310					
1/32		.0312					
	67	.0320					
	66	.0330					
	65	.0350					
	64	.0360					
	63	.0370					
	62	.0380					
	61	.0390					
	60	.0400					
	59	.0410					
	58	.0420					
	57	.0430					
	56	.0465					
3/64		.0469					
	55	.0520					
	54	.0550					
	53	.0595					
1/16		.0625	0	.060	80	3/64	1/16
	52	.0635					
	51	.0670					
	50	.0700					
	49	.0730					
	48	.0760					
5/64		.0781					
	47	.0785	1	.078	{72 64	53 53	47 47
	46	.0810					
	45	.0820					
	44	.0860					
	43	.0890					
	42	.0935	2	.086	{64 56	50 50	42 42
3/32		.0937					
	41	.0960					
	40	.0980					
	39	.0995					
	38	.1015					
	37	.1040	3	.099	{48 56	47 45	37 37
	36	.1065					

DRILL SIZES FOR MACHINE SCREWS

Fractional Size Drills Inches	Wire Gauge and Letter Size Drills	Decimal Equiv- alent Inches	Machine Screw				
			No.	O. D.	Threads Per Inch	Tap Drill	Clear. Drill
7/64		.1094					
	35	.1100					
	34	.1110					
	33	.1130					
	32	.1160			36	44	31
	31	.1200	4	.112	40	43	31
1/8		.1250			48	42	31
	30	.1285					
	29	.1360	5	.125	40	38	29
	28	.1405			44	37	29
9/64		.1406			32	36	27
	27	.1440	6	.138	32	36	27
	26	.1470			40	33	27
	25	.1495					
	24	.1520					
	23	.1540					
5/32		.1562					
	22	.1570					
	21	.1590					
	20	.1610					
	19	.1660			32	29	18
	18	.1695	8	.164	36	29	18
11/64		.1719					
	17	.1730					
	16	.1770					
	15	.1800					
	14	.1820					
	13	.1850					
3/16		.1875					
	12	.1890					
	11	.1910					
	10	.1935			24	25	9
	9	.1960	10	.190	32	21	9
	8	.1990					
	7	.2010					
13/64		.2031					
	6	.2040					
	5	.2055					
	4	.2090					
	3	.2130					
7/32		.2187					
	2	.2210			24	16	1
	1	.2280	12	.216	28	14	1
	A	.2340					
15/64		.2344					
	B	.2380					
	C	.2420					
	D	.2460					
1/4	E	.2500					
	F	.2570					
	G	.2610					

DRILL SIZES FOR MACHINE SCREWS

Fractional Size Drills Inches	Wire Gauge and Letter Size Drills	Decimal Equiv-alent Inches	Machine Screw				
			No.	O. D.	Threads Per Inch	Tap Drill	Clear. Drill
17/64		.2656	1/4	.250	20	7	17/64
	H	.2660			28	3	17/64
	I	.2720					
	J	.2770					
	K	.2810					
9/32		.2812					
	L	.2900					
	M	.2950					
19/64		.2969					
	N	.3020					
5/16		.3125					
	O	.3160					
	P	.3230					
21/64		.3281	5/16	.3125	18	F	21/64
	Q	.3320			24	I	21/64
	R	.3390					
11/32		.3437					
	S	.3480					
	T	.3580					
23/64		.3594					
	U	.3680					
3/8		.3750					
	V	.3770					
	W	.3860					
25/64		.3906	3/8	.375	16	5/16	25/64
	X	.3970			24	Q	25/64
	Y	.4040					
13/32		.4062					
	Z	.4130					
27/64		.4219					
7/16		.4375					
29/64		.4531	7/16	.4515	14	U	29/64
15/32		.4687			20	25/64	29/64
31/64		.4844					
1/2		.5000					
33/64		.5156	1/2	.500	13	27/64	33/64
					20	29/64	33/64

PIPE PLUG AND RING GAUGE SIZES

d—nominal size of pipe
D—outside diameter of pipe
n—number of threads per inch
h—depth of thread
B— minor diameter of ring gage (large end)
C— minor diameter of ring gage (small end)
G—major diameter of plug gage (large end)
F—major diameter of plug gage (small end)

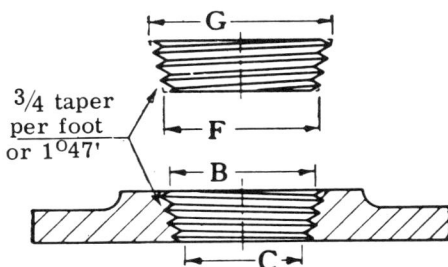

d	n	D	h	B	C	G	F
1/8	27	0.405	.029	0.355	0.339	0.404	0.388
1/4	18	0.540	.044	0.465	0.440	0.539	0.514
3/8	18	0.675	.044	0.600	0.575	0.674	0.649
1/2	14	0.840	.057	0.744	0.711	0.839	0.806
3/4	14	1.050	.057	0.954	0.920	1.049	1.015
1	11.5	1.315	.069	1.198	1.156	1.314	1.271
1 1/4	11.5	1.660	.069	1.543	1.499	1.659	1.615
1 1/2	11.5	1.900	.069	1.783	1.738	1.899	1.854
2	11.5	2.375	.069	2.258	2.211	2.374	2.327
2 1/2	8	2.875	.100	2.707	2.636	2.874	2.803
3	8	3.500	.100	3.332	3.257	3.499	3.424
3 1/2	8	4.000	.100	3.832	3.754	3.999	3.921
4	8	4.500	.100	4.332	4.251	4.499	4.418
4 1/2	8	5.000	.100	4.832	4.748	4.999	4.914
5	8	5.563	.100	5.395	5.307	5.562	5.474
6	8	6.625	.100	6.457	6.363	6.624	6.529
7	8	7.625	.100	7.457	7.356	7.624	7.523
8	8	8.625	.100	8.457	8.350	8.624	8.517
9	8	9.625	.100	9.457	9.344	9.624	9.510
10	8	10.750	.100	10.582	10.462	10.749	10.628
11	8	11.750	.100	11.582	11.456	11.749	11.622
12	8	12.750	.100	12.582	12.449	12.749	12.616
14 O.D.	8	14.000	.100	13.832	13.691	13.999	13.858
15 O.D.	8	15.000	.100	14.832	14.685	14.999	14.852
16 O.D.	8	16.000	.100	15.832	15.679	15.999	15.846

PIPE THREADS

d   = nominal size of pipe
L_1 = engagement length by hand
L_2 = thickness of full ring
E_0 = pitch diameter of plug and ring gages at small end
E_1 = pitch diameter of plug and ring gages at notch end of gage
E_2 = pitch diameter of plug and ring gages at large end of ring

The outside diameter of pipe (D), the number of threads per inch (n), and the depth of thread (h) are the same as those given on the preceding page.
To obtain the major diameters of the plug gage add (k) to E_0, E_1, and E_2, respectively. To obtain the minor diameters of the ring gage subtract (k) from E_0, E_1, and E_2 respectively.

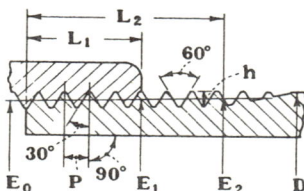

d	L_1	L_2	E_0	E_1	E_2	k
1/8	0.180	0.264	0.363	0.375	0.380	0.025
1/4	0.200	0.402	0.477	0.490	0.502	0.037
3/8	0.240	0.408	0.612	0.627	0.637	0.037
1/2	0.320	0.534	0.758	0.778	0.792	0.048
3/4	0.339	0.546	0.968	0.989	1.002	0.048
1	0.400	0.683	1.214	1.239	1.256	0.058
1 1/4	0.420	0.707	1.557	1.583	1.601	0.058
1 1/2	0.420	0.723	1.796	1.822	1.841	0.058
2	0.436	0.756	2.269	2.296	2.316	0.058
2 1/2	0.682	1.137	2.719	2.762	2.791	0.083
3	0.766	1.200	3.341	3.388	3.416	0.083
3 1/2	0.821	1.250	3.837	3.889	3.916	0.083
4	0.844	1.300	4.334	4.387	4.416	0.083
4 1/2	0.875	1.350	4.831	4.886	4.916	0.083
5	0.937	1.406	5.391	5.449	5.479	0.083
6	0.958	1.512	6.446	6.506	6.541	0.083
7	1.000	1.612	7.440	7.502	7.541	0.083
8	1.063	1.712	8.433	8.500	8.541	0.083
9	1.130	1.812	9.427	9.498	9.541	0.083
10	1.210	1.925	10.545	10.621	10.666	0.083
11	1.285	2.025	11.539	11.619	11.666	0.083
12	1.360	2.125	12.533	12.618	12.916	0.083
14 O. D.	1.562	2.250	13.775	13.873	13.916	0.083
15 O. D.	1.687	2.350	14.769	14.874	14.916	0.083
16 O. D.	1.812	2.450	15.762	15.876	15.916	0.083

AMERICAN NATIONAL THREAD
HEXAGON AND SQUARE NUT SIZES

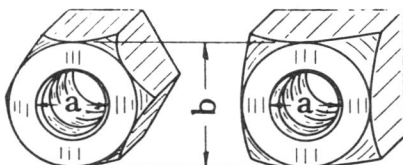

E—thickness of nut
C—distance across corners, hexagon nut
D—distance across corners, square nut

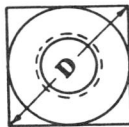

a	b	E	D	C
.0723	.23345	.0723	.33014	.26956
.0852	.25280	.0852	.35750	.29190
.0981	.27215	.0981	.38487	.31425
.1110	.29150	.1110	.41223	.33659
.1240	.3110	.1240	.43981	.35911
.1369	.33035	.1369	.46718	.38145
.1629	.36935	.1629	.52233	.42648
.1887	.40805	.1887	.57706	.47117
.2147	.44705	.2147	.63221	.51620
.250	.500	.2500	.70711	.57735
.3125	.59375	.3125	.83968	.68560
.375	.6875	.3750	.97226	.79385
.4375	.78125	.4375	1.10484	.90210
.500	.875	.5000	1.2374	1.0103
.5625	.96875	.5625	1.3700	1.1186
.625	1.0625	.6250	1.5025	1.2268
.750	1.250	.7500	1.7677	1.4433
.875	1.4375	.8750	2.0329	1.6598
1.000	1.625	1.000	2.2980	1.8763
1.125	1.8125	1.125	2.5632	2.0928
1.25	2.000	1.250	2.8284	2.3094
1.50	2.375	1.500	3.3587	2.7424
1.75	2.750	1.750	3.8890	3.1754
2.00	3.125	2.000	4.4193	3.6084
2.25	3.500	2.250	4.9497	4.0414
2.50	3.875	2.500	5.4800	4.4744
2.75	4.250	2.750	6.0103	4.9074
3.00	4.625	3.00	6.5406	5.3404

$b = a + .5a + .125$ or $1.5a + .125$
$C = 1.15b$ $D = 1.41b$

AMERICAN NATIONAL THREADS
CLASSIFICATION

Class 1 Loose Fit   Class 2 Free Fit
Class 3 Medium Fit   Class 4 Close Fit

MACHINE SCREWS AND CAP SCREWS

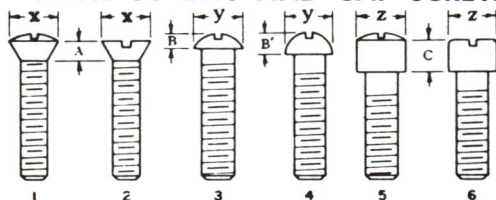

1 Oval Head   2 Flat Head   3 Button Head
4 Round Head   5 Round Fillister Head
6 Flat Fillister Head

MACHINE SCREWS
A.S.M.E.

No.	Thrd. diam.	A	B	C	X	Y	Z	Threads per inch		
1	.073	.04	.05	.05	.13	.13	.11	72 — 64		
2	.086	.05	.06	.05	.16	.15	.13	64 — 56		
3	.099	.05	.07	.06	.19	.17	.15	56 — 48		
4	.112	.06	.08	.06	.21	.20	.17	48 — 40 — 36		
5	.125	.07	.09	.07	.24	.22	.19	44 — 40 — 36		
6	.138	.08	.10	.08	.27	.24	.21	40 — 36 — 32		
7	.151	.08	.11	.09	.29	.27	.23	36 — 32 — 30		
8	.164	.09	.12	.09	.32	.29	.26	36 — 32 — 30		
9	.177	.10	.13	.10	.35	.32	.28	32 — 30 — 24		
10	.190	.10	.14	.11	.37	.34	.30	30 — 32 — 24		
12	.216	.12	.14	.12	.42	.38	.33	28 — 24		
14	.242	.13	.15	.14	.45	.42	.37	24 — 20		
	.250	.14	.16	.15	.49	.46	.40	24 — 20		
16	.268	.15	.17	.16	.50	.50	.43	22 — 20		
18	.294	.16	.19	.17	.58	.54	.47	20 — 18		
	.312	.17	.21	.19	.62	.58	.50	20 — 18		
20	.320	.17	.22	.20	.65	.61	.53	20 — 18		
22	.346	.19	.22	.21	.68	.64	.55	18 — 16		
24	.372	.20	.23	.22	.72	.66	.58	16 — 18		
	.375	.21	.24	.23	.75	.69	.61	16 — 18		

CAP SCREWS

Thrd. Diam.	A	B′	C	X	Y	Z	Threads per inch
.125	.07	.10	.10	.25	.19	.25	40
.1875	.11	.13	.13	.37	.31	.31	24
.250	.14	.18	.16	.50	.42	.37	20
.3125	.18	.23	.19	.62	.56	.43	18
.375	.22	.26	.23	.75	.62	.56	16
.4375	.22	.31	.28	.81	.75	.62	14
.500	.22	.34	.32	.87	.81	.74	13
.5625	.25	.40	.36	1.00	.93	.80	12
.625	.29	.42	.40	1.10	1.00	.86	11
.750	.37	.52	.48	1.40	1.20	.99	10

HEXAGON HEAD CAP SCREWS

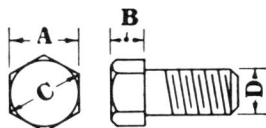

D	A	C	B
.25	.4375	.488	.1875
.3125	.500	.557	.2343
.375	.5625	.628	.2812
.4375	.625	.698	.3281
.50	.750	.840	.375
.5625	.8125	.910	.4218
.625	.875	.980	.4687
.75	1.000	1.121	.5625
.875	1.125	1.261	.6562
1.000	1.3125	1.473	.75
1.125	1.500	1.684	.8437
1.25	1.6875	1.896	.9375

AMERICAN NATIONAL THREAD
DRILL SIZES, PITCH DIAMETER, HELIX ANGLE, COARSE THREAD, 70% THREAD

	Diam.	N	Drill Sizes	Pitch Diam.	Helix Angle
(1)	.073	64	53	.0629	4° 31′
(2)	.086	56	50	.0744	4° 22′
(3)	.099	48	5/64	.0855	4° 26′
(4)	.112	40	44	.0958	4° 45′
(5)	.125	40	38	.1088	4° 11′
(6)	.138	32	36	.1177	4° 50′
(8)	.164	32	29	.1437	3° 57′
(10)	.190	24	27	.1629	4′ 39′
(12)	.216	24	11/64	.1889	4° 1′
	.250	20	9	.2175	4° 11′
	.3125	18	F	.2764	3° 39′
	.375	16	5/16	.3344	3° 24′
	.4375	14	23/64	.3911	3° 19′
	.500	13	27/64	.4500	3° 7′
	.5625	12	31/64	.5084	2° 59′
	.625	11	17/32	.5660	2° 55′
	.750	10	21/32	.6850	2° 39′
	.875	9	49/64	.8028	2° 31′
	1.000	8	55/64	.9188	2° 29′
	1.125	7	63/64	1.0322	2° 31′
	1.250	7	1 7/64	1.1572	2° 15′
	1.500	6	1 21/64	1.3917	2° 11′
	1.750	5	1 35/64	1.6201	2° 15′
	2.000	4.5	1 49/64	1.8557	2° 11′
	2.250	4.5	2 1/32	2.1057	1° 55′
	2.500	4	2 1/4	2.3376	1° 57′
	2.750	4	2 1/2	2.5876	1° 46′
	3.000	4	2 3/4	2.8376	1° 36′
	3.000	3.5	2 23/32	2.8144	1° 53′

UNIFIED AND AMERICAN SCREW THREADS
Basic Dimensions

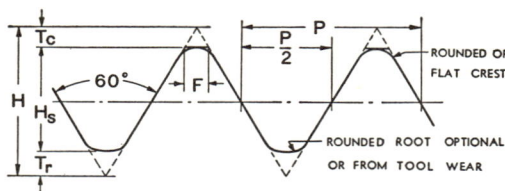

$$P = \frac{1}{\text{NO. THREADS PER IN.}}$$
$$H = .86603\ P$$
$$H_s = .61343\ P$$
$$F = .125\ P$$
$$T_c = .10825\ P$$
$$T_r = .14434\ P$$

Screw or Bolt Size	Threads per Inch			Pitch	Outside Diameter	Basic† Pitch Diameter	Minor Diameter	Flat at Crest	Section at Minor Diameter
	Coarse UNC or NC	Fine UNF or NF	Extra Fine NEF			Inches			Sq.Inches
0		80		.01250	.0600	.0519	.0447	.00156	.0015
1	64	72		.01563 .01389	.0730	.0629 .0640	.0538 .0560	.00195 .00174	.0022 .0024
2	56	64		.01786 .01563	.0860	.0744 .0759	.0641 .0668	.00223 .00195	.0031 .0034
3	48	56		.02083 .01786	.0990	.0855 .0874	.0734 .0771	.00260 .00223	.0041 .0045
4	40	48		.02500 .02083	.1120	.0958 .0985	.0813 .0864	.00312 .00260	.0050 .0057
5	40	44		.02500 .02273	.1250	.1088 .1102	.0943 .0971	.00312 .00284	.0067 .0072
6	32	40		.03125 .02500	.1380	.1177 .1218	.0997 .1073	.00391 .00312	.0075 .0087
8	32	36		.03125 .02778	.1640	.1437 .1460	.1257 .1299	.00391 .00347	.0120 .0128
10	24	32		.04167 .03125	.1900	.1629 .1697	.1389 .1517	.00521 .00391	.0145 .0175
12	24	28	32	.04167 .03571 .03125	.2160	.1889 .1928 .1957	.1649 .1722 .1777	.00521 .00446 .00391	.0206 .0226 .0242
¼	20	28	32	.05000 .03571 .03125	.250	.2175 .2268 .2297	.1887 .2062 .2117	.00625 .00446 .00391	.0269 .0326 .0344
5⁄16	18	24	32	.05556 .04167 .03125	.3125	.2764 .2854 .2922	.2443 .2614 .2742	.00694 .00521 .00391	.0454 .0524 .0581

† British: Effective Diameter.

Courtesy New Departure Division of General Motors

UNIFIED AND AMERICAN SCREW THREADS
Basic Dimensions

| Screw or Bolt Size | Threads per Inch | | | Pitch | Outside Diameter. | Basic† Pitch Diameter | Minor Diameter | Flat at Crest | Section at Minor Diameter |
	Coarse UNC or NC	Fine UNF or NF	Extra Fine NEF		Inches				Sq. Inches
⅜	16	24	32	.06250 .04167 .03125	.3750	.3344 .3479 .3547	.2983 .3239 .3367	.00781 .00521 .00391	.0678 .0809 .0878
⁷⁄₁₆	14	20	28	.07143 .05000 .03571	.4375	.3911 .4050 .4143	.3499 .3762 .3937	.00893 .00625 .00446	.0933 .1090 .1201
½	13 12	20	28	.07692 .08333 .05000 .03571	.500	.4500 .4459 .4675 .4768	.4056 .3978 .4387 .4562	.00962 .01042 .00625 .00446	.1257 .1205 .1486 .1616
⁹⁄₁₆	12	18	24	.08333 .05556 .04167	.5625	.5084 .5264 .5354	.4603 .4943 .5114	.01042 .00694 .00521	.1620 .1888 .2030
⅝	11	18	24	.09091 .05556 .04167	.6250	.5660 .5889 .5979	.5135 .5568 .5739	.01136 .00694 .00521	.2018 .2400 .2560
¹¹⁄₁₆			24	.04167	.6875	.6604	.6364	.00521	.3151
¾	10	16	20	.10000 .06250 .05000	.750	.6850 .7094 .7175	.6273 .6733 .6887	.01250 .00781 .00625	.3020 .3513 .3685
¹³⁄₁₆			20	.05000	.8125	.7800	.7512	.00625	.4388
⅞	9	14	20	.11111 .07143 .05000	.8750	.8028 .8286 .8425	.7387 .7874 .8137	.01389 .00893 .00625	.4193 .4805 .5153
¹⁵⁄₁₆			20	.05000	.9375	.9050	.8762	.00625	.5975
1	8	12 14	20	.12500 .08333 .07143 .05000	1.0000	.9188 .9459 .9536 .9675	.8466 .8978 .9124 .9387	.01562 .01042 .00893 .00625	.5510 .6245 .6404 .6866
1 ¹⁄₁₆			18	.05556	1.0625	1.0264	.9943	.00694	.7702
1 ⅛	7	12	18	.14286 .08333 .05556	1.1250	1.0322 1.0709 1.0889	.9497 1.0228 1.0568	.01786 .01042 .00694	.6931 .8118 .8705
1 ³⁄₁₆			18	.05556	1.1875	1.1514	1.1193	.00694	.9770
1 ¼	7	12	18	.14286 .08333 .05556	1.250	1.1572 1.1959 1.2139	1.0747 1.1478 1.1818	.01786 .01042 .00694	.8898 1.0237 1.0895

† British: Effective Diameter.

UNIFIED AND AMERICAN SCREW THREADS

Basic Dimensions

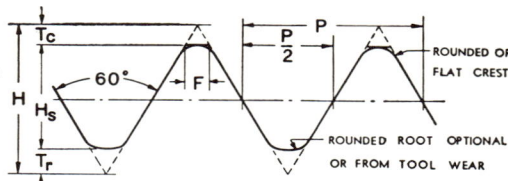

Diagram of thread profile (60°, ROUNDED OR FLAT CREST, ROUNDED ROOT OPTIONAL OR FROM TOOL WEAR)

$$P = \frac{1}{\text{NO. THREADS PER IN.}}$$
$$H = .86603\ P$$
$$H_s = .61343\ P$$
$$F = .125\ P$$
$$T_c = .10825\ P$$
$$T_r = .14434\ P$$

Screw at Bolt Size	Threads per Inch			Pitch	Outside Diameter	Basic† Pitch Diameter	Minor Diameter	Flat at Crest	Section at Minor Diameter
	Coarse UNC or NC	Fine UNF or NF	Extra Fine NEF			Inches			Sq. Inches
1 5/16			18	.05556	1.3125	1.2764	1.2443	.00694	1.2082
1 3/8	6	12	18	.16667 .08333 .05556	1.3750	1.2667 1.3209 1.3389	1.1705 1.2728 1.3068	.02083 .01042 .00694	1.0541 1.2602 1.3330
1 7/16			18	.05556	1.4375	1.4014	1.3693	.00694	1.4640
1 1/2	6	12	18	.16667 .08333 .05556	1.5000	1.3917 1.4459 1.4639	1.2955 1.3978 1.4318	.02083 .01042 .00694	1.2938 1.5212 1.6011
1 9/16			18	.05556	1.5625	1.5264	1.4943	.00694	1.7444
1 5/8			18	.05556	1.6250	1.5889	1.5568	.00694	1.8937
1 11/16			18	.05556	1.6875	1.6514	1.6193	.00694	2.0493
1 3/4	5		16	.20000 .06250	1.7500	1.6201 1.7094	1.5046 1.6733	.02500 .00781	1.7441 2.1873
2	4½		16	.22222 .06250	2.0000	1.8557 1.9594	1.7274 1.9233	.02778 .00781	2.3001 2.8917
2 1/4	4½			.22222	2.2500	2.1057	1.9774	.02778	3.0212
2 1/2	4			.25000	2.5000	2.3376	2.1933	.03125	3.7161
2 3/4	4			.25000	2.7500	2.5876	2.4433	.03125	4.6194
3	4			.25000	3.0000	2.8376	2.6933	.03125	5.6209
3 1/4	4			.25000	3.2500	3.0876	2.9433	.03125	6.7205
3 1/2	4			.25000	3.5000	3.3376	3.1933	.03125	7.9183
3 3/4	4			.25000	3.7500	3.5876	3.4433	.03125	9.2143
4	4			.25000	4.0000	3.8376	3.6933	.03125	10.6084

† British: Effective Diameter.

SCREW THREAD SYSTEMS

AMERICAN (BRIGGS) STANDARD AND WHITWORTH* PIPE THREADS

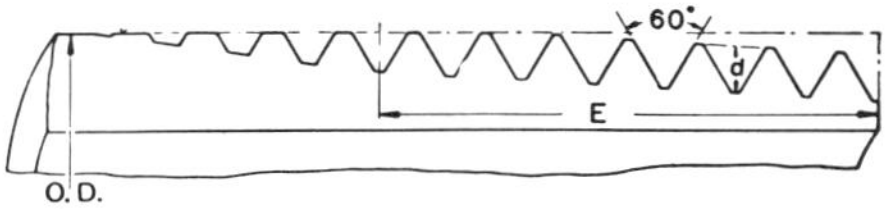

$$\text{Pitch} = \frac{1}{\text{No. of thr'ds per in.}}$$

d = Pitch × .8

E = Pitch (.8 × O.D. + 6.8)

Taper of pipe end = ¾″ per foot

Nominal size of pipe	No. of threads per inch		Pitch diameter at end of pipe		Root diameter at end of pipe		Depth of thread		Length of normal engagement by hand	Length of effective thread		Tap drill size	
	Brigg	Whitworth	Brigg	Whitworth	Brigg	Whitworth	Brigg	Whitworth		Brigg	Whitworth	Brigg	Whitworth
1/8	27	28	.3635	.3650	.334	.337	.0296	.0230	3/16	.264	.264	21/64	5/16
1/4	18	19	.4774	.4807	.433	.451	.0444	.0335	3/16	.402	.402	27/64	27/64
3/8	18	19	.6120	.6153	.568	.589	.0444	.0335	1/4	.408	.408	9/16	9/16
1/2	14	14	.7584	.7584	.701	.734	.0571	.0455	5/16	.534	.534	11/16	11/16
5/8		14		.8561		.811		.0455	11/32		.539		25/32
3/4	14	14	.9677	.9677	.911	.950	.0571	.0455	11/32	.546	.546	29/32	29/32
7/8		14		1.1241		1.098		.0455	11/32		.554		1 1/16
1	11 1/2	11	1.2136	1.2090	1.144	1.193	.0696	.0580	13/32	.683	.714	1 1/8	1 1/8
1 1/4	11 1/2	11	1.5571	1.5525	1.488	1.534	.0696	.0580	13/32	.707	.739	1 15/32	1 15/32
1 1/2	11 1/2	11	1.7961	1.7914	1.727	1.766	.0696	.0580	13/32	.724	.756	1 23/32	1 23/32
1 3/4		11		1.9905		2.000		.0580	13/32		.771		1 15/16
2	11 1/2	11	2.2690	2.2642	2.199	2.231	.0696	.0580	7/16	.757	.791	2 3/16	2 5/32
2 1/4		11		2.5131		2.471		.0580	1/2		.809		2 13/32
2 1/2	8	11	2.7195	2.7619	2.620	2.844	.1000	.0580	11/16	1.138	.827	2 9/16	2 25/32
2 3/4		11		3.0850		3.094		.0580	11/16		.851		3 1/32
3	8	11	3.3406	3.3840	3.241	3.344	.1000	.0580	3/4	1.200	.873	3 3/16	3 9/32
3 1/4		11		3.6330		3.584		.0580	3/4		.891		3 1/2
3 1/2	8	11	3.8375	3.8820	3.738	3.834	.1000	.0580	13/16	1.250	.909	3 11/16	3 3/4
3 3/4		11		4.1307		4.084		.0580	13/16		.927		4
4	8	11	4.3344	4.3795	4.234	4.334	.1000	.0580	27/32	1.300	.945	4 3/16	4 1/4
4 1/2	8	11	4.8313	4.8773	4.731	4.834	.1000	.0580	7/8	1.350	.982		
5	8	11	5.3907	5.4377	5.291	5.334	.1000	.0580	15/16	1.406	1.023		
5 1/2		11		5.8727		5.834		.0580	15/16		1.055		
6	8	11	6.4461	6.4949	6.346	6.334	.1000	.0580	31/32	1.513	1.100		

*Whitworth pipe thread may also be cut straight without taper.

SQUARE THREADS

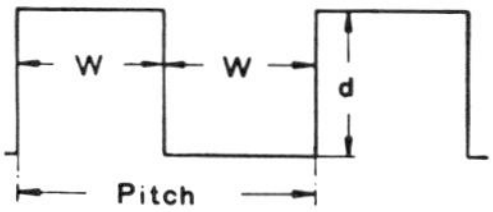

$$\text{Pitch} = \frac{1}{\text{No. of thr'ds per in.}}$$

d = Pitch × 7/16

w = Pitch × 1/2

Diam. inches	No. of thds. per in.	Pitch diam. inches	Root diam. inches	Depth of thread inches	Wth. of thread inches	Area at root of thd. sq. in.	Diam. inches	No. of thds. per in.	Pitch diam. inches	Root diam. inches	Depth of thread inches	Wth. of thread inches	Area at root of thd. sq. in.
1/4	10	.2063	.1625	.0438	.0500	.0207	1 1/4	3 1/2	1.1250	1.0000	.1250	.1429	.7854
5/16	9	.2639	.2153	.0486	.0556	.0364	1 3/8	3	1.2292	1.0834	.1458	.1667	.9219
3/8	8	.3204	.2658	.0546	.0625	.0557	1 1/2	3	1.3542	1.2084	.1458	.1667	1.1469
7/16	7	.3750	.3125	.0625	.0714	.0767	1 5/8	2 3/4	1.4659	1.3068	.1591	.1818	1.3412
1/2	6 1/2	.4328	.3656	.0672	.0769	.1050	1 3/4	2 1/2	1.5750	1.4000	.1750	.2000	1.5394
9/16	6	.4896	.4167	.0729	.0833	.1364	1 7/8	2 1/2	1.7000	1.5250	.1750	.2000	1.8265
5/8	5 1/2	.5458	.4666	.0792	.0909	.1710	2	2 1/4	1.8056	1.6111	.1945	.2222	2.0386
11/16	5	.6000	.5125	.0875	.1000	.2063	2 1/4	2 1/4	2.0556	1.8611	.1945	.2222	2.8486
3/4	5	.6625	.5750	.0875	.1000	.2597	2 1/2	2	2.2813	2.0626	.2187	.2500	3.3413
13/16	4 1/2	.7153	.6181	.0972	.1111	.3001	2 3/4	2	2.5313	2.3126	.2187	.2500	4.2004
7/8	4 1/2	.7778	.6806	.0972	.1111	.3638	3	1 3/4	2.7500	2.5000	.2500	.2857	4.9087
15/16	4	.8282	.7188	.1094	.1250	.4058	3 1/4	1 3/4	3.0000	2.7500	.2500	.2857	5.9396
1	4	.8907	.7813	.1094	.1250	.4794	3 1/2	1 5/8	3.2258	2.9615	.2643	.3077	7.0488
1 1/8	3 1/2	1.0000	.8750	.1250	.1429	.6013	3 3/4	1 1/2	3.4584	3.1667	.2917	.3333	8.0594
1 1/4	3 1/2	1.1250	1.0000	.1250	.1429	.7854	4	1 1/2	3.7084	3.4167	.2917	.3333	9.1686

Courtesy New Departure Division of General Motors Corp.

SCREW THREAD SYSTEMS

ACME 29° SCREW THREADS

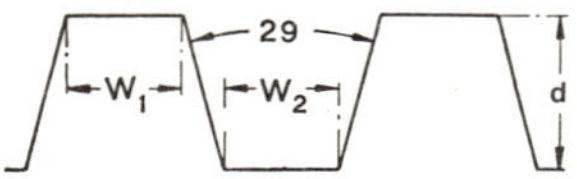

$$\text{pitch} = \frac{1}{\text{No. of threads per in.}}$$

$$d = \tfrac{1}{2}\,\text{pitch} + .01''$$

$$w_1 = .3707 \times \text{pitch}$$

$$w_2 = w_1 - .0052''$$

No. of threads per in.	Pitch	Depth of thread inches	Width of thread		Width of space	
			at top inches	bottom inches	at top inches	bottom inches
1	1.0000	.5100	.3707	.6345	.6293	.3655
1 1/3	.7500	.3850	.2780	.4772	.4720	.2728
2	.5000	.2600	.1853	.3199	.3147	.1801
3	.3333	.1767	.1235	.2150	.2098	.1183
4	.2500	.1350	.0927	.1625	.1573	.0875
5	.2000	.1100	.0741	.1311	.1259	.0689
6	.1667	.0933	.0618	.1101	.1049	.0566
7	.1428	.0814	.0530	.0951	.0899	.0478
8	.1250	.0725	.0463	.0839	.0787	.0411
9	.1111	.0655	.0413	.0751	.0699	.0361
10	.1000	.0600	.0371	.0681	.0629	.0319

BOLTS AND NUTS

U.S. STANDARD, WHITWORTH, AMERICAN STANDARD
HEXAGONAL CASTELLATED NUTS

Dia. of bolt in.	Tensile str'th stress 6000 lbs./sq. in. U.S. Std.	Width across flats square and hexagonal			Width across corners				Heighth of head					Slot in castellated nuts	
					hexagonal			square	bolts		nuts				
		U.S. Std.	Whitworth	Castellated	U.S. Std.	Whitworth	Castellated	U.S. Std.	U.S. Std.	Whitworth	U.S. Std.	Whitworth	Castellated	Width	Depth
1/4	160	1/2	.523	7/16	.578	.61	.488	.707	1/4	.225	1/4	.255	9/32	5/64	3/32
5/16	270	19/32	.598	1/2	.686	.69	.557	.840	19/64	.275	5/16	.315	21/64	5/64	3/32
3/8	410	11/16	.708	9/16	.794	.82	.628	.972	11/32	.335	3/8	.385	13/32	1/8	1/8
7/16	560	25/32	.818	5/8	.902	.95	.699	1.105	25/64	.385	7/16	.445	29/64	1/8	1/8
1/2	760	7/8	.918	3/4	1.011	1.06	.840	1.237	7/16	.445	1/2	.505	9/16	1/8	3/16
9/16	1000	31/32	1.006	7/8	1.119	1.17	.980	1.370	31/64	.495	9/16	.565	39/64	5/32	3/16
5/8	1210	1 1/16	1.096	15/16	1.227	1.27	1.051	1.502	17/32	.555	5/8	.635	23/32	5/32	1/4
11/16			1.196			1.39				.605		.695			
3/4	1810	1 1/4	1.296	1 1/8	1.444	1.50	1.263	1.768	5/8	.665	3/4	.755	13/16	5/32	1/4
13/16			1.386			1.61				.715		.815			
7/8	2520	1 7/16	1.476	1 5/16	1.660	1.71	1.474	2.033	23/32	.775	7/8	.885	29/32	5/32	1/4
1	3300	1 5/8	1.666	1 1/2	1.877	1.93	1.686	2.298	13/16	.885	1	1.005	1	5/32	1/4
1 1/8	4160	1 13/16	1.855	1 11/16	2.093	2.15	1.898	2.563	29/32	.99	1 1/8	1.14	1 5/32	7/32	5/16
1 1/4	5350	2	2.045	1 7/8	2.310	2.37	2.109	2.828	1	1.10	1 1/4	1.26	1 1/4	7/32	5/16
1 3/8	6340	2 3/16	2.215		2.527	2.56		3.093	1 3/32	1.21	1 3/8	1.39			
1 1/2	7770	2 3/8	2.405	2 1/4	2.743	2.78	2.533	3.358	1 3/16	1.32	1 1/2	1.51	1 1/2	1/4	3/8
1 5/8	9090	2 9/16	2.575		2.960	2.98		3.623	1 9/32	1.43	1 5/8	1.64			
1 3/4	10470	2 3/4	2.755		3.176	3.19		3.889	1 3/8	1.54	1 3/4	1.76			
1 7/8	12300	2 15/16			3.393			4.154	1 15/32		1 7/8				
2	13800	3 1/8	3.145		3.609	3.64		4.419	1 9/16	1.76	2	2.01			
2 1/4	18100	3 1/2	3.543		4.043	4.10		4.949	1 3/4	1.98	2 1/4	2.26			
2 1/2	22300	3 7/8	3.883		4.476	4.49		5.479	1 15/16	2.20	2 1/2	2.51			
2 3/4	27700	4 1/4	4.173		4.909	4.83		6.010	2 1/8	2.42	2 3/4	2.76			
3	32500	4 5/8	4.523		5.342	5.23		6.540	2 5/16	2.64	3	3.01			
3 1/4	39000	5	4.840		5.775	5.60		7.070	2 1/2	2.85	3 1/4	3.26			
3 1/2	45300	5 3/8	5.170		6.208	5.98		7.600	2 11/16	3.07	3 1/2	3.51			
3 3/4	51800	5 3/4	5.540		6.641	6.41		8.131	2 7/8	3.29	3 3/4	3.76			
4	59700	6 1/8	5.940		7.074	6.87		8.661	3 1/16	3.51	4	4.01			
4 1/4	68000	6 1/2			7.508			9.191	3 1/4		4 1/4				
4 1/2	76500	6 7/8	6.808		7.941	7.88		9.721	3 7/16	3.96	4 1/2	4.52			
4 3/4	85500	7 1/4			8.374			10.252	3 5/8		4 3/4				
5	94000	7 5/8	7.788		8.807	9.01		10.782	3 13/16	4.40	5	5.02			
5 1/4	105500	8			9.240			11.312	4		5 1/4				
5 1/2	116000	8 3/8	8.835		9.673	10.22		11.842	4 3/16	4.83	5 1/2	5.52			
5 3/4	127000	8 3/4			10.106			12.373	4 3/8		5 3/4				
6	138000	9 1/8	9.985		10.539	11.55		12.903	4 9/16	5.27	6	6.02			

Courtesy New Departure Division of General Motors Corp.

CISTERNS, TANKS AND BARRELS

In measuring cisterns, tanks, reservoirs, barrels, etc., the barrel is figured at 31½ gallons and the hogshead at 63 gallons.

A gallon of water weighs about 8 pounds avoirdupois, and contains 231 cubic inches.

A pint is generally estimated as weighing a pound.

How to Find the Capacity of Round Cisterns and Tanks.

RULE: Multiply the square of the diameter in feet by the depth in feet and this result by .1865 for the capacity in barrels, or by 5.875 (5⅞) for the capacity in gallons.

EXAMPLE: How many barrels will a round cistern 5 feet in diameter and 8 feet deep hold? How many gallons?

SOLUTION: $5 \times 5 \times 8 = 200$.
  $200 \times .1865 = 37.3$ barrels.
  $200 \times 5.875 = 1175$ gallons.

How to Find the Capacity of Square Cisterns, Tanks and Watering Troughs.

RULE: Multiply the length, width and depth in feet together and this product by 7½ (or for exact results by 7.48) and the result will be the number of gallons.

For capacity in barrels multiply by .2375.

For small tanks and troughs reduce feet to inches then multiply the dimensions together and divide result by 231 for gallons.

EXAMPLE: How many gallons will a square cistern 6 × 6 and 9 feet deep hold? How many barrels?

SOLUTION: $6 \times 6 \times 9 = 324 \times 7½ = 2430$ gallons.
  $288 \times .2375 = 68.4$ barrels.

EXAMPLE: What is the capacity of a small watering trough 6 feet long, 2 feet wide, and 10 inches deep?

SOLUTION: $6 \times 12 \times 2 \times 12 \times 10 = 17280$ square inches.
  $17280 \div 231 = 75$ gallons nearly.

RECTANGULAR TANKS

NUMBER OF U.S. GALLONS FOR ONE FOOT OF DEPTH

Length of Tank

Width of Tank	2 ft	2 ft 6 in	3 ft	3 ft 6 in	4 ft	4 ft 6 in	5 ft	5 ft 6 in	6 ft	6 ft 6 in	7 ft	7 ft 6 in	8 ft	8 ft 6 in	9 ft	9 ft 6 in	10 ft	10 ft 6 in	11 ft	11 ft 6 in	12 ft
2 ft	29.92	37.40	44.88	52.36	59.84	67.32	74.81	82.29	89.77	97.25	104.73	112.21	119.69	127.17	134.65	142.13	149.61	157.09	164.57	172.05	179.53
2 ft 6 in		46.75	56.10	65.45	74.80	84.16	93.51	102.86	112.21	121.56	130.91	140.26	149.61	158.96	168.31	177.66	187.01	196.36	205.71	215.06	224.41
3 ft			67.32	78.54	89.77	100.99	112.21	123.43	134.65	145.87	157.09	168.31	179.53	190.75	201.97	213.19	224.41	235.63	246.86	258.07	269.30
3 ft 6 in				91.64	104.73	117.82	130.91	144.00	157.09	170.18	183.27	196.36	209.45	222.54	235.63	248.73	261.82	274.90	288.00	301.09	314.18
4 ft					119.69	134.65	149.61	164.57	179.53	194.49	209.45	224.41	239.37	254.34	269.30	284.26	299.22	314.18	329.14	344.10	359.06
4 ft 6 in						151.48	168.31	185.14	201.97	218.80	235.63	252.47	269.30	286.13	302.96	319.79	336.62	353.45	370.28	387.11	403.94
5 ft							187.01	205.71	224.41	243.11	261.82	280.52	299.22	317.92	336.62	355.32	374.03	392.72	411.43	430.13	448.83
5 ft 6 in								226.28	246.86	267.43	288.00	308.57	329.14	349.71	370.28	390.85	411.43	432.00	452.57	473.14	493.71
6 ft									269.30	291.74	314.18	336.62	359.06	381.50	403.94	426.39	448.83	471.27	493.71	516.15	538.59
6 ft 6 in										316.05	340.36	364.67	388.98	413.30	437.60	461.92	486.23	510.54	534.85	559.16	583.47
7 ft											366.54	392.72	418.91	445.09	471.27	497.45	523.64	549.81	575.99	602.18	628.36
7 ft 6 in												420.78	448.83	476.88	504.93	532.98	561.04	589.08	617.14	645.19	673.24
8 ft													478.75	508.67	538.59	568.51	598.44	628.36	658.28	688.20	718.12
8 ft 6 in														540.46	572.25	604.05	635.84	667.63	699.42	731.21	763.00
9 ft															605.92	639.58	673.25	706.90	740.56	774.23	807.89
9 ft 6 in																675.11	710.65	746.17	781.71	817.24	852.77
10 ft																	748.05	785.45	822.86	860.26	897.66
10 ft 6 in																		824.73	864.00	903.26	942.56
11 ft																			905.14	946.27	987.43
11 ft 6 in																				989.29	1032.3
12 ft																					1077.2

Courtesy Posey Iron Works, Lancaster, Pa.

CAPACITIES OF HORIZONTAL CYLINDRICAL TANKS*

On the next 4 pages, there will be found a table for determining the volumes of materials contained in horizontal cylindrical tanks of different diameters filled to various depths.

This table makes it unnecessary to perform the tedious and rather complicated calculations otherwise required to determine volumes for this type of tank when partially filled

While this table has been computed to apply to tanks with their ends squared off, it is sufficiently accurate for general use in connection with tanks having convex or concave ends provided the convexities or concavities are not too extreme.

The example below is intended to make clear the method of applying the table to a specific problem:

Example: Given a horizontal cylindrical tank 68 inches in diameter and 32 feet long, and containing 17 inches of liquid. It is desired to know the volume occupied by the liquid.

First, determine the total volume of the tank. Reading across the top horizontal column under "Diameter in Inches", locate 68"—the diameter of the tank. Following vertically downward to the bottom of this column, it will be found that the capacity per foot of length of a 68" tank is 25.2 cubic feet.

Since the tank is 32 feet long, its total volume is:

$$32 \times 25.2 = 806.4 \text{ cu. ft.}$$

Locating the depth of liquid, 17", in the vertical column on the extreme left entitled "Depth Inches", and reading horizontally to the right until the column 68" is reached, it will be found that 17" represents 19.5% of the total volume of this tank.

Therefore, the volume occupied by the liquid is:

$$806.4 \times .195 = 157.2 \text{ cu. ft.}$$

*Courtesy Allied Chemical

HORIZONTAL CYLINDRICAL TANKS

PER CENTS OF TOTAL CAPACITIES FOR DIAMETERS FROM 48" TO 68"

DIAMETERS IN INCHES

Depth Ins.	48"	50"	52"	54"	56"	58"	60"	62"	64"	66"	68"
	Per Cent	Per Cent	Per Cent	Per Cent	Per Cent	Per Cent	Per Cent	Per Cent	Per Cent	Per Cent	Per Cent
1	0.51	0.48	0.44	0.42	0.40	0.38	0.37	0.35	0.33	0.32	0.30
2	1.43	1.34	1.26	1.19	1.12	1.08	1.02	0.98	0.93	0.89	0.85
3	2.6	2.4	2.3	2.2	2.1	2.0	1.9	1.8	1.7	1.6	1.6
4	4.0	3.7	3.5	3.3	3.2	3.0	2.9	2.7	2.6	2.5	2.4
5	5.5	5.2	4.9	4.6	4.4	4.2	4.0	3.8	3.6	3.5	3.3
6	7.2	6.8	6.4	6.1	5.8	5.5	5.2	5.0	4.7	4.5	4.3
7	9.0	8.5	8.1	7.6	7.2	6.9	6.6	6.2	5.9	5.7	5.4
8	11.0	10.3	9.8	9.2	8.8	8.4	7.9	7.6	7.2	6.9	6.6
9	13.0	12.2	11.6	11.0	10.4	9.9	9.4	9.0	8.6	8.2	7.8
10	15.1	14.2	13.4	12.8	12.1	11.5	11.0	10.5	10.0	9.5	9.1
11	17.2	16.3	15.4	14.6	13.9	13.2	12.5	12.0	11.5	10.9	10.5
12	19.5	18.5	17.5	16.5	15.7	14.9	14.2	13.6	13.0	12.4	11.9
13	21.9	20.7	19.5	18.5	17.6	16.7	16.0	15.2	14.6	13.9	13.3
14	24.3	22.9	21.7	20.6	19.5	18.6	17.7	16.9	16.2	15.5	14.8
15	26.7	25.2	24.0	22.7	21.5	20.5	19.6	18.7	17.8	17.1	16.4
16	29.3	27.6	26.2	24.8	23.6	22.4	21.4	20.5	19.5	18.7	18.0
17	31.7	30.0	28.4	27.0	25.7	24.4	23.3	22.3	21.3	20.4	19.5
18	34.2	32.4	30.7	29.2	27.8	26.4	25.2	24.1	23.1	22.1	21.2
19	36.8	34.9	33.0	31.4	29.9	28.5	27.2	26.0	24.9	23.8	22.8
20	39.4	37.3	35.5	33.7	32.1	30.6	29.1	27.9	26.7	25.6	24.5
21	42.0	39.9	37.8	36.0	34.2	32.7	31.2	29.8	28.5	27.4	26.3
22	44.7	42.4	40.2	38.3	36.4	34.8	33.3	31.8	30.4	29.2	28.0
23	47.3	44.9	42.6	40.6	38.7	36.9	35.3	33.8	32.3	31.0	29.8
24	50.0	47.4	45.2	42.9	40.9	39.1	37.4	35.7	34.3	32.8	31.5
25	52.7	50.0	47.6	45.3	43.2	41.2	39.5	37.7	36.2	34.7	33.3
26	55.3	52.6	50.0	47.6	45.4	43.4	41.5	39.8	38.1	36.6	35.1
27	58.0	55.1	52.4	50.0	47.7	45.6	43.7	41.8	40.1	38.5	37.0
28	60.6	57.6	54.8	52.4	50.0	47.8	45.8	43.8	42.1	40.4	38.8
29	63.2	60.1	57.4	54.7	52.3	50.0	47.8	45.9	44.0	42.3	40.7
30	65.8	62.7	59.8	57.1	54.6	52.2	50.0	47.9	46.0	44.2	42.5
31	68.3	65.1	62.2	59.4	56.8	54.4	52.2	50.0	48.0	46.1	44.4
32	70.8	67.6	64.5	61.7	59.1	56.6	54.2	52.1	50.0	48.0	46.2
33	73.3	70.0	67.0	64.0	61.3	58.8	56.3	54.1	52.0	50.0	48.1
34	75.7	72.4	69.3	66.3	63.6	60.9	58.5	56.2	54.0	52.0	50.0
35	78.1	74.8	71.6	68.6	65.8	63.1	60.5	58.2	56.0	53.9	51.9
36	80.5	77.1	73.8	70.8	67.9	65.2	62.6	60.2	57.9	55.8	53.8
37	82.8	79.3	76.0	73.0	70.1	67.3	64.7	62.3	59.9	57.7	55.6
38	84.9	81.5	78.3	75.2	72.2	69.4	66.7	64.3	61.9	59.6	57.5
39	87.0	83.7	80.5	77.3	74.3	71.5	68.8	66.2	63.8	61.5	59.3

CAPACITIES IN CUBIC FEET PER ONE FOOT OF LENGTH

	12.6	13.6	14.7	15.9	17.1	18.3	19.6	21.0	22.3	23.8	25.2
40	89.0	85.8	82.5	79.4	76.4	73.6	70.9	68.2	65.7	63.4	61.2
41	91.0	87.8	84.6	81.5	78.5	75.6	72.8	70.2	67.7	65.3	63.0
42	92.8	89.7	86.6	83.5	80.5	77.6	74.8	72.1	69.6	67.2	64.9
43	94.5	91.5	88.4	85.4	82.4	79.5	76.7	74.0	71.5	69.0	66.7
44	96.0	93.2	90.2	87.2	84.3	81.4	78.6	75.9	73.3	70.8	68.5
45	97.4	94.8	91.9	89.0	86.1	83.3	80.4	77.7	75.1	72.6	70.2
46	98.6	96.3	93.6	90.8	87.9	85.1	82.3	79.5	76.9	74.4	72.0
47	99.5	97.6	95.1	92.4	89.6	86.8	84.0	81.3	78.7	76.2	73.7
48	100.0	98.7	96.5	93.9	91.2	88.5	85.8	83.1	80.5	77.9	75.5
49		99.5	97.7	95.4	92.8	90.1	87.5	84.8	82.2	79.6	77.2
50		100.0	98.7	96.7	94.2	91.6	89.0	86.4	83.8	81.3	78.8
51			99.6	97.8	95.6	93.1	90.6	88.0	85.4	82.9	80.5
52			100.0	98.8	96.8	94.5	92.1	89.5	87.0	84.5	82.0
53				99.6	97.9	95.8	93.4	91.0	88.5	86.1	83.6
54				100.0	98.9	97.0	94.8	92.4	90.0	87.6	85.2
55					99.6	98.0	96.0	93.8	91.4	89.1	86.7
56					100.0	98.9	97.1	95.0	92.8	90.5	88.1
57						99.6	98.1	96.2	94.1	91.8	89.5
58						100.0	99.0	97.3	95.3	93.1	90.9
59							99.6	98.2	96.4	94.3	92.2
60							100.0	99.0	97.4	95.5	93.4
61								99.6	98.3	96.5	94.6
62								100.0	99.1	97.5	95.7
63									99.7	98.4	96.7
64									100.0	99.1	97.6
65										99.7	98.4
66										100.0	99.1
67											99.7
68											100.0
69											
70											
71											
72											
73											
74											
75											
76											
77											
78											
79											
80											
81											
82											
83											
84											

HORIZONTAL CYLINDRICAL TANKS

PER CENTS OF TOTAL CAPACITIES FOR DIAMETERS FROM 70" TO 84"

DIAMETERS IN INCHES

Depth Ins.	70" Per Cent	72" Per Cent	73" Per Cent	74" Per Cent	75" Per Cent	76" Per Cent	78" Per Cent	80" Per Cent	82" Per Cent	84" Per Cent
1	0.29	0.28	0.27	0.26	0.25	0.25	0.24	0.23	0.23	0.22
2	0.81	0.78	0.76	0.75	0.73	0.72	0.69	0.67	0.64	0.62
3	1.5	1.4	1.4	1.4	1.3	1.3	1.3	1.2	1.2	1.1
4	2.3	2.2	2.1	2.1	2.0	2.0	1.9	1.9	1.8	1.7
5	3.2	3.0	3.0	2.9	2.9	2.8	2.7	2.6	2.5	2.4
6	4.1	3.9	3.9	3.8	3.7	3.6	3.5	3.4	3.3	3.2
7	5.2	5.0	4.9	4.8	4.7	4.6	4.4	4.3	4.1	4.0
8	6.3	6.0	6.0	5.8	5.7	5.6	5.4	5.2	5.0	4.9
9	7.5	7.2	7.1	6.9	6.8	6.7	6.4	6.2	6.0	5.8
10	8.8	8.4	8.2	8.1	7.9	7.8	7.5	7.2	7.0	6.7
11	10.1	9.7	9.4	9.3	9.1	8.9	8.6	8.3	8.0	7.7
12	11.4	11.0	10.7	10.5	10.3	10.1	9.8	9.4	9.1	8.7
13	12.8	12.3	12.1	11.8	11.6	11.4	11.0	10.6	10.2	9.8
14	14.2	13.6	13.5	13.1	12.9	12.7	12.2	11.8	11.3	11.0
15	15.7	15.0	14.8	14.5	14.2	14.0	13.5	13.0	12.5	12.2
16	17.2	16.5	16.2	15.9	15.6	15.4	14.8	14.2	13.7	13.3
17	18.8	18.1	17.7	17.4	17.1	16.7	16.1	15.5	15.0	14.5
18	20.3	19.6	19.2	18.8	18.5	18.1	17.5	16.8	16.3	15.7
19	21.9	21.1	20.7	20.3	19.9	19.5	18.8	18.2	17.6	17.0
20	23.6	22.7	22.3	21.8	21.5	21.0	20.2	19.6	18.9	18.2
21	25.2	24.3	23.8	23.4	22.9	22.5	21.7	21.0	20.2	19.5
22	26.9	26.0	25.4	24.9	24.4	24.0	23.2	22.4	21.6	20.7
23	28.6	27.5	27.0	26.5	26.0	25.5	24.6	23.8	23.0	22.2
24	30.0	29.1	28.6	28.1	27.6	27.1	26.1	25.2	24.4	23.6
25	32.0	30.8	30.3	29.7	29.1	28.6	27.6	26.7	25.8	25.0
26	33.8	32.5	31.9	31.4	30.8	30.2	29.2	28.2	27.2	26.3
27	35.6	34.2	33.6	33.0	32.4	31.8	30.7	29.7	28.7	27.7
28	37.4	36.0	35.3	34.7	34.0	33.4	32.3	31.2	30.2	29.1
29	39.1	37.7	37.0	36.3	35.7	35.1	33.9	32.7	31.6	30.6
30	40.9	39.5	38.7	38.0	37.3	36.7	35.4	34.3	33.1	32.0
31	42.7	41.2	40.4	39.7	39.0	38.3	37.0	35.9	34.6	33.5
32	44.5	42.9	42.2	41.4	40.7	39.9	38.6	37.4	36.1	35.0
33	46.4	44.7	43.9	43.1	42.4	41.6	40.2	38.9	37.6	36.5
34	48.2	46.4	45.6	44.8	44.0	43.3	41.9	40.5	39.2	37.9
35	50.0	48.2	47.4	46.5	45.8	45.0	43.5	42.0	40.7	39.4
36	51.8	50.0	49.1	48.2	47.4	46.6	45.1	43.6	42.2	40.9
37	53.6	51.8	50.9	50.0	49.1	48.3	46.7	45.2	43.8	42.4
38	55.5	53.6	52.6	51.8	50.9	50.0	48.3	46.8	45.4	43.9
39	57.3	55.3	54.4	53.5	52.6	51.7	50.0	48.4	46.9	45.4

CAPACITIES IN CUBIC FEET PER ONE FOOT OF LENGTH

	26.7	28.3	29.0	29.9	30.6	31.5	33.2	34.9	36.7	38.5
40	59.1	57.1	56.1	55.2	54.2	53.4	51.7	50.0	48.4	47.0
41	60.9	58.8	57.8	56.9	56.0	55.0	53.3	51.6	50.0	48.5
42	62.6	60.5	59.6	58.6	57.6	56.7	54.9	53.2	51.6	50.0
43	64.4	62.3	61.3	60.3	59.3	58.4	56.5	54.8	53.1	51.5
44	66.2	64.0	63.0	62.0	61.0	60.1	58.1	56.4	54.6	53.0
45	68.0	65.8	64.7	63.7	62.7	61.7	59.8	58.0	56.2	54.6
46	69.7	67.5	66.4	65.3	64.3	63.3	61.4	59.5	57.8	56.1
47	71.4	69.2	68.1	67.0	66.0	64.9	63.0	61.1	59.3	57.6
48	73.1	70.9	69.7	68.6	67.6	66.6	64.6	62.6	60.8	59.1
49	74.8	72.5	71.4	70.3	69.2	68.2	66.1	64.1	62.4	60.6
50	76.4	74.0	73.0	71.9	70.9	69.8	67.7	65.7	63.9	62.1
51	78.1	75.7	74.6	73.5	72.4	71.4	69.3	67.3	65.4	63.5
52	79.7	77.3	76.2	75.1	74.0	72.9	70.8	68.8	66.9	65.0
53	81.2	78.9	77.7	76.6	75.6	74.5	72.4	70.3	68.4	66.5
54	82.8	80.4	79.3	78.2	77.1	76.0	73.9	71.8	69.8	68.0
55	84.3	81.9	80.8	79.7	78.5	77.5	75.4	73.3	71.3	69.4
56	85.8	83.5	82.3	81.2	80.1	79.0	76.8	74.8	72.8	70.9
57	87.2	85.0	83.8	82.6	81.5	80.5	78.3	76.2	74.2	72.3
58	88.6	86.4	85.2	84.1	82.9	81.9	79.8	77.6	75.6	73.7
59	89.9	87.7	86.6	85.5	84.4	83.3	81.2	79.0	77.0	75.0
60	91.2	89.0	87.9	86.9	85.8	84.6	82.5	80.4	78.4	76.4
61	92.5	90.3	89.3	88.2	87.1	86.0	83.9	81.8	79.8	77.8
62	93.7	91.6	90.6	89.5	88.4	87.3	85.2	83.2	81.1	79.3
63	94.8	92.8	91.8	90.7	89.7	88.6	86.5	84.5	82.4	80.5
64	95.9	94.0	92.9	91.9	90.9	89.9	87.8	85.8	83.7	81.8
65	96.8	95.0	94.0	93.1	92.1	91.1	89.0	87.0	85.0	83.0
66	97.7	96.1	95.1	94.2	93.3	92.2	90.2	88.2	86.3	84.3
67	98.5	97.0	96.1	95.2	94.3	93.3	91.4	89.4	87.5	85.5
68	99.2	97.8	97.0	96.2	95.3	94.4	92.5	90.6	88.7	86.7
69	99.7	98.6	97.9	97.1	96.3	95.4	93.6	91.7	89.8	87.8
70	100.0	99.2	98.6	97.9	97.1	96.4	94.6	92.8	90.9	89.0
71		99.7	99.2	98.6	97.9	97.2	95.6	93.8	92.0	90.2
72		100.0	99.7	99.2	98.7	98.0	96.5	94.8	93.0	91.3
73			100.0	99.7	99.3	98.7	97.3	95.7	94.0	92.3
74				100.0	99.7	99.3	98.1	96.6	95.0	93.3
75					100.0	99.7	98.7	97.4	95.9	94.2
76						100.0	99.3	98.1	96.7	95.1
77							99.8	98.8	97.5	96.0
78							100.0	99.3	98.2	96.8
79								99.8	98.8	97.6
80								100.0	99.4	98.3
81									99.8	98.9
82									100.0	99.4
83										99.8
84										100.0

CAPACITY OF VERTICAL CYLINDRICAL TANKS
BASED ON INSIDE DIAMETER

Inside Diameter	U.S. Gallons per inch of depth	Imperial Gallons per inch of depth	Inside Diameter	U.S. Gallons per inch of depth	Imperial Gallons per inch of depth
3′ 0″	4.406	3.669	16′ 0″	125.3	104.3
3′ 3″	5.171	4.306	16′ 3″	129.3	107.8
3′ 6″	5.998	4.994	16′ 6″	133.3	111.2
3′ 9″	6.885	5.733	16′ 9″	137.4	114.4
4′ 0″	7.833	6.523	17′ 0″	141.5	118.0
4′ 3″	8.843	7.363	17′ 3″	145.7	121.2
4′ 6″	9.914	8.255	17′ 6″	149.9	124.8
4′ 9″	11.047	9.198	17′ 9″	154.3	128.7
5′ 0″	12.240	10.192	18′ 0″	158.6	132.2
5′ 3″	13.495	11.237	18′ 6″	167.6	139.8
5′ 6″	14.810	12.320	19′ 0″	176.7	147.2
5′ 9″	16.187	13.478	19′ 6″	186.2	155.0
6′ 0″	17.626	14.677	20′ 0″	195.8	163.1
6′ 3″	19.125	15.925	20′ 6″	205.8	171.2
6′ 6″	20.851	17.366	21′ 0″	215.9	179.8
6′ 9″	22.307	18.575	21′ 6″	226.3	189.1
7′ 0″	23.990	19.976	22′ 0″	237.0	197.3
7′ 3″	25.735	21.429	22′ 6″	247.9	206.2
7′ 6″	27.540	22.932	23′ 0″	259.0	215.8
7′ 9″	29.407	24.487	23′ 6″	270.4	225.9
8′ 0″	31.334	26.091	24′ 0″	282.0	234.4
8′ 3″	33.32	27.74	24′ 6″	293.9	244.5
8′ 6″	35.37	29.45	25′ 0″	306.0	254.6
8′ 9″	37.48	31.21	25′ 6″	318.4	265.7
9′ 0″	39.66	33.05	26′ 0″	331.0	275.8
9′ 3″	41.89	35.10	26′ 6″	343.8	286.1
9′ 6″	44.19	36.80	27′ 0″	357.0	297.3
9′ 9″	46.54	38.75	27′ 6″	370.3	310.4
10′ 0″	48.96	40.80	28′ 0″	383.8	319.4
10′ 3″	51.44	42.83	29′ 0″	411.8	342.5
10′ 6″	53.98	44.95	30′ 0″	440.6	367.5
10′ 9″	56.60	47.13	31′ 0″	470.5	392.0
11′ 0″	59.24	49.33	32′ 0″	501.3	417.2
11′ 3″	61.96	51.59	33′ 0″	533.2	443.0
11′ 6″	64.75	53.92	34′ 0″	566.0	472.0
11′ 9″	67.59	56.28	35′ 0″	600.0	500.0
12′ 0″	70.50	57.90	36′ 0″	634.6	527.5
12′ 3″	73.47	61.18	37′ 0″	670.3	558.
12′ 6″	76.50	63.70	38′ 0″	707.0	588.
12′ 9″	79.59	66.27	39′ 0″	744.7	622.
13′ 0″	82.74	68.90	40′ 0″	783.4	652.
13′ 3″	85.95	71.73	41′ 0″	823.0	686.
13′ 6″	89.23	74.30	42′ 0″	863.7	719.
13′ 9″	92.56	77.05	43′ 0″	905.3	755.
14′ 0″	95.96	79.90	44′ 0″	947.9	790.
14′ 3″	99.42	82.78	45′ 0″	991.4	826.
14′ 6″	102.9	85.6	46′ 0″	1036.0	863.
14′ 9″	106.5	88.6	47′ 0″	1081.5	902.
15′ 0″	110.2	91.8	48′ 0″	1128.0	940.
15′ 3″	113.9	94.8	49′ 0″	1175.0	957.
15′ 6″	117.6	97.9	50′ 0″	1224.0	1040.
15′ 9″	121.4	103.6			

Courtesy National Wood Tank Institute

110

GAUGING CONTENTS OF 55-GAL. DRUMS

Wet Inches	70° F.	60° F.	50° F.	40° F.	30° F.	20° F.	10° F.
31	53.5	53.8					
30	51.7	52.0	52.3	52.6	52.9	53.3	53.6
29	50.1	50.3	50.6	50.9	51.2	51.5	51.8
28	48.3	48.6	48.9	49.2	49.4	49.7	50.0
27	46.6	46.9	47.1	47.4	47.7	48.0	48.3
26	44.9	45.1	45.4	45.7	45.9	46.2	46.5
25	43.2	43.4	43.7	43.9	44.1	44.5	44.7
24	41.5	41.7	41.9	42.2	42.4	42.7	42.9
23	39.6	39.9	40.1	40.4	40.6	40.8	41.1
22	37.9	38.2	38.4	38.6	38.8	39.1	39.3
21	36.2	36.4	36.7	36.9	37.1	37.3	37.5
20	34.5	34.7	34.9	35.1	35.3	35.5	35.8
19	32.8	33.0	33.2	33.4	33.6	33.8	34.0
18	31.1	31.3	31.5	31.7	31.8	32.0	32.2
17	29.4	29.6	29.7	29.9	30.1	30.3	30.4
16	27.6	27.7	27.9	28.1	28.3	28.4	28.5
15	26.0	26.1	26.3	26.4	26.6	26.7	26.8
14	24.2	24.3	24.4	24.6	24.7	24.9	25.0
13	22.4	22.6	22.7	22.8	23.0	23.1	23.2
12	20.7	20.8	20.9	21.1	21.2	21.4	21.5
11	19.0	19.1	19.2	19.4	19.5	19.6	19.7
10	17.2	17.3	17.4	17.5	17.6	17.7	17.8
9	15.5	15.6	15.7	15.8	15.9	16.0	16.0
8	13.8	13.9	14.0	14.0	14.1	14.2	14.3
7	12.1	12.1	12.2	12.3	12.4	12.4	12.5
6	10.4	10.4	10.5	10.5	10.6	10.7	10.7
5	8.7	8.7	8.8	8.8	8.9	8.9	9.0
4	6.9	7.0	7.0	7.1	7.1	7.2	7.2
3	5.1	5.2	5.2	5.2	5.3	5.3	5.3
2	3.4	3.4	3.4	3.5	3.5	3.5	3.5
1	1.7	1.7	1.7	1.7	1.7	1.8	1.8

DRUM VERTICAL

Wet Inches	70° F.	60° F.	50° F.	40° F.	30° F.	20° F.	10° F.
20	54.3	54.7	55.0	55.3	55.6	55.9	
19	52.1	52.5	52.7	53.1	53.3	53.7	54.0
18	49.7	50.0	50.3	50.6	50.9	51.2	51.5
17	47.1	47.4	47.6	47.9	48.2	48.5	48.8
16	44.3	44.5	44.8	45.1	45.3	45.6	45.9
15	41.2	41.5	41.7	42.0	42.2	42.5	42.7
14	38.1	38.4	38.6	38.8	39.0	39.2	39.5
13	34.9	35.1	35.3	35.5	35.7	36.0	36.2
12	31.6	31.8	32.0	32.2	32.4	32.5	32.7
11	28.3	28.4	28.6	28.8	29.0	29.1	29.3
10	25.0	25.1	25.3	25.4	25.6	25.7	25.8
9	21.6	21.8	21.9	22.0	22.2	22.3	22.4
8	18.4	18.5	18.6	18.7	18.9	19.0	19.1
7	15.3	15.4	15.5	15.6	15.7	15.8	15.8
6	12.3	12.3	12.4	12.5	12.6	12.6	12.7
5	9.5	9.5	9.6	9.6	9.7	9.7	9.8
4	6.8	6.8	6.9	7.0	7.0	7.1	7.1
3	4.4	4.5	4.5	4.5	4.5	4.6	4.6
2	2.4	2.4	2.4	2.5	2.5	2.5	2.5
1	0.8	0.8	0.8	0.8	0.8	0.8	0.8

DRUM HORIZONTAL

These tables are useful for general inventory purposes where it is desired to make approximate measurements.

An ordinary yardstick is inserted through the bung. The number of wet inches shown on the stick is noted. This number is located in the table under the column marked "Wet Inches." The gallons of liquid in the drum will be found opposite this number under the temperature at which the measurement was taken.

These tables were computed for 190-proof alcohol in standard ICC-17E drums but can be used for approximate measurement of other liquids.

111

Tensile Strength of Steel—55,000 pounds per square inch

Joint Efficiency—100 per cent

Inside Dia.	1/4	9/32	5/16	11/32	3/8	13/32	7/16	15/32	1/2	17/32	9/16	19/32	5/8	21/32	11/16	23/32	3/4	25/32	13/16	27/32	7/8
24	1146	1289	1432	1575	1718	1861	2005	2148	2292												
26	1058	1190	1322	1452	1587	1718	1850	1984	2117												
28	982	1104	1228	1350	1473	1596	1718	1841	1965	2086	2209										
30	916	1030	1146	1260	1375	1489	1602	1718	1833	1947	2061										
32	859	967	1074	1181	1289	1397	1502	1611	1719	1827	1934	2041	2148								
34	809	910	1011	1111	1213	1314	1415	1517	1618	1718	1820	1921	2022								
36	764	859	955	1050	1146	1241	1336	1432	1528	1623	1718	1814	1910	2005	2100						
38	723	814	904	995	1085	1176	1266	1358	1446	1539	1629	1718	1808	1900	1990						
40	687	773	859	945	1031	1117	1203	1290	1374	1460	1547	1633	1718	1805	1890	1975	2062				
42	654	736	818	900	982	1067	1146	1228	1310	1391	1472	1556	1636	1718	1800	1882	1964				
44	625	703	781	859	937	1015	1094	1171	1250	1328	1406	1485	1562	1640	1718	1796	1874	1952	2030		
46	598	672	747	822	897	971	1046	1121	1196	1270	1344	1420	1494	1569	1644	1718	1794	1868	1942		
48	573	644	716	788	859	931	1001	1073	1146	1218	1288	1361	1432	1503	1575	1647	1718	1790	1862	1933	2002
50	550	619	687	756	825	894	962	1031	1100	1169	1238	1307	1374	1444	1512	1581	1650	1718	1788	1856	1924
52	529	595	661	727	793	859	925	992	1058	1123	1190	1257	1322	1389	1453	1520	1586	1652	1718	1785	1850
54	509	573	636	700	764	827	891	955	1019	1082	1146	1210	1272	1338	1400	1464	1528	1591	1654	1718	1782
60	458	516	573	630	687	745	802	859	917	974	1032	1089	1146	1202	1260	1318	1375	1431	1490	1547	1603
66	417	469	521	573	625	677	729	782	834	886	938	990	1042	1093	1146	1198	1250	1301	1354	1407	1458
72	382	430	477	525	573	621	668	716	764	812	860	907	954	1002	1050	1098	1146	1193	1242	1290	1336
78	352	397	441	484	529	573	617	661	703	749	794	838	882	926	968	1013	1058	1101	1146	1190	1234
84	327	368	409	450	491	532	573	614	655	696	736	778	818	860	900	941	982	1022	1064	1105	1146
90	305	344	382	420	458	496	535	573	611	650	688	726	764	802	840	879	917	955	993	1031	1070
96	286	322	358	394	430	465	501	537	573	609	645	681	716	752	788	824	859	895	931	968	1002
102	270	303	337	371	405	438	472	506	539	573	607	641	674	708	742	775	810	843	876	910	944
108	254	287	318	350	382	414	445	478	509	541	573	605	636	669	700	732	764	796	827	860	891
114	241	272	302	332	362	392	422	453	483	513	543	573	603	634	664	694	724	754	784	814	844
120	229	258	286	315	344	372	401	430	458	487	516	545	573	602	630	659	687	716	745	774	802
126	218	246	273	300	328	355	382	409	436	464	491	518	546	573	600	628	655	683	710	737	764
132	208	234	260	287	312	339	365	391	417	443	469	495	521	547	573	599	625	651	677	704	729
138	199	224	249	274	299	324	349	374	398	424	449	474	498	524	548	573	598	623	648	673	698
144	191	215	239	262	287	310	334	358	382	406	430	454	478	501	525	549	573	597	621	645	668

The safe working pressure is found by dividing the above bursting pressures by the factor of safety and multiplying the quotient by the efficiency of the longitudinal joint. **Example:** Shell 60 in. diam. x ½ in. thick, factor of safety 5; butt and double strap joint, double riveted efficiency 81.3%; $\frac{917}{5} \times .813 = 149$ lbs.

Courtesy Posey Iron Works, Lancaster, Pa.

UNDERWRITERS' LABORATORY SPECIFICATIONS FOR UNDERGROUND HORIZONTAL STORAGE TANKS

Horizontal tanks shall not exceed the maximum capacities, diameters, or lengths for the corresponding gauges of metal outlined in the following table, except as noted below.

U. S. S. Gauge Metal	Approx. Thickness Inches	Maximum Capacity U. S. Gal.	Maximum Diameter Inches	Maximum Length of Shell Feet
16	1/16	285	38	8
14	5/64	560	46	11
12	7/64	1,100	56	14
7	3/16	4,000*	84*	22*
3	1/4	12,000*	126*	32*
0	5/16	20,000*	132*	42*
000	3/8	30,000*	132*	50*

*To take care of miscalculations and mistakes in fabrication, for tanks made of No. 7 or heavier gauge metal, a tolerance of 10 per cent in capacity and a tolerance of 5 per cent in either the diameter or the length will be permitted. This does not mean that tanks made of No. 7 or heavier gauge stocks should be intentionally designed to have capacities, diameters, or lengths in excess of the nominal maximums designated above for such stocks.

SPECIAL

Tanks made of 5/16" or 3/8" metal and constructed as required by the Standard may employ diameters up to and including 144". Tanks having diameters of from 133" to 144" shall not be labelled until the manufacturer has obtained advices from the transportation company stating that the tank can be accepted for delivery to the customer.

Tanks up to 30,000 gallons capacity for storing Class III liquids (flash point above 70° F. and below 200° F., closed cup tester) may be made of 1/4" material, if adequate internal bracing is provided.

SHELL SEAMS

Shell and head seams may be riveted or welded.

HEADS

Flat flanged, braced heads; dished heads, or flanged and dished heads, are permissible, when the proper joints are used, in accordance with requirements.

TESTS

Before painting, tanks shall be tested and proven tight against leakage under a test pressure of not less than 5 nor more than 10 pounds per square inch.

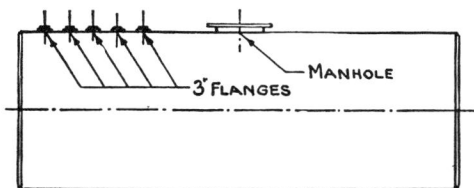

SUGGESTED OPENINGS FOR UNDER-GROUND TANKS

Note: Specify exact size and location of openings required.

PART FIVE

BUILDING AND CONSTRUCTION

TABLE OF BOARD FEET FOR VARIOUS SIZES AND LENGTHS OF LUMBER

This table may be used for estimating forms and other timber work. Figures given are board feet. Lumber is usually priced by thousands of board feet. A piece 1 inch thick, 12 inches wide and 1 foot long constitutes 1 foot board measure.

Size of Timber in Inches	LENGTH OF PIECE IN FEET							
	10	12	14	16	18	20	22	24
1 x 2	1⅔	2	2⅓	2⅔	3	3⅓	3⅔	4
1 x 3	2½	3	3½	4	4½	5	5½	6
1 x 4	3⅓	4	4⅔	5⅓	6	6⅔	7⅓	8
1 x 5	4⅙	5	5⅚	6⅔	7½	8⅓	9⅙	10
1 x 6	5	6	7	8	9	10	11	12
1 x 8	6⅔	8	9⅓	10⅔	12	13⅓	14⅔	16
1 x 10	8⅓	10	11⅔	13⅓	15	16⅔	18⅓	20
1 x 12	10	12	14	16	18	20	22	24
1 x 14	11⅔	14	16⅓	18⅔	21	23⅓	25⅔	28
1 x 16	13⅓	16	18⅔	21⅓	24	26⅔	29⅓	32
1 x 20	16⅔	20	23⅓	26⅔	30	33⅓	36⅔	40
1¼ x 4	4⅙	5	5⅚	6⅔	7½	8⅓	9⅙	10
1¼ x 6	6¼	7½	8¾	10	11¼	12½	13¾	15
1¼ x 8	8⅓	10	11⅔	13⅓	15	16⅔	18⅓	20
1¼ x 10	10⅓	12½	14½	16⅔	18⅔	20⅚	22⅚	25
1¼ x 12	12½	15	17½	20	22½	25	27½	30
1½ x 4	5	6	7	8	9	10	11	12
1½ x 6	7½	9	10½	12	13½	15	16½	18
1½ x 8	10	12	14	16	18	20	22	24
1½ x 10	12½	15	17½	20	22½	25	27½	30
1½ x 12	15	18	21	24	27	30	33	36
2 x 4	6⅔	8	9⅓	10⅔	12	13⅓	14⅔	16
2 x 6	10	12	14	16	18	20	22	24
2 x 8	13⅓	16	18⅔	21⅓	24	26⅔	29⅓	32
2 x 10	16⅔	20	23⅓	26⅔	30	33⅓	36⅔	40
2 x 12	20	24	28	32	36	40	44	48
2 x 14	23⅓	28	32⅔	37⅓	42	46⅔	51⅓	56
2 x 16	26⅔	32	37½	42⅔	48	53⅓	58⅔	64
2½ x 12	25	30	35	40	45	50	55	60
2½ x 14	29⅙	35	40⅚	46⅔	52½	58⅓	64⅙	70
2½ x 16	33⅓	40	46⅔	53⅓	60	66⅔	73⅓	80
3 x 6	15	18	21	24	27	30	33	36
3 x 8	20	24	28	32	36	40	44	48
3 x 10	25	30	35	40	45	50	55	60
3 x 12	30	36	42	48	54	60	66	72
3 x 14	35	42	49	56	63	70	77	84
3 x 16	40	48	56	64	72	80	88	96
4 x 4	13⅓	16	18⅔	21⅓	24	26⅔	29⅓	32
4 x 6	20	24	28	32	36	40	44	48
4 x 8	26⅔	32	37⅓	42⅔	48	53⅓	58⅔	64
4 x 10	33⅓	40	46⅔	53⅓	60	66⅔	73⅓	80
4 x 12	40	48	56	64	72	80	88	96
4 x 14	46⅔	56	65⅓	74⅔	84	93⅓	102⅔	112
6 x 6	30	36	42	48	54	60	66	72
6 x 8	40	48	56	64	72	80	88	96
6 x 10	50	60	70	80	90	100	110	120
6 x 12	60	72	84	96	108	120	132	144
6 x 14	70	84	98	112	126	140	154	168
6 x 16	80	96	112	128	144	160	176	192
8 x 8	53⅓	64	74⅔	85⅓	96	106⅔	117⅓	128
8 x 10	66⅔	80	93⅓	106⅔	120	133⅓	146⅔	160
8 x 12	80	96	112	128	144	160	176	192

Courtesy Universal Atlas Cement Co.

BUILDING CONSTRUCTION

Roof Elevations

The Gable is a space in the form of a triangle on the end of a building with a common double roof.

The Pitch of the roof is the relation which the height of the ridge above the level of the roof-plates bears to the span, or the distance between the studs on which the roof rests.

Quarter Pitch is a roof that is one-fourth, a third pitch one that is one-third, and and a half pitch one that is one-half as high as the width of the building.

The Span is the width of the building.

Area of a Gable End

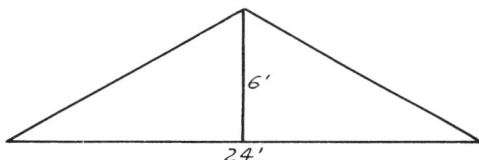

RULE: Multiply the width of the building by the height of the roof and take one-half of the result for the number of square feet. If the roof is "quarter pitch" find the area in square feet by multiplying width of the roof by ⅛ of itself.

Rules for Measuring Lumber

1. A FOOT OF LUMBER is one foot long, one foot wide and one inch thick. This is called a Board Foot.
2. PIECE STUFF OR DIMENSION STUFF is lumber that is two or more inches thick and of uniform width and length.
3. SCANTLING is usually from three to four inches wide and from two to four inches thick.
4. JOIST is two-inch lumber of any width.
5. PLANK is two inches in thickness and wider than a scantling.
Rule for 12-foot Boards: Find the width of the boards in inches and add together, and the sum obtained will be equal to the number of feet in the pile. (Each inch in width equals one foot of lumber.)

LUMBER

Figuring the Number of Pieces within a Given Number of Feet Board Measure

When a certain job calls for a given number of feet board measure of lumber and the price has been determined, it will in many instances be necessary to find the number of certain sized pieces required.

EXAMPLE: Find the number of pieces of $2'' \times 6'' \times 20'$ which should be delivered for an order of 2,500 f.b.m.

SOLUTION:

$$\frac{2'' \times \cancel{6}'' \times 20}{\underset{2}{\cancel{12}}} = 20 \text{ f.b.m. in each piece}$$

$$2,500 \div 20 = 120.5 \text{ pcs. or } 121 \text{ pcs. of } 2'' \times 6'' \times 20'$$

Finding the Number of Linear Feet of Lumber for a Given Number of Feet Board Measure

Smaller sized lumber is generally figured in linear feet. If an estimate calls for 135 feet board measure of $1'' \times 3''$ cross bridging and it is necessary to find the total linear feet, proceed as follows:

$$\frac{1 \times \cancel{3}}{\underset{4}{\cancel{12}}} = \frac{1}{4}, \text{ number of f.b.m. in each lin. ft. of material}$$

$$\frac{135}{\frac{1}{4}} = 540 \qquad \text{number of lin. ft. of material required}$$

STANDARD SIZES OF LUMBER SURFACED ON FOUR SIDES

Nominal Size	Thickness	Width
1" × 2"	25/32"	1⅝"
1" × 3"	25/32"	2⅝"
1" × 4"	25/32"	3⅝"
1" × 5"	25/32"	4⅝"
1" × 6"	25/32"	5⅝"
1" × 8"	25/32"	7½"
1" × 10"	25/32"	9½"
1" × 12"	25/32"	11½"
2" × 4"	1⅝"	3⅝"
2" × 6"	1⅝"	5⅝"
2" × 8"	1⅝"	7½"
2" × 10"	1⅝"	9½"
2" × 12"	1⅝"	11½"
4" × 6"	3⅝"	5½"
4" × 8"	3⅝"	7½"
4" × 10"	3⅝"	9½"
6" × 6"	5½"	5½"
6" × 8"	5½"	7½"
6" × 10"	5½"	9½"
8" × 8"	7½"	7½"
8" × 10"	7½"	9½"
8" × 12"	7½"	11½"

LUMBER COMPUTATIONS IN FOOT BOARD MEASURE FOR GIVEN LENGTHS

Size, In.	Length, Ft.							
	8'	10'	12'	14'	16'	18'	20'	22'
1" × 2"	1⅓	1⅔	2	2⅓	2⅔	3	3⅓	3⅔
1" × 3"	2	2½	3	3½	4	4½	5	5½
1" × 4"	2⅔	3⅓	4	4⅔	5⅓	6	6⅔	7⅓
1" × 5"	3⅓	4⅙	5	5⅚	6⅔	7½	8⅓	9⅙
1" × 6"	4	5	6	7	8	9	10	11
1" × 8"	5⅓	6⅔	8	9⅓	10⅔	12	13⅓	14⅔
1" × 10"	6⅔	8⅓	10	11⅔	13⅓	15	16⅔	18⅓
1" × 12"	8	10	12	14	16	18	20	22
2" × 4"	5⅓	6⅔	8	9⅓	10⅔	12	13⅓	14⅔
2" × 6"	8	10	12	14	16	18	20	22
2" × 8"	10⅔	13⅓	16	18⅔	21⅓	24	26⅔	29⅓
2" × 10"	13⅓	16⅔	20	23⅓	26⅔	30	33⅓	36⅔
2" × 12"	16	20	24	28	32	36	40	44
4" × 4"	10⅔	13⅓	16	18⅔	21⅓	24	26⅔	29⅓
4" × 6"	16	20	24	28	32	36	40	44
4" × 8"	21⅓	26⅔	32	37⅓	42⅔	48	53⅓	58⅔
4" × 10"	26⅔	33⅓	40	46⅔	53⅓	60	66⅔	73⅓
6" × 6"	34	30	36	42	48	54	60	66
6" × 8"	32	40	48	56	64	72	80	88
6" × 10"	40	50	60	70	80	90	100	110
8" × 8"	42⅔	53⅓	64	74⅔	85⅓	96	106⅔	117⅓
8" × 10"	53⅓	66⅔	80	93⅓	106⅔	120	133⅓	146⅔
8" × 12"	64	80	96	112	128	144	160	176

LUMBER

Rapid Lumber Computations in Foot Board Measure

1 × 3	Divide lin. ft. by 4
1 × 4	Divide lin. ft. by 3
1 × 6	Divide lin. ft. by 2
1 × 8	Multiply lin. ft. by 2, and divide by 3
1 × 10	Multiply lin. ft. by 10, and divide by 12
1 × 12	Lin. ft. and f.b.m. the same
2 × 3	Divide lin. ft. by 2
2 × 4	Multiply lin. ft. by 2, and divide by 3
2 × 8	Add to lin. ft. ⅓ of amount
2 × 10	Multiply lin. ft. by 10, and divide by 6
2 × 12	Multiply lin. ft. by 2
3 × 3	Multiply lin. ft. by 3, and divide by 4
3 × 4	Lin. ft. and f.b.m. the same
3 × 6	Add to lin. ft. ½ the amount
3 × 8	Multiply lin. ft. by 2
3 × 10	Multiply lin. ft. by 10, and divide by 4
3 × 12	Multiply lin. ft. by 3
4 × 4	Add to lin. ft. ⅓ of amount
4 × 6	Multiply lin. ft. by 2
4 × 8	Multiply lin. ft. by 3, and subtract ⅓ lin. ft. from amount
4 × 10	Multiply lin. ft. by 10, and divide by 3
4 × 12	Multiply lin. ft. by 4
8 × 8	Multiply lin. ft. by 5⅓
10 × 10	Multiply lin. ft. by 100, and divide by 12
12 × 12	Multiply lin. ft. by 12
14 × 14	Multiply lin. ft. by 16⅓
16 × 16	Multiply lin. ft. by 21⅓
18 × 18	Multiply lin. ft. by 27
20 × 20	Multiply lin. ft. by 100, and divide by 3
22 × 22	Multiply lin. ft. by 40⅓
24 × 24	Multiply lin. ft. by 48

ESTIMATING EXTERIOR & INTERIOR WALL STUDDING

The number of studding in each wall section can be found by dividing the length of the section by the center-to-center distance between the studding, counting any fraction as one additional studding.

For inside partitions, add one additional studding to the number found.

For exterior wall construction with only a single studding for a corner post, add one additional studding to the number previously found.

For exterior wall construction in which corner posts consist of two studding, add three additional studding to the number previously found.

In estimating the number of studding in any wall adjacent to two other walls for which ·lumber for corner posts has already been included, subtract one from the number of studding previously found.

EXAMPLE: Find the number of 2" × 4" studding required for the outside walls and inside partition walls of the lakeside cottage shown on the following page. Assume a studding spacing of 16" on center and a studding height of 8'-0".

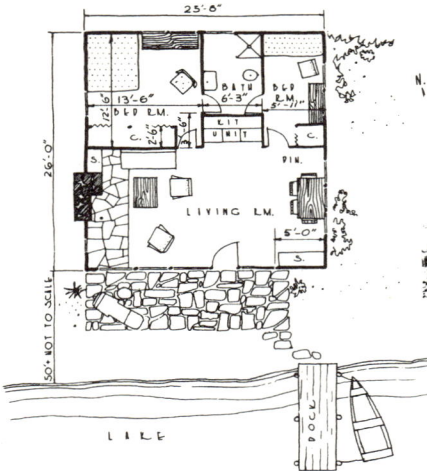

LAKESIDE COTTAGE

SOLUTION: The length of the outside walls and inside partitions as determined by scale measurements from the top to the bottom of the floor plan are as follows:

25'-8" + 6'-3" + 2'-10" + 25'-8" + 5'-0" = 65'-5", combined lengths of walls taken horizontally.

The lengths of the outside walls and inside walls taken vertically and from left to right are as follows:

26'-0" + 2'-6" + 3'-6" + 12'-6" + 12'-6" + 26'-0" = 83'-0", combined lengths of these walls.

65'-5" + 83'-0" = 148'-5" or 149', total length of combined walls.

Considerable additional material is required for constructing corner posts and framing around openings for doors and windows. An allowance of one studding per foot is commonly made in estimating the lumber required to construct these wall frames. Therefore, the number of linear feet of outside wall and inside partitions is the number of studding needed.

The total linear length is 149', which is also the number of pieces of 2" × 4" × 8' studding needed.

If the outside walls require a different length of studding from the inside partitions, the number of studding for the outside walls and inside partitions must be found separately.

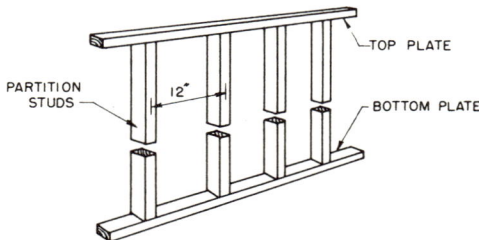

DEFINITIONS FOR MECHANICS

An angle is the opening between two lines that have a different direction.

When two straight lines cross each other so as to form four equal angles, each angle is called a right angle.

An acute angle is less than a right angle. An obtuse angle is greater than a right angle.

A triangle is a figure having three sides.

A surface having four straight lines and four right angles is called a rectangle.

A rectangle whose sides are equal is called a square.

The perimeter of a figure is the distance around it.

An arc is any part of the circumference of a circle.

A chord is a line drawn through the circle and ending on the circumference.

A quadrant is a quarter circle.

A tangent is a line that touches a circle but does not cut it.

A polygon is a figure bounded by straight lines.

The following figures show the principal polygons used with numbers of sides of each:

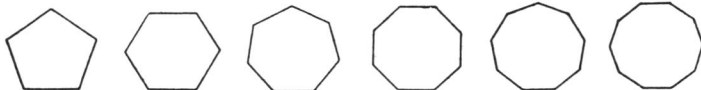

| Pentagon. | Hexagon. | Heptagon. | Octagon. | Nonagon. | Decagon. |

Concentric circles are circles that have the same center and the space included between their circumference is called a ring.

WIRE NAILS TO THE POUND

	Number to the ℔.	Length in inches
3 penny fine...............................	778	1⅛
3 penny common..........................	568	1¼
4 penny common..........................	316	1½
6 penny common..........................	181	2
8 penny common..........................	106	2½
10 penny common..........................	69	3
16 penny common..........................	49	3½
20 penny common..........................	31	4
40 penny common..........................	18	5
60 penny common..........................	11	6
8 penny fence..............................	82	2½
10 penny fence..............................	50	3

RESIDENTIAL CONSTRUCTION DATA

Standard dead load computation for residential floor tier of wood joists, cross-bridging, underfloor, hardwood, linoleum, or bonded finish flooring, and also lath and plaster ceiling: 17 lb. per square foot. No ceiling, deduct 8 lb. per square foot. For a tile floor instead of wood, add 25 lb.

STONE WORK

A cord of stone like a cord of wood is 8 feet long, 4 feet wide and 4 feet high and contains 128 cubic feet.

A perch of stone work is 16½ feet long, 1½ feet high and 1 foot thick and contains 24¾ cubic feet.

Usually 2¾ cubic feet of mortar and filling are contained in each perch of stone-work.

How to Find the Number of Perches in a Wall

RULE: Multiply together length, height and thickness in feet, and divide this product by 24¾ (or multiply by .0404) and the result will be the number of perches in the wall.

EXAMPLE: A wall is 40 feet long, 15 feet high and 2 feet thick. How many perches?

SOLUTION: 40×15×2÷24¾=48 12/25 perches, or
40×15×2×.0404=48.48.

How to Find the Number of Cords of Stone in a Pile

RULE: Multiply together the length, width and height in feet and divide by 128.

EXAMPLE: How many cord of stone in a pile 24 feet long, 8 feet wide, and 4 feet high?

SOLUTION: 24×8×4÷128=6 cord.

BRICK MASONRY

Bricks are of different sizes, varying according to custom of State or locality. The Baltimore Brick is 8¼ x 4⅛ x 2⅜ inches; the Maine brick 7½ x 3⅜ x 2⅜ inches; the Michigan brick 8½ x 4⅛ x 2⅜ inches; the New York brick 8 x 3½ x 2¼ inches, and the Fire brick 9⅛ x 4⅝ x 2⅜ inches. They are estimated and sold by the thousand. A common brick is 8 inches long, 4 inches wide and 2 inches thick, and contains 64 cubic inches. Twenty-seven bricks make one cubic foot of wall without mortar, or 22½ bricks one cubic foot with mortar, the mortar filling about 1/6 of the space.

Five courses of common brick with mortar equal one foot in height on a chimney.

Laid flat it takes 4½ bricks to a square foot; on edge it requires 9.

One cubic foot of brick work with common mortar weighs from 100 to 110 pounds.

A bricklayers hod will hold 20 common bricks; the ordinary load, however, is 16 walling or 12 facing bricks.

One cask or barrel of lime mixed with ⅝ yards of sand will make sufficient mortar to lay 1,000 bricks.

How to Find the Number of Common Bricks in a Wall or Building

RULE: Multiply together the length, height and thickness of the wall in feet and the result again by 22½ and the product will be the number of bricks in the wall.

For a wall 8 inches thick, multiply the length and height in feet together and that result by 14 and the product will equal the number of bricks.

When doors and windows occur in the wall, multiply their height, width and thickness together, and deduct the result from the solid contents of the wall before multiplying by 22½ or 14 as the case may be.

EXAMPLE: How many bricks in a wall 60 feet long, 15 feet high and 2 feet thick?

SOLUTION: 60 x 15 x 2 x 22½=40,500 bricks.

EXAMPLE: How many bricks in a wall 40 feet long, 10 feet high, and 8 inches thick?

SOLUTION: 40 x 10 x 14=5,600 bricks.

BRICK MASONRY

MORTAR MIXES REQUIRED TO LAY 1,000 COMMON BRICK

Kind of Mortar	Lime, Lb.	Cement, Bbl.	Sand, Cu. Ft.
1:3 lime mortar	180	......	18
2:1:9 lime-cement mortar	115	.50	18
1:3 cement mortar, 10% lime	16	1.50	18
Brixment cement mortar	......	1.25	15
Masonry cement mortar	......	1.25	15
Kosmortar	......	1.25	15

NUMBER OF ROMAN BRICK REQUIRED FOR 1 SQ. FT. OF WALL
Actual Brick Size 12" × 1½" × 4"

Wall Thickness	Width of Vertical or End Joint—Same as Horizontal or Bed Joint						
	⅛	¼	⅜	½	⅝	¾	⅞
4	7.31	6.71	6.20	5.76	5.367	5.01	4.70
8	14.62	13.42	12.40	11.52	10.734	10.02	9.40
12	21.93	20.13	18.60	17.28	16.101	15.03	14.10
16	29.24	26.84	24.80	23.04	21.468	20.04	18.80
20	36.55	33.55	31.00	28.80	26.835	25.05	23.50
24	43.86	40.26	37.20	34.56	32.202	30.06	28.20

NUMBER OF ENGLISH BRICK REQUIRED FOR 1 SQ. FT. OF WALL
Actual Brick Size 9" × 3" × 4½"

Wall* Thickness	Width of Vertical or End Joints—Same as Horizontal or Bed Joints						
	⅛	¼	⅜	½	⅝	¾	⅞
4½ or 1 Brick	5.14	4.71	4.54	4.33	4.12	3.28	3.81
9½ or 2 Brick	10.28	9.42	9.08	8.66	8.24	6.56	7.62
14½ or 3 Brick	15.42	14.13	13.62	12.99	12.36	9.84	11.43
21½ or 4 Brick	20.56	18.84	18.16	17.32	16.48	13.12	15.24
24½ or 5 Brick	25.70	23.55	22.70	21.65	20.60	16.40	19.05
29½ or 6 Brick	30.84	28.26	27.24	25.98	24.72	19.68	22.86

*Note Wall thicknesses include ½" motar joints between brick.

BRICK MASONRY

NUMBER OF COMMON BRICK LAID PER EIGHT-HOUR DAY

Class or Work	Mortar Joints Style	Kind of Mortar	Average No. of Brick Laid per 8-hr. Day
8" walls, 1-story bungalows, garages, two-flat buildings, residences	Cut	Lime	850 to 950
	Struck	Lime	800 to 900
12" walls, ordinary construction, apartment buildings, houses, garages, factories, · stores, store and apartment buildings, schools	Cut	Lime	950 to 1,050
	Struck	Lime	925 to 975
	Cut	Cement	825 to 900
	Struck	Cement	750 to 850
16" walls; heavy warehouse, factory, and industrial work. Straight walls	Cut	Lime	1,100 to 1,225
	Struck	Lime	1,000 to 1,125
	Cut	Mortar	950 to 1,050
	Struck	Mortar	900 to 1,000
Backing-up face brick, cut stone, terra-cotta on steel or concrete skeleton frame buildings. First-grade workmanship. Walls 8" to 12" thick	Cut	Lime	825 to 900
	Struck	Lime	750 to 850
	Cut	Cement	725 to 800
	Struck	Cement	700 to 775
Public buildings, first-grade workmanship. Schools; college and university buildings; courthouses; state capitols; public libraries, etc.; 12" to 20" walls	Cut	Lime	850 to 950
	Struck	Lime	800 to 900
	Cut	Cement	750 to 850
	Struck	Cement	700 to 800
Powerhouses and other structures, having high walls 12" to 20" thick, without intermediate floors	Cut	Lime	1,100 to 1,200
	Struck	Lime	1,000 to 1,100
	Cut	Cement	925 to 1,050
	Struck	Cement	875 to 950
Basement foundation walls, having brick	Cut	Cement	750 to 850
	Struck	Cement	700 to 800
Common brick foundation walls 8" to 12" thick; ordinary workmanship	Cut	Lime	1,000 to 1,100
	Struck	Lime	900 to 975
	Cut	Cement	900 to 975
	Struck	Cement	825 to 900
Chimneys and stacks, common brick 1'−4" to 2'−0" square, 15'−0" above roof, 4" to 8" walls	Struck	Lime	500 to 550
Large chimneys and stacks, 3'−0" to 4'−0" square, 15'−0" to 30'−0" high above roof	Struck	Lime	550 to 600
Large brick stacks 100' to 150' high, walls from 1'−8" at base to 12" at top	Struck	Lime	650 to 750

BRICK MASONRY

NUMBER OF BRICKS LAID PER HOUR

Walls	4" Brick	8" Brick	12" Brick
Common brick:			
Flush joint	80	120	150
Struck joint	72	110	140
Face brick:			
Running bond, cut joint	70	115	150
Running bond, V joint	60	110	145
Running bond, concave joint	60	110	145
Running bond, raked joint	50	90	125
Enameled brick	20 to 30		

BREAKDOWN OF COST AND LABOR TIME PER 1,000

FACE BRICK (SELECTED COMMON)

Brick delivered	$ 37
Mortar, hoist, scaffolding	8
Mason 16 hr.	40
Helper 12 hr.	21
Total cost per 1,000 brick	$106

WATER-STRUCK FACE BRICK

Brick delivered	$ 57.00
Mortar, hoist, etc.	9.50
Mason 20 hr.	50.00
Helper 14 hr.	24.50
Total cost per 1,000 brick	$141.00

SHALE FACE BRICK

Brick delivered	$ 67
Mortar, hoist, etc.	9
Mason 22 hr.	55
Helper 16 hr.	28
Total cost per 1,000 brick	$159

BRICK IN BRICK VENEER WALL
(1,000 brick cover 150 sq. ft.)

Brick delivered	$ 37
Mortar including coloring 14 cu. ft.	7
Ties 200 @ $.05	10
Nailing ties in place (5 hr.)	10
Mason 16 hr.	40
Helper 12 hr.	21
Total cost per 1,000 brick	$125

BRICK MASONRY

NUMBER OF MODULAR BRICK REQUIRED FOR
1 SQ. FT. OF WALL.
Actual Brick Size 7½ × 2⅙ × 3½ (Nominal Size 8" × 4" × 2⅔")

Wall Thickness	Width of Vertical or End Joints—Same as Horizontal or Bed Joint						
	⅛	¼	⅜	½	⅝	¾	⅞
4	7.72	7.71	7.46	6.75	6.42	6.00	5.71
8	15.44	15.42	14.92	13.50	12.84	12.00	11.42
12	23.16	23.13	22.38	20.25	19.26	18.00	17.13
16	30.88	30.84	29.84	26.00	25.68	24.00	22.84
20	38.6	38.55	37.30	33.75	32.10	30.00	28.55
24	46.32	46.26	44.76	40.50	38.52	36.00	34.26

How to Make the Curves for Brick and Stone Arches

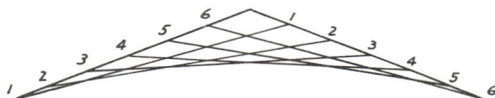

Measure the width, and draw the figure as above. If the points in 1, 2, 3, 4, etc. are equal on both sides, the curve will be an exact part of a circle.

PAINTING

The most accurate and perhaps the best method of estimating painting is to find the actual surface area to be painted from the plans and specifications or to take actual field measurements. As in everything else, painting costs are based on two major items, namely, labor and material. The cost of labor depends on the present-day labor scales, and the cost of material depends on the grade, or quality, and quantity of paint used. Estimating the quantities of material by finding the surface areas to be painted is relatively simple, but the labor quantities present a much more difficult problem.

For example: A plain wall surface may have the same surface area as a cornice, but it takes much longer to paint the cornice owing to its height, which requires the erection of scaffolding. Care must be taken in pricing any piece of work, as conditions on each job are different. The following table, giving methods of measuring and listing painting quantities, is based on the actual performance of numberous jobs and represents a fairly accurate method of establishing quantities.

PAINT — QUANTITIES REQUIRED

Description of Item	Unit of Measure	Multiply by Factor
Clapboards or drop siding (no deductions for areas less than 10' × 10')	Find actual area	Add 10% to surface
Shingle siding (no deductions for areas less than 10' × 10')	Find actual area	1½ times area
Brick, wood, stucco, cement, stone walls (no deductions for areas less than 10' × 10')	Find actual area	
Eaves—plain, painted same color as side walls	Find actual area	1½ times area
Eaves—different color from side walls	Find actual area	2 times area
Eaves—with rafters running through	Find actual area	3 times area
Eaves—over 20' above ground	Find actual area	Add ½ of area to each 10' of height
Eaves—over brick, stucco, or stone walls	Find actual area	3 times area
Exterior cornices:		
Plain	Find actual area	2 times area
Fancy	Find actual area	3 times area
Down spouts and gutters:		
Plain	Find actual area	2 times area
Fancy	Find actual area	3 times area
Blinds and shutters:		
Plain	Area of outer faces	2 times area
Slatted	Area of outer faces	4 times area
Columns and pilasters:		
Plain	Area, sq. ft.	
Fluted	Area, sq. ft.	1½ times area
Paneled	Area, sq. ft.	2 times area
Moldings:		
If under 12" in girth	Figure 1 sq. ft. per lin. ft.	
If over 12" in girth	Take actual area	
Exterior doors and frames:		
Figure no door less than 3' × 7', allow for frame, add 2' to width and 1' to height	Figure all doors 40 sq. ft.	2 times area for both sides
Containing small lights of glass	Add 2 sq. ft. for each additional light	2 times area for both sides
Door frames only (no door)	Allow area of opening for both sides	
Exterior windows:		
Figure no window less than 3' × 6'; add 2' to both width and height of opening	Figure all windows 40 sq. ft.	
Sash containing more than one light	Add 2 sq. ft. for each additional light	
Interior doors, jambs, and casings:		
Figure no door less than 3' × 7', allow for frame, add 2' to width and 1' to height	Figure all doors 40 sq. ft.	Do not deduct for glass in doors
Containing small lights of glass	Add 2 sq. ft. for each additional light	2 times area for both sides of door
Stairs:		
Add 2' to length of treads and risers to allow for stair strings. Figure 2' width of tread and riser	Multiply width (2') by length of thread. Then multiply by Number of treads, for total sq. ft.	
Wood ceilings	Find actual area	No deductions for openings less than 10' × 10'
Floors	Actual area	
Plastered walls and ceilings	Actual area of wall and ceiling, sq. ft.	Do not deduct for door and window openings
Radiators	For each front foot, multiply face area by 7	
Bookcases, cupboards, closets	Find area of front	Multiply area (front) by 3
Wainscoting:		
Plain	Find actual area	
Paneled	Find actual area	Multiply area by 2

MATERIAL AND LABOR REQUIRED
FOR ONE COAT OF PAINT

Material	Sq. Ft. per Gal.	Sq. Ft. per Hr.
Paint, lead and oil, outside	400 to 450	150 to 200
Paint, lead and oil, walls	450	200
Paint, lead and oil, trim	450	175
Ready-mixed paint	450	
Aluminum paint	600	250
Floor paint	400	300
Cement paint on rough concrete	150 to 400	125 to 300
Calcimine	300 or 2 lb.	250
Flat paint on walls	450	175
Flat paint on trim	450	150
Enamel on trim	400	125
Enamel on walls	400	150
Red lead on wood	350	250
Red lead on metal	700	125 to 150
Filler on trim	300	175
Filler on floors	300	250
Varnish on floors	400	300
Varnish on trim	400	150
Varnish remover	150	
Shellac on floors	400	300
Shellac on trim	400	175
Shingle stain (dip)	40	
Shingle stain (brushed)	160	150
Shingle stain (creosote)	200	150
Varnish stain	400	200
Glue size	1,000	1,000
Glazing liquid	500	400
Linseed oil (boiled)	400	400
Turpentine tint	250	
Undercoat	450	175
Plastic paint	75 sq. yd.	
Window frames and sash		4

CEMENT AND HOW TO USE IT

The word "Concrete" itself is of Latin origin, meaning "grown together" and implies a body formed by separate particles of different materials combined into a solid mass.

Kinds of Cement.—There are two general kinds, Natural and Portland cement. The raw material from which natural cement is made is found in a natural state and is made by calcining (burning) cement rock, but the temperature required is considerably lower than that needed for making Portland cement.

Portland Cement, however, is the kind used almost exclusively in this country and is manufactured in about 25 different states. The raw materials used by different plants vary greatly, nor is the chemical composition the same, so that it cannot be reduced to a formula.

What Portland Cement is.—So far, then, as it is possible to give an accurate definition, Portland cement may be defined as any cement which, on being tested, will manifest the characteristic properties that engineers have agreed to associate with the name "Portland" and which will meet the requirements that have been accepted as standard.

Raw Materials.—As a matter of fact, however, the raw materials are limestone (also chalk and marl, which are really forms of limestone), clay, shale and slate, also blast-furnace slag. These in proper proportion are heated to a temperature at which melting begins (2000° to 4000°F). The resulting cement clinker is then ground to an impalpable powder to which a very small percentage of gypsum is added.

How to Use Cement.—In using cement for concrete work it is necessary to mix it with water and aggregates—these aggregates consist of sand, crushed stone or gravel. That is to say, you must use either cement, sand and gravel or cement, sand and crushed stone, or any material that can take the place of gravel or crushed stone. These must be thoroughly mixed and the proper amount of water added.

The Proportions required for different kinds of cement or concrete construction are shown in the preceding section. For example for a rich mixture 1:2:4 means one part cement, 2 parts sand and 4 parts gravel or crushed stone.

By Consistency is meant the relative wetness of the mixture. VERY WET is mushy enough to run readily off the shovel. MEDIUM WET is wet enough to make it jelly-like. DRY MIXTURE is about like damp earth.

APPROXIMATE MIXTURES FOR
VARIOUS CLASSES OF CONCRETE WORK

Kind of Work	Mixture	Consistency
Abutments	Rich to Ordinary	Medium
Arches	Rich to Medium	Medium
Backing for Masonry	Lean	Medium to Dry
Beams, Reinforced	Rich to Medium	Very Wet
Beams, Plain	Rich to Medium	Very Wet to Medium
Building Blocks	Rich to Medium	Very Wet to Medium
Cisterns	Rich to Medium	Very Wet to Medium
Columns, Reinforced	Rich	Very Wet
Conduits, Water................	Rich	Very Wet
Coping	Rich to Medium	Medium
Culverts, Reinforced	Medium to Ordinary	Medium
Culverts, Plain	Medium to Ordinary	Medium
Driveways	Same as Sidewalks	
Fence Posts	Rich	Very Wet to Medium
Floors, Reinforced.............	Rich to Ordinary	Very Wet to Medium
Floors, Ordinary Ground	Medium to Ordinary	Medium
Footings.....................	Orindary to Lean	Medium
Foundations, Heavy Vibrating Machinery	Rich	Very Wet to Medium
Foundations, Ordinary Machinery....	Medium	Medium
Foundations, Thin Walls	Rich to Medium	Very Wet to Medium
Foundations, Thick Walls..........	Medium to Lean	Medium to Dry
Girders, Reinforced	Rich to Medium	Very Wet
Girders, Plain.................	Same as Beams	
Gutters	Same as Sidewalks	
Pavements	Same as Sidewalks	
Piers.......................	Rich to Ordinary	Medium
Reservoirs	Rich to Medium	Very Wet to Medium
Roof Slabs	Medium to Ordinary	Medium
Sewers, Reinforced	Rich to Medium	Medium
Sewers, Plain	Medium	Medium
Sidewalks (Base)	Medium to Ordinary	Medium to Dry
Sidewalks (Sub-Base)	Ordinary to Lean	Medium to Dry
Silos	Rich to Medium	Very Wet to Medium
Tanks	Rich to Medium	Very Wet to Medium
Walls, Dwelling Houses	Rich to Medium	Very Wet to Medium
Walls, Large Buildings...........	Rich to Medium	Very Wet to Medium
(Compression and Tension)		
Walls, Large Buildings	Medium to Ordinary	Medium
(Compression Only)		
Walls, Massive	Medium to Ordinary	Medium
Walls, Retaining	Medium to Ordinary	Medium
Walls, Thin Foundations	Rich to Medium	Very Wet to Medium
Walls, Tunnel	Medium to Ordinary	Medium

NOTE—The above facts and table are used by permission of W. A. Radford, editor-in-chief of the "Cement World," etc.

CONCRETE FOUNDATIONS, FLOORS AND WALLS

To determine the quantity of cement (barrels), sand (cubic yards), and pebbles (cubic yards) in a concrete floor base, measuring 10'-0" × 15'-0", proceed as follows:

$$10 \times 15 = 150 \text{ sq. ft.}$$

For 100 sq. ft. of 3" floor base, in the above table, the quantity of

Cement = 1.62 bbl.
Sand   = .48 cu. yd.
Pebbles = .71 cu. yd.

Therefore, multiply

$$1.5 \times 1.62 = 2.43 \text{ bbl. of cement}$$
$$1.5 \times .48 = .72 \text{ cu. yd. of sand}$$
$$1.5 \times .71 = 1.06 \text{ cu. yd. of pebbles}$$

For 225 sq. ft. of floor base, multiply the values in the table by 2.25.

AMOUNTS OF MATERIALS FOR 100 SQ. FT. OF WALL AREA

Thick-ness of Wall, In.	Mixture					
	1:2½:5			1:2:4		
	Cement, Bbl.	Sand, Cu. Yd.	Pebbles, Cu. Yd.	Cement, Bbl.	Sand, Cu. Yd.	Pebbles, Cu. Yd.
6	2.30	.85	1.70	2.70	.83	1.66
8	3.08	1.13	2.26	3.70	1.10	2.20
10	3.85	1.41	2.82	4.63	1.37	2.70
12	4.60	1.70	3.40	5.56	1.66	3.30
15	5.76	2.12	4.24	6.93	2.06	4.12
18	6.90	2.55	5.10	8.34	2.49	4.98

QUANTITIES FOR 100 SQ. FT. OF WEARING SURFACE OR TOPCOAT

Thickness, In.	Proportions				
	1:2		1:1:1		
	Cement, Bbl.	Sand, Cu. Yd.	Cement, Bbl.	Sand, Cu. Yd.	Pebbles, Cu. Yd.
½	.51	.15			
¾	.75	.23			
1	1.00	.29	1.00	.15	.15
1¼	1.26	.37	1.26	.19	.19
1½	1.51	.45	1.51	.23	.23
2	2.00	.59	2.00	.30	.30

CONCRETE FOUNDATIONS, FLOORS AND WALLS

SURFACE-COVERING CAPACITY OF MORTAR
FROM ONE BAG OF CEMENT

Mixture of Parts by Volume		Thickness of Coat				
		¼"	⅜"	½"	¾"	1"
Cement	Sand	Sq. Ft.	Sq. Ft.	Sq. Ft.	Sq. Ft.	Sq. Ft.
1	1	66	44	33	22	16
1	1½	84	56	42	28	21
1	2	101	67	50	33	25
1	2½	118	78	59	39	29
1	3	136	90	68	45	34
1	3½	153	102	76	51	42
1	4	171	113	85	57	38

SQUARE FEET OF CONCRETE FLOOR OR SIDEWALK
OBTAINABLE FROM 1 CUBIC YARD OF CONCRETE

In. Thick	No. Sq. Ft.	In. Thick	No. Sq. Ft.	In. Thick	No. Sq. Ft.	In. Thick	No. Sq. Ft.
1	324	4	81	7	46	10	32
1¼	259	4¼	76	7¼	44	10¼	31
1½	216	4½	72	7½	43	10½	31
1¾	185	4¾	68	7¾	42	10¾	30
2	162	5	65	8	40	11	29½
2¼	144	5¼	62	8¼	39	11¼	29
2½	130	5½	59	8½	38	11½	28
2¾	118	5¾	56	8¾	37	11¾	27½
3	108	6	54	9	36	12	27
3¼	100	6¼	52	9¼	35	12¼	26½
3½	93	6½	50	9½	34	12½	26
3¾	86	6¾	48	9¾	33	12¾	25½

AMOUNT OF CONCRETE IN ONE-BAG BATCH FOR
DIFFERENT PROPORTIONS OF SAND AND GRAVEL

Proportions	Amount of Concrete in One-bag Batch	
	Cu. Ft.	Cu. Yd.
1:1½:3	3.53	.131
1:2:3	3.90	.145
1:2:3½	4.22	.156
1:2:4	4.50	.167
1:2½:4	4.88	.181
1:2½:4½	5.17	.192
1:2½:5	5.40	.202
1:3:5	5.81	.215
1:3:5½	6.11	.226
1:3:6	6.38	.236

CONCRETE FOUNDATIONS, FLOORS AND WALLS

COLORS TO BE USED IN CONCRETE FLOOR FINISH

Color Desired	Commercial Names of Colors for Use in Cement	Lb. of Color Required per Sack of Cement to Obtain	
		Light Shade	Medium Shade
Grays, blue-black, and black	Germantown Lampblack*,	½	1
	or, carbon black*, or,	½	1
	black oxide of Manganese*,	1	2
	or mineral black*	1	2
Blue shade	Ultramarine blue	5	9
Brownish red to dull brick red	Red oxide of iron	5	9
Bright red to vermilion	Mineral turkey red	5	9
Red sandstone to purplish red	Indian red	5	9
Brown to reddish brown	Metallic brown (oxide)	5	9
Buff, Colonial tint, and yellow	Yellow ocher, or	5	9
	yellow oxide	2	4
Green shade	Chromium oxide, or	5	9
	greenish-blue ultramarine	6	

*Only first-quality lampblack should be used. Carbon black is light and requires very thorough mixing. Black oxide or mineral black is probably most advantageous for general use. For black, use 11 lb. oxide per sack of cement.

MATERIAL REQUIRED FOR 100 SQUARE FEET OF CONCRETE FLOOR BASE

Thick-ness, In.	Proportions								
	1:2:3			1:2:4			1:2½:5		
	Cement, Bbl.	Sand, Cu. Yd.	Pebbles, Cu. Yd.	Cement, Bbl.	Sand, Cu. Yd.	Pebbles, Cu. Yd.	Cement, Bbl.	Sand, Cu. Yd.	Pebbles, Cu. Yd.
3	1.62	.48	.71	1.38	.41	.82	1.15	.43	.85
3½	1.89	.56	.83	1.61	.48	.96	1.35	.50	1.00
4	2.16	.64	.95	1.84	.55	1.10	1.54	.56	1.23
4½	2.43	.72	1.07	2.07	.62	1.24	1.73	.63	1.26
5	2.68	.80	1.19	2.31	.69	1.37	1.92	.70	1.41

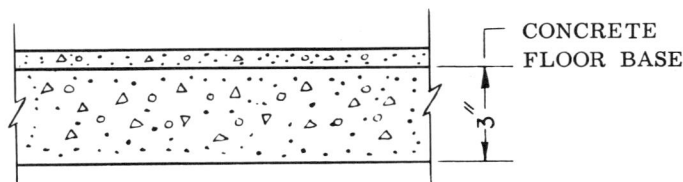

CONCRETE
FLOOR BASE

SUITABLE MIXTURES FOR CONCRETE CONSTRUCTION

	One-mixture Concrete Construction	Two-course Slab	
Foundation walls and footings	1:2¾:4 1:3:5 1:2½:5		
Basement walls	1:2½:4 1:2¾:4		
Basement walls—waterproof	1:2¼:3 1:2½:3½ 1:2½:4½		
Retaining walls	1:2:3½ 1:3:5		
Steps	1:2¼:3		
Lintels	1:2:4		
Swimming pools	1:2:3 1:2½:3		
Barnyard pavements	1:3:5		
Beam filling	1:3:4		
Fence posts	1:1:1½ 1:1¾:2 1:2:3 1:2¼:2½		
Floors:		Base	Top
One-course	1:1¾:4 1:2½:3		
Heavy-duty, one-course	1:1:2 1:1¼:2		
Farm buildings: One-course	1:2¼:3		
Two-course		1:2¼:3 1:2½:4	1:1½ 1:2
Driveways:			
One-course	1:2:3½ 1:2¼:3 1:2½:3		
Two-course		1:2¼:3 1:2½:4	1:1½ 1:2 1:1:1½
Sidewalks:			
One-course	1:2¼:3 1:2½:4		
Two-course		1:2¼:3 1:2½:4	1:1½ 1:2

WATER-CEMENT RATIOS FOR
VARIOUS TYPES OF CONSTRUCTION AND EXPOSURE CONDITIONS

Type or location of structure	Severe or moderate climate, wide range of temperature, rain, and long freezing spells or frequent freezing and thawing. gal/sk			Mild climate, rain or semi-arid; rarely snow or frost. gal/sk		
	Thin sections	Moderate sections	Mass sections	Thin sections	Moderate sections	Mass sections
A. At the water line in hydraulic or waterfront structures or portions of such structures where complete saturation or intermittent saturation is possible, but not where the structure is continuously submerged in water.	5	5½	6	5	5½	6
B. Portions of hydraulic or waterfront structures some distance from water line, but subject to frequent wetting by water.	5½	6	6	5½	6½	7
C. Ordinary exposed structures, buildings and portions of bridges not coming under above groups.	6	6½	7	6	7	7½
D. Complete continuous submergence in water.	6	6½	7	6	6½	7
E. Concrete deposited through water.	*	5½	5½	*	5½	5½
F. Pavement slabs directly on ground. Wearing slabs Base slabs	5½ 6½	* *	* *	6 7	* *	* *
G. Special case: For concrete not exposed to the weather, such as interiors of buildings and portions of structures entirely below ground, no exposure hazard is involved and the water-cement ratio should be selected on the basis of the strength and workability requirements.						

*These sections not practicable for the purpose intended.

135

AGE-COMPRESSIVE-STRENGTH RELATION
FOR TYPES I AND III PORTLAND CEMENTS

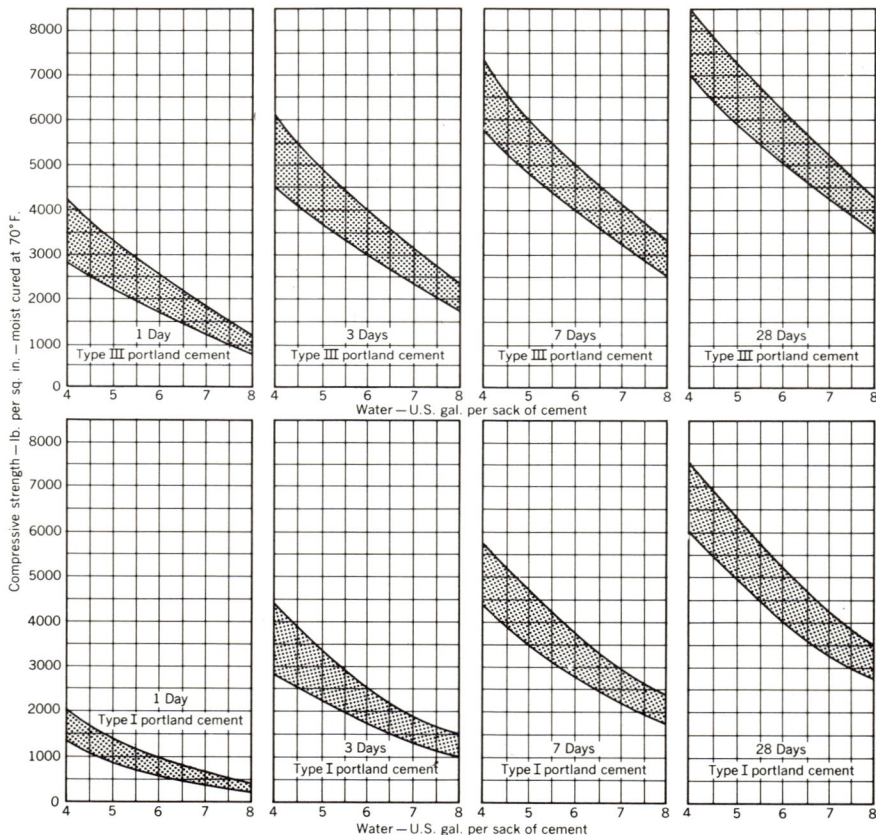

A large majority of the tests for compressive strength made by many laboratories using a variety of materials complying with the specifications of the American Society for Testing Materials is in the area within the band curves.

SOLID CONCRETE SLABS — SINGLE SPANS (OR SIMPLE SPANS SIMPLY SUPPORTED)

Approx. Balanced Reinforcement

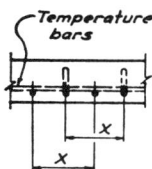

Temperature bars

Slab Thickness (in.)	3	3½	4	4½	5	5½	6	6½	7	7½	8	8½	9	9½	10
Temp. Bars #	#3	#3	#3	#3	#3	#4	#4	#4	#4	#4	#4	#5	#5	#5	#5
Spacing (in.)	15	15½	13½	12	11	18	16½	15	14	13	12½	18	17	16	15½
Bottom and Truss Bars #	#3	#3	#4	#4	#4	#5	#5	#5	#5	#5	#5	#6	#6	#6	#6
Distance "x" (in.)	8	6	10	8	8	10	10	9	8	7	7	9	9	8	8
Steel Percentage	1.33	1.43	1.33	1.43	1.25	1.40	1.26	1.26	1.30	1.37	1.28	1.32	1.24	1.31	1.24
Weight of Slab (psf)	38	44	50	56	63	69	75	81	88	94	100	106	113	119	125

Span	\[Safe Superimposed Load (psf)\]														
	3	3½	4	4½	5	5½	6	6½	7	7½	8	8½	9	9½	10
4'-0	436	739	686	1011	1167	1291	1435	1769							
4'-6	348	574	604	897	1028	1131	1268	1554	1932						
5'-0	275	457	539	796	920	1011	1135	1401	1732						
5'-6	220	370	480	720	832	923	1025	1269	1562	1941					
6'-0	179	304	411	595	710	835	935	1142	1432	1796	1920	1894			
6'-6	147	252	342	498	595	765	857	1059	1312	1631	1770	1744	1867		
7'-0	121	211	288	422	505	695	790	977	1211	1504	1635	1609	1727		
7'-6	101	178	244	360	431	597	682	841	1044	1298	1417	1494	1607	1931	
8'-0	84	151	209	310	371	516	590	729	907	1129	1233	1394	1497	1801	1915
8'-6	70	129	179	268	322	449	514	636	793	989	1081	1270	1366	1644	1755
9'-0	58	110	154	233	280	393	451	559	698	873	953	1122	1206	1453	1552
9'-6	48	94	133	203	245	346	397	493	617	773	845	996	1071	1292	1380
10'-0	40	81	116	178	215	305	351	437	548	689	753	888	956	1154	1233
10'-6		69	100	156	189	270	311	389	489	616	674	796	856	1036	1107
11'-0			87	137	167	240	277	347	438	553	605	716	770	933	997
11'-6			75	121	147	214	247	311	393	498	545	646	695	843	902
12'-0			65	106	130	191	220	289	354	449	492	584	629	765	818
12'-6				94	115	170	197	250	319	407	446	530	571	696	744
13'-0				82	101	152	177	225	288	369	405	482	519	634	678
13'-6				72	89	136	158	203	261	335	368	439	473	579	620
14'-0					79	122	142	183	236	305	335	401	432	530	568
14'-6					69	109	127	165	214	278	306	367	395	486	521
15'-0					60	97	114	149	195	253	279	336	362	447	478
15'-6						86	102	134	177	231	255	308	332	411	440
16'-0							91	121	160	211	233	282	304	378	405
16'-6							81	109	145	193	213	259	279	348	373
17'-0							72	98	132	176	195	238	257	321	345
17'-6							64	88	119	161	178	218	236	296	318
18'-0								79	108	147	163	201	217	274	294
18'-6								70	98	134	149	184	199	253	271
19'-0								62	88	122	136	169	183	233	251
19'-6									79	111	124	155	168	215	232
20'-0									71	101	113	142	154	199	214

$\dfrac{l}{t} = 32$ { Max Span for Floor Slabs

Courtesy Concrete Reinforcing Steel Institute.

DEAD WEIGHTS OF MASONRY, IN POUNDS
PER CUBIC FOOT

MASONRY:—   *Weight (pcf)*

Cinder concrete fill... 60
Concrete, cinder.. 100
Concrete, slag... 130
Concrete, stone.. 144
Concrete, reinforced stone.. 150
Brick masonry, soft.. 110
Brick masonry, common... 125
Brick masonry, pressed... 140
Dry rubble masonry, sandstone, bluestone.......................... 110
Dry rubble masonry, limestone, marble............................. 125
Dry rubble masonry, granite, gneiss............................... 130
Mortar rubble masonry, sandstone, bluestone....................... 130
Mortar rubble masonry, limestone, marble.......................... 150
Mortar rubble masonry, granite, gneiss............................ 155
Ashlar sandstone, bluestone....................................... 140
Ashlar limestone, marble.. 160
Ashlar granite, gneiss.. 165

BEARING CAPACITIES OF SOILS
(Boston Building Code)

Class	Material	Allowable Bearing Value (Tons Per Sq Ft)
1	Massive bedrock without laminations, such as granite, diorite and other granite rocks; and also gneiss, trap rock, folsite and thoroughly cemented conglomerates, such as the Roxbury Puddingstone, all in sound condition (sound condition allows some cracks).	100 *
2	Laminated rocks, such as slate and schist, in sound condition (some cracks allowed).	35
3	Shale in sound condition (some cracks allowed).	10
4	Residual deposits of shattered or broken bedrock of any kind except shale.	10
5	Hardpan.	10
6	Gravel, sand-gravel mixtures, compact.	5
7	Gravel, sand-gravel mixtures, loose; sand, coarse, compact.	4
8	Sand, coarse, loose; sand, fine, compact.	3
9	Sand, fine, loose.	1
10	Hard clay.	6
11	Medium clay.	4
12	Soft clay.	1
13	Rock flour or any deposit of unusual character not provided for herein.	(Values to be fixed by the Commissioner)

***** But not greater than the value of the footing resting upon it.**

PROPERTIES OF STEEL REINFORCING BARS

Nominal dimensions—round sections				
Bar designation, No.	Unit weight per ft., lb.	Diameter, in.	Cross-sectional area, sq.in.	Perimeter, in.
2	0.167	0.250	0.05	0.786
3	0.376	0.375	0.11	1.178
4	0.668	0.500	0.20	1.571
5	1.043	0.625	0.31	1.963
6	1.502	0.750	0.44	2.356
7	2.044	0.875	0.60	2.749
8	2.670	1.000	0.79	3.142
9	3.400	1.128	1.00	3.544
10	4.303	1.270	1.27	3.990
11	5.313	1.410	1.56	4.430

COMMON STYLES OF WELDED WIRE FABRIC—TWO-WAY TYPES

Style designation	Spacing of wires, in.		Size of wires, AS&W gage		Sectional area, sq.in. per ft.		Weight, lb. per 100 sq. ft.
	Longit.	Trans.	Longit.	Trans.	Longit.	Trans.	
2 × 2—10/10	2	2	10	10	.086	.086	60
2 × 2—12/12*	2	2	12	12	.052	.052	37
2 × 2—14/14*	2	2	14	14	.030	.030	21
3 × 3—8/8	3	3	8	8	.082	.082	58
3 × 3—10/10	3	3	10	10	.057	.057	41
3 × 3—12/12*	3	3	12	12	.035	.035	25
3 × 3—14/14*	3	3	14	14	.020	.020	14
4 × 4—4/4	4	4	4	4	.120	.120	85
4 × 4—6/6	4	4	6	6	.087	.087	62
4 × 4—8/8	4	4	8	8	.062	.062	44
4 × 4—10/10	4	4	10	10	.043	.043	31
4 × 4—12/12*	4	4	12	12	.026	.026	19
4 × 4—13/13*	4	4	13	13	.020	.020	14
6 × 6—0/0	6	6	0	0	.148	.148	107
6 × 6—1/1	6	6	1	1	.126	.126	91
6 × 6—2/2	6	6	2	2	.108	.108	78
6 × 6—3/3	6	6	3	3	.093	.093	68
6 × 6—4/4	6	6	4	4	.080	.080	58
6 × 6—4/6	6	6	4	6	.080	.058	50
6 × 6—5/5	6	6	5	5	.067	.067	49
6 × 6—6/6	6	6	6	6	.058	.058	42
6 × 6—7/7	6	6	7	7	.049	.049	36
6 × 6—8/8	6	6	8	8	.041	.041	30
6 × 6—9/9	6	6	9	9	.035	`.035	25
6 × 6—10/10	6	6	10	10	.029	.029	21

*Usually furnished only in galvanized wire.

A two-way fabric—for a given size of longitudinal wires—is any style in which the sectional area of transverse steel is greater than the minimum required for proper fabrication because the transverse wires either have a spacing that is less than the permissible maximum, or are of larger size than the permissible minimum. Two-way fabrics are not necessarily limited to styles in which both longitudinal and transverse wires have the same size and spacing, as indicated in the above table. Courtesy American Concrete Institute.

COMMON STYLES OF WELDED WIRE FABRIC—ONE-WAY TYPES

Style designation	Spacing of wires, in.		Size of wires, AS&W gage		Sectional area, sq.in. per ft.		Weight, lb. per 100 sq. ft.
	Longit.	Trans.	Longit.	Trans.	Longit.	Trans.	
2 × 12—0/6	2	12	0	6	.443	.029	166
2 × 16—0/6	2	16	0	6	.443	.022	163
2 × 16—1/7	2	16	1	7	.377	.018	140
2 × 16—2/8	2	16	2	8	.325	.015	119
2 × 16—3/8	2	16	3	8	.280	.015	104
2 × 16—4/9	2	16	4	9	.239	.013	89
2 × 16—5/10	2	16	5	10	.202	.011	75
2 × 16—6/10	2	16	6	10	.174	.011	65
2 × 16—7/11	2	16	7	11	.148	.009	55
3 × 16—2/8	3	16	2	8	.216	.015	83
3 × 16—3/8	3	16	3	8	.187	.015	72
3 × 16—4/9	3	16	4	9	.159	.013	61
4 × 16—3/8	4	16	3	8	.140	.015	56
4 × 16—4/9	4	16	4	9	.120	.013	48
4 × 16—5/10	4	16	5	10	.101	.011	40
4 × 16—6/10	4	16	6	10	.087	.011	35
4 × 16—7/11	4	16	7	11	.074	.009	30
4 × 16—8/12	4	16	8	12	.062	.007	25
4 × 16—9/12	4	16	9	12	.052	.007	21
4 × 12—4/9	4	12	4	9	.120	.017	49
4 × 12—5/7	4	12	5	7	.101	.025	45
4 × 12—5/10	4	12	5	10	.101	.014	42
4 × 12—6/10	4	12	6	10	.087	.014	36
4 × 12—7/11	4	12	7	11	.074	.011	31
4 × 12—8/12	4	12	8	12	.062	.009	26
4 × 12—9/12	4	12	9	12	.052	.009	22
4 × 8—7/11	4	8	7	11	.074	.017	33
4 × 8—8/12	4	8	8	12	.062	.013	27
4 × 8—9/12	4	8	9	12	.052	.013	23
4 × 8—10/12	4	8	10	12	.043	.013	20
6 × 12—00/4	6	12	00	4	.172	.040	78
6 × 12—0/0	6	12	0	0	.148	.074	81
6 × 12—0/3	6	12	0	3	.148	.047	72
6 × 12—1/1	6	12	1	1	.126	.063	69
6 × 12—1/4	6	12	1	4	.126	.040	61
6 × 12—2/2	6	12	2	2	.108	.054	59
6 × 12—2/5	6	12	2	5	.108	.034	52
6 × 12—3/3	6	12	3	3	.093	.047	51
6 × 12—4/4	6	12	4	4	.080	.040	44
6 × 12—6/6	6	12	6	6	.058	.029	32

The above styles are used mostly in building construction. Although the above styles are termed "one-way" fabrics—since in each case the transverse wires are of minimum permissible size and have maximum permissible spacing — actually they have some transverse reinforcing effectiveness by virtue of the amount of transverse steel provided. Courtesy American Concrete Institute.

RECOMMENDED THICKNESSES OF CONCRETE SLABS IN INCHES

Basement floors for dwellings	4
Private garage floors	4 to 5
Porch floors	4 to 5
Stock barn floors	5 to 6
Poultry-house floors	4
Hog-house floors	4
Milkhouse floors	4
Granary floors	5
Impliment-shed floors	6
Tile floor bases	2½
Driveways and approaches	6 to 8
Sidewalks	4 to 6

PERIODIC CHART OF THE ELEMENTS

IA	IIA	IIIB	IVB	VB	VIB	VIIB	VIII	VIII	VIII	IB	IIB	IIIA	IVA	VA	VIA	VIIA	INERT GASES
1 H 1.0080																1 H 1.0080	2 He 4.003
3 Li 6.940	4 Be 9.013											5 B 10.82	6 C 12.011	7 N 14.008	8 O 16.000	9 F 19.00	10 Ne 20.183
11 Na 22.991	12 Mg 24.32											13 Al 26.98	14 Si 28.09	15 P 30.975	16 S 32.066	17 Cl 35.457	18 Ar 39.944
19 K 39.100	20 Ca 40.08	21 Sc 44.96	22 Ti 47.90	23 V 50.95	24 Cr 52.01	25 Mn 54.94	26 Fe 55.85	27 Co 58.94	28 Ni 58.71	29 Cu 63.54	30 Zn 65.38	31 Ga 69.72	32 Ge 72.60	33 As 74.91	34 Se 78.96	35 Br 79.916	36 Kr 83.80
37 Rb 85.48	38 Sr 87.63	39 Y 88.92	40 Zr 91.22	41 Nb 92.91	42 Mo 95.95	43 Tc (97)	44 Ru 101.1	45 Rh 102.91	46 Pd 106.4	47 Ag 107.880	48 Cd 112.41	49 In 114.82	50 Sn 118.70	51 Sb 121.76	52 Te 127.61	53 I 126.91	54 Xe 131.30
55 Cs 132.91	56 Ba 137.36	57 *La 138.92	72 Hf 178.50	73 Ta 180.95	74 W 183.86	75 Re 186.22	76 Os 190.2	77 Ir 192.2	78 Pt 195.09	79 Au 197.0	80 Hg 200.61	81 Tl 204.39	82 Pb 207.21	83 Bi 209.00	84 Po (210)	85 At (210)	86 Rn (222)
87 Fr (223)	88 Ra (226)	89 †Ac (227)															

* LANTHANUM SERIES

58 Ce 140.13	59 Pr 140.92	60 Nd 144.27	61 Pm (147)	62 Sm 150.35	63 Eu 152.0	64 Gd 157.26	65 Tb 158.93	66 Dy 162.51	67 Ho 164.94	68 Er 167.27	69 Tm 168.94	70 Yb 173.04	71 Lu 174.99

† ACTINIUM SERIES

90 Th (232)	91 Pa (231)	92 U 238.07	93 Np (237)	94 Pu (242)	95 Am (243)	96 Cm (247)	97 Bk (247)	98 Cf (249)	99 Es (254)	100 Fm (253)	101 Md (256)	102 No (253)	103 Lux (OVER)

141

MATERIALS FOR SMALL FOUNDATION WALLS OF CONCRETE

Wall 7 Feet High—Material Needed for Each 10-Foot Length

Thickness Inches	1:2¼:3 Mixture			1:2¾:4 Mixture		
	Cement Sacks	Sand Cubic Feet	Stone Cubic Feet	Cement Sacks	Sand Cubic Feet	Stone Cubic Feet
8	10 4/5	24 1/10	32 7/10	8 3/5	24 1/10	34 2/5
9	12 1/5	26 1/5	37	9 7/10	26 1/5	39
10	13 1/2	30 1/5	41	10 4/5	30 1/5	43 1/5
12	16 2/5	36 1/3	49 1/4	12 9/10	36 1/3	51 4/5
18	24 1/3	54 1/2	73 4/5	19 2/5	54 1/2	77 7/10

Wall 8 Feet High—Material Needed for Each 10-Foot Length

	Cement Sacks	Sand Cubic Feet	Stone Cubic Feet	Cement Sacks	Sand Cubic Feet	Stone Cubic Feet
8	12 2/5	27 3/4	37 3/5	9 9/10	27 3/4	39 3/5
9	13 9/10	31 1/10	42 1/5	11 1/10	31 1/10	44 1/2
10	15 4/10	34 1/2	46 4/5	12 3/10	34 1/2	49 1/4
12	18 1/2	41 1/2	56 1/3	14 4/5	41 1/2	59 1/3
18	27 7/10	62 1/10	84 1/3	22 1/5	62 1/10	88 4/5

Wall 9 Feet High—Material Needed for Each 10-Foot Length

	Cement Sacks	Sand Cubic Feet	Stone Cubic Feet	Cement Sacks	Sand Cubic Feet	Stone Cubic Feet
8	13 9/10	31 1/5	42 1/3	11 1/10	31 1/5	44 1/2
9	15 3/5	35	47 1/2	12 1/2	35	50
10	13 4/5	38 4/5	52 7/10	17 3/10	38 4/5	55 1/2
12	16 7/10	46 3/5	63 1/3	16 7/10	46 3/5	66 2/3
18	31 1/4	70	95	25	70	100

Material for Each 10-Foot Length of Footings—1:2¾ :4 Mixture

Size (Height x Width)	Cement Sacks	Sand Cubic Feet	Stone Cubic Feet
6″ x 12″	9/10	2 3/5	3 7/10
7″ x 14″	1 1/5	3 1/2	5 1/3
8″ x 16″	1 3/5	4 3/5	6 3/5
9″ x 18″	2 4/5	5 4/5	8 1/3
10″ x 20″	2 7/10	7 1/5	10 3/10
12″ x 24″	3 7/10	10 2/5	14 4/5
15″ x 30″	5 3/4	16 1/5	23 1/10

Courtesy Universal Atlas Cement Co.

CONCRETE BLOCK QUANTITIES

Number of 16-in. Concrete Block per Course for Solid Walls in Buildings of Various Sizes.*

SIZE OF BLDG. IN FEET	2	4	6	8	10	12	14	16	18	20	22	24	26	28	30	32	34	36	38	40
2	4	7	10	13	16	19	22	25	28	31	34	37	40	43	46	49	52	55	58	61
4	7	10	13	16	19	22	25	28	31	34	37	40	43	46	49	52	55	58	61	64
6	10	13	16	19	22	25	28	31	34	37	40	43	46	49	52	55	58	61	64	67
8	13	16	19	22	25	28	31	34	37	40	43	46	49	52	55	58	61	64	67	70
10	16	19	22	25	28	31	34	37	40	43	46	49	52	55	58	61	64	67	70	73
12	19	22	25	28	31	34	37	40	43	46	49	52	55	58	61	64	67	70	73	76
14	22	25	28	31	34	37	40	43	46	49	52	55	58	61	64	67	70	73	76	79
16	25	28	31	34	37	40	43	46	49	52	55	58	61	64	67	70	73	76	79	82
18	28	31	34	37	40	43	46	49	52	55	58	61	64	67	70	73	76	79	82	85
20	31	34	37	40	43	46	49	52	55	58	61	64	67	70	73	76	79	82	85	88
22	34	37	40	43	46	49	52	55	58	61	64	67	70	73	76	79	82	85	88	91
24	37	40	43	46	49	52	55	58	61	64	67	70	73	76	79	82	85	88	91	94
26	40	43	46	49	52	55	58	61	64	67	70	73	76	79	82	85	88	91	94	97
28	43	46	49	52	55	58	61	64	67	70	73	76	79	82	85	88	91	94	97	100
30	46	49	52	55	58	61	64	67	70	73	76	79	82	85	88	91	94	97	100	103
32	49	52	55	58	61	64	67	70	73	76	79	82	85	88	91	94	97	100	103	106
34	52	55	58	61	64	67	70	73	76	79	82	85	88	91	94	97	100	103	106	109
36	55	58	61	64	67	70	73	76	79	82	85	88	91	94	97	100	103	106	109	112
38	58	61	64	67	70	73	76	79	82	85	88	91	94	97	100	103	106	109	112	115
40	61	64	67	70	73	76	79	82	85	88	91	94	97	100	103	106	109	112	115	118
42	64	67	70	73	76	79	82	85	88	91	94	97	100	103	106	109	112	115	118	121
44	67	70	73	76	79	82	85	88	91	94	97	100	103	106	109	112	115	118	121	124
46	70	73	76	79	82	85	88	91	94	97	100	103	106	109	112	115	118	121	124	127
48	73	76	79	82	85	88	91	94	97	100	103	106	109	112	115	118	121	124	127	130
50	76	79	82	85	88	91	94	97	100	103	106	109	112	115	118	121	124	127	130	133
52	79	82	85	88	91	94	97	100	103	106	109	112	115	118	121	124	127	130	133	136
54	82	85	88	91	94	97	100	103	106	109	112	115	118	121	124	127	130	133	136	139
56	85	88	91	94	97	100	103	106	109	112	115	118	121	124	127	130	133	136	139	142
58	88	91	94	97	100	103	106	109	112	115	118	121	124	127	130	133	136	139	142	145
60	91	94	97	100	103	106	109	112	115	118	121	124	127	130	133	136	139	142	145	148

*Explanation: To find the number of block for any building always use outside measurements. A basement 22 feet by 32 feet, for example, would require 79 block for one course all around. Multiply 79 by the number of courses needed. Thus a 10-course basement would require a total of 790 block for the solid wall, from which deductions should be made for windows and doors. If any dimension is an odd number such as 22 feet by 31 feet see table for nearest smaller size; for example, 22 feet by 30 feet, and add 1½ block per row.

Courtesy Universal Atlas Cement Co.

PART SIX

PIPING AND PLUMBING

GRAPHIC SYMBOLS FOR PIPE FITTINGS AND VALVES

ASA Z 32.2.3 1949 Extract
(Reaffirmed 1953)*

	Flanged	Screwed	Bell & Spigot	Welded	Soldered
1 BUSHING					
2 CAP					
3 CROSS					
3.1 Reducing					
3.2 Straight Size					
4 CROSSOVER					
5 ELBOW					
5.1 45 Degree					
5.2 90-Degree					
5.3 Turned Down					
5.4 Turned Up					
5.5 Base					
5.6 Double Branch					
5.7 Long Radius					
5.8 Reducing					
5.9 Side Outlet (Outlet Down)					
5.10 Side Outlet (Outlet Up)					
5.11 Street					
6 JOINT					
6.1 Connecting Pipe					
6.2 Expansion					
7 LATERAL					
8 ORIFICE FLANGE					

*Published by the A.S.M.E.

GRAPHIC SYMBOLS FOR PIPE FITTINGS AND VALVES

	Flanged	Screwed	Bell & Spigot	Welded	Soldered
9 REDUCING FLANGE	⊣▷				
10 PLUGS					
10.1 Bull Plug	⊣▷		◯		
10.2 Pipe Plug		◁	€		
11 REDUCER					
11.1 Concentric	⊣▷⊢	▷	▷▷	▷	▷
11.2 Eccentric	⊣▷⊢	▷	▷	▷	▷
12 SLEEVE	╂··╂	╂··╂	⊰···⊱	⋇··⋇	⊙···⊙
13 TEE					
13.1 (Straight Size)					
13.2 (Outlet Up)	⊢⊙⊣	⊢⊙⊣	⊰⊙€	⋇⊙⋇	⊙⊙⊙
13.3 (Outlet Down)	⊢⊙⊣	⊢⊙⊣	⊰⊖€	⋇⊖⋇	⊙⊖⊙
13.4 (Double Sweep)					
13.5 Reducing					
13.6 (Single Sweep)					
13.7 Side Outlet (Outlet Down)					
13.8 Side Outlet (Outlet Up)					
14 UNION	⫲	⫲		⋇⫲	⊙⫲⊙
15 ANGLE VALVE					
15.1 Check					
15.2 Gate (Elevation)					
15.3 Gate (Plan)	⊗⊣	⊗⊢		⊗⋇	
15.4 Globe (Elevation)					
15.5 Globe (Plan)	⊗⊣	⊗⊣		⊗⋇	⊗▷
15.6 Hose Angle	Same as	Symbol	23.1		
16 AUTOMATIC VALVE					
16.1 By-Pass					
16.2 Governor-Operated					
16.3 Reducing					

147

GRAPHIC SYMBOLS FOR PIPE FITTINGS AND VALVES

	Flanged	Screwed	Bell & Spigot	Welded	Soldered
17 CHECK VALVE 17.1 Angle Check 17.2 (Straight Way)	Same as	Symbol	15.1		
18 COCK					
19 DIAPHRAGM VALVE					
20 FLOAT VALVE					
21 GATE VALVE 21.1[1]					
21.2 Angle Gate	Same as	Symbols	15.2-15.3		
21.3 Hose Gate	Same as	Symbol	23.2		
21.4 Motor-Operated					
22 GLOBE VALVE 22.1					
22.2 Angle Globe	Same as	Symbols	15.4-15.5		
22.3 Hose Globe	Same as	Symbol	23.3		
22.4 Motor-Operated					
23 HOSE VALVE					
23.1 Angle					
23.2 Gate					
23.3 Globe					
24 LOCKSHIELD VALVE					
25 QUICK OPENING VALVE					
26 SAFETY VALVE					
27 STOP VALVE	Same as	Symbol	21.1		

GRAPHIC SYMBOLS FOR PIPING

ASA Z 32.2.3 1949 Extract

(Reaffirmed 1953)*

AIR CONDITIONING

28 Brine Return — — —BR— — —

29 Brine Supply ———— B ————

30 Circulating Chilled or Hot-Water Flow ————CH————

31 Circulating Chilled or Hot-Water Return — — –CHR— — —

32 Condenser Water Flow Flow ————— C —————

33 Condenser Water Return — — —CR— — —

34 Drain ———— D ————

35 Humidification Line — . —— H —— . —

36 Make-up Water —— . —— . —— . —

37 Refrigerant Discharge ————RD————

38 Refrigerant Liquid ————RL————

39 Refrigerant Suction — — —RS — — —

HEATING

40 Air-Relief Line — — — — — — —

41 Boiler Blow Off —— —— —— ——

42 Compressed Air ———— A ————

43 Condensate or Vacuum Pump Discharge — —o— —o— —o— —

44 Feedwater Pump Discharge —oo— —oo— —oo—

45 Fuel-Oil Flow ———— FOF————

46 Fuel-Oil Return — — — FOR— — —

47 Fuel-Oil Tank Vent — — — FOV— — —

48 High-Pressure Return — / — / — /

49 High-Pressure Steam — / — / — /

50 Hot-Water Heating Return — — — — — — —

51 Hot-Water Heating Supply ————————

52 Low-Pressure Return — — — — — — —

53 Low-Pressure Steam ————————

54 Make-Up Water —— . —— . —— . —

55 Medium Pressure Return — / — — / —

56 Medium Pressure Steam — / — — / —

PLUMBING

57 Acid Waste ————ACID————

58 Cold Water — . — . — . — . —

59 Compressed Air ———— A ————

60 Drinking Water Flow —— . —— . —— . —

61 Drinking Water Return —— . . —— . . ——

62 Fire Line — F ———— F —

63 Gas — G ———— G—

64 Hot Water —— . . —— . . ——

65 Hot-Water Return — — . . — — . . —

66 Soil, Waste or Leader (Above Grade) ————————

67 Soil, Waste or Leader (Below Grade) — — — — — — —

68 Vacuum Cleaning — V ———— V —

69 Vent — — — — — — — — —

PNEUMATIC TUBES

70 Tube Runs ════════

SPRINKLERS

71 Branch and Head —o———— o—

72 Drain — s — — — s —

73 Main Supplies ———— s ————

149

GRAPHIC SYMBOLS FOR PLUMBING

ASA Y32.4 1955 Extract*

1 Autopsy Table	AT	10 Drain	□ FD
2 Bath	B-1 B-2, etc.	11 Drinking Fountain	□ DF-1 DF-2, etc.
USE SPECIFICATION TO DESCRIBE		USE SPECIFICATION TO DESCRIBE	
3 Bed Pan Washer	BPW	12 Gas Outlet	T G
4 Bed Pan Sterilizer	BPS	13 Range	R
5 Bidet	O O B	14 Grease Trap	GT
6 Can Washer	O CW	15 Hose Bibb	T HB
7 Cleanout	O CO	16 Hose Rack	⬛O HR
8 Dental Unit	O DU	17 Hot Water Tank	O HWT
		18 Laundry Tray	LT
9 Dish Washer	DW	19 Lavatories	L-1 L-2, etc.
*Published by the A.S.M.E.		USE SPECIFICATION TO DESCRIBE	
		20 Meter	O M

HEAT LOSS FROM BARE PIPE SURFACES

Losses given in B.t.u. per hour, per linear foot of bare pipe
at various temperature differences.

Nominal pipe size, inches	Sq. ft. of pipe surface, per lin. ft.	Temperature difference, degrees F.					
		50°	100°	150°	200°	250°	300°
½ 0.220		21.5	47.3	79.2	117.3	162.3	215.2
¾ 0.275		26.8	59.2	99.0	146.6	202.9	269.0
1 ....0.344		33.5	74.0	123.8	183.4	253.8	336.4
1¼ 0.435		42.4	93.6	156.6	231.9	320.9	425.4
1½ 0.498		48.6	107.2	179.3	265.4	367.4	487.0
2 ....0.622		60.7	133.9	223.9	331.5	458.9	608.3
2½ 0.753		73.4	162.1	271.1	401.4	555.6	736.4
3 ....0.917		89.4	197.3	330.1	488.8	676.6	896.8
4 ....1.178		114.9	253.5	424.1	627.9	869.1	1152.0

STANDARD WROUGHT-IRON AND STEEL PIPE

Diameter — Nominal internal, inches	Diameter — Actual external, inches	Diameter — Actual internal, inches	Nominal thickness, inches	Circumference External, inches	Transverse area — External square inches	Transverse area — Internal square inches	Transverse area — Metal, square inches	Length pipe per sq. ft. External surface, feet	Length of pipe containing 1 cu. ft., feet	Area of external surface per linear foot, sq. ft.
3 ...	3.500	3.068	.216	10.996	9.621	7.393	2.2280	1.091	19.470	.917
3½ ...	4.000	3.548	.226	12.566	12.566	9.887	2.6790	.955	14.570	1.047
4 ...	4.500	4.026	.237	14.137	15.904	12.730	3.4740	.849	11.310	1.178
4½ ...	5.000	4.506	.247	15.708	19.635	15.947	3.6880	.763	9.030	1.309
5 ...	5.563	5.047	.258	17.477	24.306	20.006	4.3000	.686	7.198	1.456
6 ...	6.625	6.065	.280	20.813	34.472	28.888	5.5840	.577	4.980	1.734
7 ...	7.625	7.023	.301	23.955	45.664	38.738	6.9260	.501	3.720	1.996
8 ...	8.625	7.981	.322	27.096	58.426	50.027	8.3990	.442	2.878	2.257
9 ...	9.625	8.941	.342	30.238	72.760	62.786	9.9740	.396	2.294	2.519
10 ...	10.750	10.020	.365	33.772	90.763	78.855	11.9080	.355	1.826	2.817
11 ...	11.750	11.000	.375	39.914	108.434	95.033	13.4010	.325	1.510	3.073
12 ...	12.750	12.000	.375	40.055	127.677	113.098	14.5790	.299	1.270	3.337

FLOW OF WATER AND PRESSURE DROP THROUGH STANDARD-WEIGHT PIPE

Nom. Pipe Size → / Q ↓	¾ v	¾ p	1 v	1 p	1¼ v	1¼ p	1½ v	1½ p	2 v	2 p	2½ v	2½ p	3 v	3 p	4 v	4 p
5	3.0	3.6	1.9	1.1	1.1	0.3	0.8	0.1	0.5	.04	0.3	.02				
10	6.0	10.3	3.7	3.9	2.1	1.0	1.6	0.5	1.0	0.1	0.7	.05	0.4	.02		
15	9.0	27.0	5.6	8.2	3.2	2.1	2.4	1.0	1.4	0.3	1.0	.12	0.7	.04		
20	12.0	49.0	7.4	14.4	4.3	3.7	3.1	1.7	1.9	0.5	1.3	0.2	0.9	.07		
25	15.0	72.0	9.3	21.6	5.4	5.5	3.9	2.5	2.4	0.7	1.7	0.3	1.1	0.1		
30			11.1	31.0	6.4	7.8	4.7	3.5	2.9	1.0	2.0	0.4	1.3	0.1		
40			14.9	52.6	8.6	13.7	6.3	6.0	3.8	1.7	2.7	0.7	1.7	0.2	1.0	.06
50					10.7	20.5	7.9	9.1	4.8	2.6	3.4	1.1	2.2	0.4	1.3	.09
60					12.8	28.8	9.4	13.0	5.7	3.6	4.0	1.5	2.6	0.5	1.5	.13
70					14.9	38.2	11.0	17.2	6.7	4.8	4.7	2.0	3.0	0.7	1.8	.18
80							12.6	22.4	7.6	6.1	5.4	2.6	3.5	0.9	2.0	.23
90							14.1	27.4	8.6	7.6	6.0	3.2	3.9	1.1	2.3	.28
100							15.7	33.1	9.6	9.3	6.7	3.9	4.3	1.3	2.5	.34
125							19.6	50.4	11.9	14.4	8.4	6.0	5.4	2.0	3.1	0.5
150									14.3	20.1	10.1	8.4	6.5	2.8	3.8	0.7
175									16.7	26.7	11.7	11.1	7.6	3.8	4.4	1.0
200									19.1	33.9	13.4	14.4	8.7	4.9	5.0	1.3

Nom. Pipe Sizes in Inches
Q = Gallons per minute
v = Velocity in feet per second
p = Pressure drop in p.s.i. per 100 ft. of pipe in fairly smooth condition

The above table is based on the empirical flow formula of E. W. Schoder of Cornell University and applies to standard-weight cast iron and wrought iron or wrought steel pipe having a fairly smooth interior. The formula is as follows:

$$p = 0.38 \ \frac{v\ 1.86}{d\ 1.25}$$

where p = pressure drop in pounds per square inch per 100 feet of pipe, v = velocity of water flow in feet per second and d = inside diameter of pipe in inches.

SOFT SOLDER FLUXES

Description	Form	Application	Remarks
NONCORROSIVE			
Rosin and alcohol	Liquid	Copper, brass, tinned, cadmium or silver-plated surfaces	General use, surfaces are very clean.
Oleic acid	Liquid	Same as above	Same as above.
Rosin and naphtha	Liquid	Same as above	For slightly oily surfaces. Danger, very inflammable.
Analine phosphate	Paste	Copper, brass, aluminum, bronze, rolled zinc (not zinc die castings), carbon steel, nickel, and nickel alloys	Most active noncorrosive flux available. Ventilation necessary for continuous work. Residue may be electrically conductive.
CORROSIVE			
Zinc chloride and ammonium chloride plus water.	Liquid	Copper, brass, aluminum, bronze, rolled zinc (not zinc die castings), carbon steel, nickel, and nickel alloys.	General use, not suitable for work immersed in insulating oil or in contact with insulating materials.
Zinc chloride and petrolatum	Paste	Same as above	Use where paste flux is more convenient than a liquid.
Zinc chloride plus water	Liquid	Brass	An ammonia-free flux suitable for brasses to lessen the dangers of season cracking.
Acid type	Liquid	Stainless steel	Very corrosive.

PIPE — DIMENSIONS AND PROPERTIES

Nom. Dia. In.	Outside Dia. In.	Inside Dia. In.	Thickness In.	Wt. per Ft, Lb. Plain Ends	Wt. per Ft, Lb. Thread & Cplg.	Threads per Inch	Outside Dia. In.	Length In.	Weight Lb.	I In.⁴	A In.²	r In.
		DIMENSIONS						COUPLINGS			PROPERTIES	
					STANDARD							
1/8	.405	.269	.068	.24	.25	27	.562	7/8	.03	.001	.072	.12
1/4	.540	.364	.088	.42	.43	18	.685	1	.04	.003	.125	.16
3/8	.675	.493	.091	.57	.57	18	.848	1 1/8	.07	.007	.167	.21
1/2	.840	.622	.109	.85	.85	14	1.024	1 3/8	.12	.017	.250	.26
3/4	1.050	.824	.113	1.13	1.13	14	1.281	1 5/8	.21	.037	.333	.33
1	1.315	1.049	.133	1.68	1.68	11 1/2	1.576	1 7/8	.35	.087	.494	.42
1 1/4	1.660	1.380	.140	2.27	2.28	11 1/2	1.950	2 1/8	.55	.195	.669	.54
1 1/2	1.900	1.610	.145	2.72	2.73	11 1/2	2.218	2 3/8	.76	.310	.799	.62
2	2.375	2.067	.154	3.65	3.68	11 1/2	2.760	2 5/8	1.23	.666	1.075	.79
2 1/2	2.875	2.469	.203	5.79	5.82	8	3.276	2 7/8	1.76	1.530	1.704	.95
3	3.500	3.068	.216	7.58	7.62	8	3.948	3 1/8	2.55	3.017	2.228	1.16
3 1/2	4.000	3.548	.226	9.11	9.20	8	4.591	3 5/8	4.33	4.788	2.680	1.34
4	4.500	4.026	.237	10.79	10.89	8	5.091	3 5/8	5.41	7.233	3.174	1.51
5	5.563	5.047	.258	14.62	14.81	8	6.296	4 1/8	9.16	15.16	4.300	1.88
6	6.625	6.065	.280	18.97	19.19	8	7.358	4 1/8	10.82	28.14	5.581	2.25
8	8.625	8.071	.277	24.70	25.00	8	9.420	4 5/8	15.84	63.35	7.265	2.95
8	8.625	7.981	.322	28.55	28.81	8	9.420	4 5/8	15.84	72.49	8.399	2.94
10	10.750	10.192	.279	31.20	32.00	8	11.721	6 1/8	33.92	125.4	9.178	3.70
10	10.750	10.136	.307	34.24	35.00	8	11.721	6 1/8	33.92	137.4	10.07	3.69
10	10.750	10.020	.365	40.48	41.13	8	11.721	6 1/8	33.92	160.7	11.91	3.67
12	12.750	12.090	.330	43.77	45.00	8	13.958	6 1/8	48.27	248.5	12.88	4.39
12	12.750	12.000	.375	49.56	50.71	8	13.958	6 1/8	48.27	279.3	14.38	4.38
					EXTRA STRONG							
1/8	.405	.215	.095	.31	.32	27	.582	1 1/8	.05	.001	.093	.12
1/4	.540	.302	.119	.54	.54	18	.724	1 3/8	.07	.004	.157	.16
3/8	.675	.423	.126	.74	.75	18	.898	1 5/8	.13	.009	.217	.20
1/2	.840	.546	.147	1.09	1.10	14	1.085	1 7/8	.22	.020	.320	.25
3/4	1.050	.742	.154	1.47	1.49	14	1.316	2 1/8	.33	.045	.433	.32
1	1.315	.957	.179	2.17	2.20	11 1/2	1.575	2 3/8	.47	.106	.639	.41
1 1/4	1.660	1.278	.191	3.00	3.05	11 1/2	2.054	2 7/8	1.04	.242	.881	.52
1 1/2	1.900	1.500	.200	3.63	3.69	11 1/2	2.294	2 7/8	1.17	.391	1.068	.61
2	2.375	1.939	.218	5.02	5.13	11 1/2	2.870	3 5/8	2.17	.868	1.477	.77
2 1/2	2.875	2.323	.276	7.66	7.83	8	3.389	4 1/2	3.43	1.924	2.254	.92
3	3.500	2.900	.300	10.25	10.46	8	4.014	4 1/2	4.13	3.894	3.016	1.14
3 1/2	4.000	3.364	.318	12.51	12.82	8	4.628	4 5/8	6.29	6.280	3.678	1.31
4	4.500	3.826	.337	14.98	15.39	8	5.233	4 5/8	8.16	9.610	4.407	1.48
5	5.563	4.813	.375	20.78	21.42	8	6.420	5 1/8	12.87	20.67	6.112	1.84
6	6.625	5.761	.432	28.57	29.33	8	7.482	5 1/8	15.18	40.49	8.405	2.20
8	8.625	7.625	.500	43.39	44.72	8	9.596	6 1/8	26.63	105.7	12.76	2.88
10	10.750	9.750	.500	54.74	56.94	8	11.958	6 5/8	44.16	211.9	16.10	3.63
12	12.750	11.750	.500	65.42	68.02	8	13.958	6 5/8	51.99	361.5	19.24	4.34
					DOUBLE-EXTRA STRONG							
1/2	.840	.252	.294	1.71	1.73	14	1.085	1 7/8	.22	.024	.504	.22
3/4	1.050	.434	.308	2.44	2.46	14	1.316	2 1/8	.33	.058	.718	.28
1	1.315	.599	.358	3.66	3.68	11 1/2	1.575	2 3/8	.47	.140	1.076	.36
1 1/4	1.660	.896	.382	5.21	5.27	11 1/2	2.054	2 7/8	1.04	.341	1.534	.47
1 1/2	1.900	1.100	.400	6.41	6.47	11 1/2	2.294	2 7/8	1.17	.568	1.885	.55
2	2.375	1.503	.436	9.03	9.14	11 1/2	2.870	3 5/8	2.17	1.311	2.656	.70
2 1/2	2.875	1.771	.552	13.70	13.87	8	3.389	4 1/2	3.43	2.871	4.028	.84
3	3.500	2.300	.600	18.58	18.79	8	4.014	4 1/2	4.13	5.992	5.466	1.05
3 1/2	4.000	2.728	.636	22.85	23.16	8	4.628	4 5/8	6.29	9.848	6.721	1.21
4	4.500	3.152	.674	27.54	27.95	8	5.233	4 5/8	8.16	15.28	8.101	1.37
5	5.563	4.063	.750	38.55	39.20	8	6.420	5 1/8	12.87	33.64	11.34	1.72
6	6.625	4.897	.864	53.16	53.92	8	7.482	5 1/8	15.18	66.33	15.64	2.06
8	8.625	6.875	.875	72.42	73.76	8	9.596	6 1/8	26.63	162.0	21.30	2.76

LARGE O. D. PIPE

Pipe 14″ and larger is sold by actual O. S. diameter and thickness.
Sizes 14″, 15″, and 16″ are available regularly in thicknesses varying by 1/8″ from 1/4″ to 1″, inclusive.

Courtesy Posey Iron Works, Lancaster, Pa.

IRON PIPE SIZES

Nominal Pipe Size Inches	Outside Diameter (D) Inches	Schedule No. See Note 1	Wall Thickness (t) Inches	Inside Diameter (d) Inches	Area of Metal (A) Square Inches	Transverse Internal Area Square Inches	Transverse Internal Area See Note 2 Sq Ft	Moment of Inertia (I) Inches to 4th Power	Weight of Pipe Pounds per foot	Weight of Water Pounds per foot of pipe	External Surface Sq Ft per foot of pipe	Section Modulus $\left(2\frac{I}{D}\right)$
⅛	0.405	40s	.068	.269	.0720	.0568	.00040	.00106	.244	.025	.106	.00525
		80x	.095	.215	.0925	.0364	.00025	.00122	.314	.016	.106	.00600
¼	0.540	40s	.088	.364	.1250	.1041	.00072	.00331	.424	.045	.141	.01227
		80x	.119	.302	.1574	.0710	.00050	.00377	.535	.031	.141	.01395
⅜	0.675	40s	.091	.493	.1670	.1910	.00133	.00729	.567	.083	.178	.02160
		80x	.126	.423	.2173	.1405	.00098	.00862	.738	.061	.178	.02554
½	0.840	40s	.109	.622	.2503	.3040	.00211	.01709	.850	.132	.220	.04069
		80x	.147	.546	.3200	.2340	.00163	.02008	1.087	.102	.220	.04780
		160	.187	.466	.3836	.1706	.00118	.02212	1.300	.074	.220	.05269
		...xx	.294	.252	.5043	.050	.00035	.0242	1.714	.022	.220	.05772
¾	1.050	40s	.113	.824	.3326	.5330	.00371	.03704	1.130	.231	.275	.07055
		80x	.154	.742	.4335	.4330	.00300	.04479	1.473	.188	.275	.08531
		160	.218	.614	.5698	.2961	.00206	.05269	1.940	.128	.275	.10038
		...xx	.308	.434	.7180	.148	.00103	.05792	2.440	.064	.275	.11030
1	1.315	40s	.133	1.049	.4939	.8640	.00600	.08734	1.678	.375	.344	.1328
		80x	.179	.957	.6388	.7190	.00499	.1056	2.171	.312	.344	.1606
		160	.250	.815	.8365	.5217	.00362	.1251	2.840	.230	.344	.1903
		...xx	.358	.599	1.0760	.282	.00196	.1405	3.659	.122	.344	.2136
1¼	1.660	40s	.140	1.380	.6685	1.495	.01040	.1947	2.272	.649	.435	.2346
		80x	.191	1.278	.8815	1.283	.00891	.2418	2.996	.555	.435	.2913
		160	.250	1.160	1.1070	1.057	.00734	.2839	3.764	.458	.435	.3421
		...xx	.382	.896	1.534	.630	.00438	.3411	5.214	.273	.435	.4110
1½	1.900	40s	.145	1.610	.7995	2.036	.01414	.3099	2.717	.882	.497	.3262
		80x	.200	1.500	1.068	1.767	.01225	.3912	3.631	.765	.497	.4118
		160	.281	1.338	1.429	1.406	.00976	.4824	4.862	.608	.497	.5080
		...xx	.400	1.100	1.885	.950	.00660	.5678	6.408	.42	.497	.5977
2	2.375	40s	.154	2.067	1.075	3.355	.02330	.6657	3.652	1.45	.622	.5606
		80x	.218	1.939	1.477	2.953	.02050	.8679	5.022	1.28	.622	.7309
		160	.343	1.689	2.190	2.241	.01556	1.162	7.440	.97	.622	.979
		...xx	.436	1.503	2.656	1.774	.01232	1.311	9.029	.77	.622	1.311C

154

Nom.	O.D.	Sched.										
2½	2.875	40s	.203	2.469	1.704	4.788	.03322	1.530	5.79	2.07	.753	1.064
		80x	.276	2.323	2.254	4.238	.02942	1.924	7.66	1.87	.753	1.339
		160	.375	2.125	2.945	3.546	.02463	2.353	10.01	1.54	.753	1.638
		..xx	.552	1.771	4.028	2.464	.01710	2.871	13.70	1.07	.753	1.997
3	3.500	40s	.216	3.068	2.228	7.393	.05130	3.017	7.58	3.20	.916	1.724
		80x	.300	2.900	3.016	6.605	.04587	3.894	10.25	2.86	.916	2.225
		160	.437	2.626	4.205	5.416	.03761	5.032	14.32	2.35	.916	2.876
		..xx	.600	2.300	5.466	4.155	.02885	5.993	18.58	1.80	.916	3.424
3½	4.000	40s	.226	3.548	2.680	9.886	.06870	4.788	9.11	4.29	1.047	2.394
		80x	.318	3.364	3.678	8.888	.06170	6.280	12.51	3.84	1.047	3.140
4	4.500	40s	.237	4.026	3.174	12.73	.0840	7.233	10.79	5.50	1.178	3.214
		80x	.337	3.826	4.407	11.50	.07986	9.610	14.98	4.98	1.178	4.271
		120	.437	3.626	5.578	10.33	.0717	11.65	19.00	4.47	1.178	5.176
		160	.531	3.438	6.621	9.28	.0645	13.27	22.51	4.02	1.178	5.900
		..xx	.674	3.152	8.101	7.80	.0542	15.28	27.54	3.38	1.178	6.793
5	5.563	40s	.258	5.047	4.300	20.01	.1390	15.16	14.62	8.67	1.456	5.451
		80x	.375	4.813	6.112	18.19	.1263	20.67	20.78	7.88	1.456	7.431
		120	.500	4.563	7.953	16.35	.1136	25.73	27.10	7.09	1.456	9.253
		160	.625	4.313	9.696	14.61	.1015	30.03	32.96	6.33	1.456	10.800
		..xx	.750	4.063	11.340	12.97	.0901	33.63	38.55	5.61	1.456	12.090
6	6.625	40s	.280	6.065	5.581	28.89	.2006	28.14	18.97	12.51	1.734	8.46
		80x	.432	5.761	8.405	26.07	.1810	40.49	28.57	11.29	1.734	12.22
		120	.562	5.501	10.70	23.77	.1650	49.61	36.40	10.30	1.734	15.07
		160	.718	5.189	13.32	21.15	.1469	58.97	45.30	9.16	1.734	17.81
		..xx	.864	4.897	15.64	18.84	.1308	66.33	53.16	8.16	1.734	20.02
8	8.625	20	.250	8.125	6.57	51.85	.3601	57.72	22.36	22.47	2.258	13.39
		30	.277	8.071	7.26	51.16	.3553	63.35	24.70	22.17	2.258	14.69
		40s	.322	7.981	8.40	50.03	.3474	72.49	28.55	21.70	2.258	16.81
		60	.406	7.813	10.48	47.94	.3329	88.73	35.64	20.77	2.258	20.58
		80x	.500	7.625	12.76	45.66	.3171	105.7	43.39	19.78	2.258	24.51
		100	.593	7.439	14.96	43.46	.3018	121.3	50.87	18.83	2.258	28.14
		120	.718	7.189	17.84	40.59	.2819	140.5	60.63	17.59	2.258	32.61
		140	.812	7.001	19.93	38.50	.2673	153.7	67.76	16.68	2.258	35.65
		..xx	.875	6.875	21.30	37.12	.2578	162.0	72.42	16.10	2.258	37.56
		160	.906	6.813	21.97	36.46	.2532	165.9	74.69	15.80	2.258	38.48

Note 1: The letters "s", "x" and "xx" in the column of Schedule Numbers indicate Standard, Extra Strong, and Double Extra Strong Pipe, respectively.
Note 2: The values shown in square feet for the Transverse Internal Area also represent the volume in cubic feet per foot of pipe length.

Courtesy Platecoil Division, Tranter Manufacturing, Inc.

155

TABLE OF PIPING VOLUMES

STANDARD PIPE DATA

NOMINAL PIPE DIAM. IN INCHES	ACTUAL INSIDE DIAM. IN INCHES	LENGTH IN FEET CONTAINING ONE CUBIC FOOT	GALLONS IN ONE LINEAL FOOT
1/8	.269	2526.000	.0030
1/4	.364	1383.800	.0054
3/8	.493	754.360	.0099
1/2	.622	473.910	.0158
3/4	.824	270.030	.0277
1	1.049	166.620	.0449
1 - 1/4	1.308	96.275	.0777
1 - 1/2	1.610	70.733	.1058
2	2.067	49.913	.1743
2 - 1/2	2.469	30.077	.2487
3	3.068	19.479	.3840
3 - 1/2	3.548	14.565	.5136
4	4.026	11.312	.6613
4 - 1/2	4.560	9.030	.8284
5	5.047	7.198	1.0393
6	6.065	4.984	1.5008
8	7.981	2.878	2.5988
10	10.020	1.826	4.0963

CARGO CAPACITY CONVERSION TABLE

Gallons*	Barrels	Tons
2,100,000 to 4,200,000	50,000 to 100,000	7,500 to 15,000
4,200,000 to 6,300,000	100,000 to 150,000	15,000 to 22,500
6,300,000 to 8,400,000	150,000 to 200,000	22,000 to 30,000
8,400,000 to 10,500,000	200,000 to 250,000	30,000 to 37,500
10,500,000 to 12,600,000	250,000 to 300,000	37,500 to 45,000
12,600,000 to 14,700,000	300,000 to 350,000	45,000 to 52,500
14,700,000 to 16,800,000	350,000 to 400,000	52,500 to 60,000

*Based on crude oil 42 gallon barrel

DIMENSIONS AND WEIGHTS OF COPPER AND RED BRASS PIPE, STANDARD PIPE SIZES

(Applicable to ASTM Designations B 42, B 43, and B 188.)
ASTM B251—56T Extract*

Pipe Size, In.	Nominal Dimensions, in.			Cross-Sectional Area of Bore, sq. in.	Nominal Weight, lb per ft	
	Outside Diameter	Inside Diameter	Wall Thickness		Red Brass	Copper
REGULAR						
1/8	0.405	0.281	0.062	0.062	0.253	0.259
1/4	0.540	0.376	0.082	0.110	0.447	0.457
3/8	0.675	0.495	0.090	0.192	0.627	0.641
1/2	0.840	0.626	0.107	0.307	0.934	0.955
3/4	1.050	0.822	0.114	0.531	1.27	1.30
1	1.315	1.063	0.126	0.887	1.78	1.82
1 1/4	1.660	1.368	0.146	1.47	2.63	2.69
1 1/2	1.900	1.600	0.150	2.01	3.13	3.20
2	2.375	2.063	0.156	3.34	4.12	4.22
2 1/2	2.875	2.501	0.187	4.91	5.99	6.12
3	3.500	3.062	0.219	7.37	8.56	8.75
3 1/2	4.000	3.500	0.250	9.62	11.2	11.4
4	4.500	4.000	0.250	12.6	12.7	12.9
5	5.562	5.062	0.250	20.1	15.8	16.2
6	6.625	6.125	0.250	29.5	19.0	19.4
8	8.625	8.001	0.312	50.3	30.9	31.6
10	10.750	10.020	0.365	78.8	45.2	46.2
12	12.750	12.000	0.375	113.	55.3	56.5
EXTRA–STRONG						
1/8	0.405	0.205	0.100	0.033	0.363	0.371
1/4	0.540	0.294	0.123	0.068	0.611	0.625
3/8	0.675	0.421	0.127	0.139	0.829	0.847
1/2	0.840	0.542	0.149	0.231	1.23	1.25
3/4	1.050	0.736	0.157	0.425	1.67	1.71
1	1.315	0.951	0.182	0.710	2.46	2.51
1 1/4	1.660	1.272	0.194	1.27	3.39	3.46
1 1/2	1.900	1.494	0.203	1.75	4.10	4.19
2	2.375	1.933	0.221	2.94	5.67	5.80
2 1/2	2.875	2.315	0.280	4.21	8.66	8.85
3	3.500	2.892	0.304	6.57	11.6	11.8
3 1/2	4.000	3.358	0.321	8.86	14.1	14.4

STEAM PIPE CAPACITIES

For 30 psig and 150 psig Steam Systems, capacity in pounds per hour (using Sch. 40 iron pipe).

Std Pipe Size-In	30 psig System			150 psig System		
	Drop In Pressure Lb/100 Ft Length					
	¼ Lb	½ Lb	1 Lb	¼ Lb	½ Lb	1 Lb
¾	22	31	45	41	58	82
1	46	63	89	82	117	165
1¼	100	141	199	185	262	370
1½	154	219	309	287	407	575
2	313	444	627	583	825	1170
2½	516	730	1030	959	1360	1920
3	940	1330	1880	1750	2480	3500
3½	1410	2000	2830	2630	3720	5250
4	2000	2830	4000	3720	5260	7430
5	3640	5230	7390	6880	9730	13800
6	6030	8590	12100	11300	16000	22600
8	12600	17900	25300	23500	33200	47000

From — Heating, Ventilating, Air Conditioning Guide 1958, p. 534.
Note: While the pressure drop to use depends on individual circumstances, a drop of ½ lb will usually be satisfactory.

CARRYING CAPACITY OF REFRIGERATION LINES

In tons of refrigeration for installations having average lengths of pipe and number of fittings.
(For estimating purposes only.)

Iron Pipe Size	AMMONIA		Type L Copper Tube Size OD	Approx. Equivalent Sch. 40 Iron Pipe Size	METHYLCHLORIDE		FREON - 12	
	Liquid Line	Suction Line Evap Temp 5F			Liquid Line	Suction Line Evap Temp 40F	Liquid Line	Suction Line Evap Temp 40F
⅜	13.6		⅜	¼	3.0		1.0	
½	24.2	2.0	½	⅜	6.4	0.9	2.8	0.4
¾	56.7	3.7	⅝	½	10.6	1.2	4.7	0.7
1	99.0	6.8	¾	¾	17.0	1.8	7.3	1.1
1¼	170	11.3	⅞	¾	23.5	2.5	10.0	1.5
1½	264	16.0	1⅛	1	42.2	4.5	20.6	2.8
2	477	26.8	1⅜	1¼	66.5	7.0	33.6	4.5
2½		41.6	1⅝	1½	80.0	10.0	52.0	6.7
			2⅛	2	139.0	18.0	70.0	11.7

For more complete data see — American Society of Refrigeration Engineers Data Book — Design 1957-58, Page 9-06.
The above suction line capacities may be approximately doubled to indicate effective capacities of Platecoil.

Courtesy Platecoil Division, Tranter Manufacturing, Inc.

PLASTIC PIPE SIZE CHART

| Size In. | Standard Size in Inches | | | | | |
| | SWP | | Schedule 40 i.p.s.* | | Schedule 80 i.p.s.* | |
	O.D.	I.D.	O.D.	I.D.	O.D.	I.D.
1/2	.600	.500	.840	.622	.840	.546
3/4	.855	.750	1.050	.824	1.050	.742
1	1.140	1.000	1.315	1.049	1.315	.957
1 1/4	1.420	1.250	1.660	1.380	1.660	1.278
1 1/2	1.730	1.500	1.900	1.610	1.900	1.500
2	2.250	2.000	2.375	2.067	2.375	1.939
2 1/2	2.570	2.320	2.875	2.469	2.875	2.277
3	3.250	3.000	3.500	3.065	3.500	2.842
4	4.100	3.800	4.500	4.026	4.500	3.749
5	5.110	4.750	5.563		5.563	
6	6.220	5.760	6.625	6.065	6.625	5.761

*Iron pipe size.

SIZES AVAILABLE IN PLASTIC PIPE

Size	Cellulose Acetate Butyrate (Tenite II)	Acrylonitrile Resin-Rubber (Kralastic)	Polyvinyl Chloride	Polyester	Polyethylene	Polyvinyidene Chloride (Saran)
Schedule 40	x	x	x		x	
Schedule 80		x	x		x	x
SWP	x	x	x			

Special dimensions suggested for new gas services and mains not over 60 psi or 100°F—and "pull through" service in old metal lines

Nominal Size	1/2"	3/4"	1"	1 1/4"	1 3/4"
O.D.	.625	.875	1.125	1.375	1.875

| Size | Wall Thickness Required in Inches | | | | | |
| | Cellulose Acetate Butyrate (Tenite II) | | Polyvinyl Chloride Type I | | PVC Type II Styrene Acrylonitrile | |
	IPS (new)	SWP (old)	IPS (new)	SWP (old)	IPS (new)	SWP (old)
1/2"	.090	.062	.090	.062	.090	.062
3/4"	.090	.062	.090	.062	.090	.062
1"	.090	.062	.090	.062	.090	.062
1 1/4"	.090	.062	.090	.062	.090	.062
1 1/2"	.090	.062	.090	.062	.090	.062
2"	.110		.090		.090	
2 1/2"	.135		.100		.110	
3"	.160		.120		.125	
4"	.205		.145		.155	
5"	.250		.170		.190	
6"	.300		.200		.220	

NATIONAL STD. FIRE-HOSE COUPLING SCREW THREAD

	2 1/2	3	3 1/2	4 1/2
Nominal inside diameter of hose coupling (C)....	2 1/2	3	3 1/2	4 1/2
Number of threads per inch....................	7 1/2	6	6	4
Total length of threaded part of coupling and hydrant nipple, external thread (see L, fig. 1)...	1	1 1/8	1 1/8	1 1/4
Distance from face of nipple to start of second turn (see I, fig. 1)......................	1/4	5/16	5/16	7/16
Depth of coupling swivel to washer seat (see H, fig. 1).................................	15/16	1 1/16	1 1/16	1 3/16
Distance from face of coupling swivel to start of second turn (see J, fig. 1)............	3/16	1/4	1/4	3/8
Depth of thread of coupling swivel (see T, fig. 1)..	11/16	13/16	13/16	13/16
Nipple (external thread) cylindrical to base of thread.................................	—	—	—	—
Coupling (internal thread) cylindrical to base of thread.................................	—	—	—	—
Outer ends of external and internal thread should be terminated by the "Higbee Cut" on FULL THREAD to avoid crossing and mutilation of thread (see figs. 1, 2 & 3 of A. S. A. B26)................................	—	—	—	—
American (National) Form of thread must be used.....................................	—	—	—	—

All dimensions given in inches.

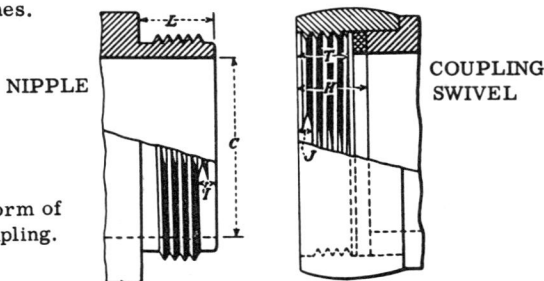

NIPPLE

COUPLING SWIVEL

Fig. 1. Typical Form of Standard Coupling.

POLYETHYLENE PIPE

Polyethylene pipe is flexible and is by far the most popular plastic pipe. Its use is generally restricted to cold water where light weight, corrosion resistance and ease of installation have insured its acceptance. It is available in forms for potable water and in lower cost pipe for other applications.

USES	LIMITATIONS
Jet well tubing........	Flexibility in above-ground installations
Sprinkler systems	Temperature
Mine drainage tubing..	Working pressure
Farm water systems..	Attacked by petroleum products and by some other chemicals

PHYSICAL PROPERTIES

Specific gravity .... .92
Tensile strength @ room temp. ... 1,500
Elongation at break per cent 400
Heat distortion point, $^\circ$F ....
Notched impact strength .... .16
Recommended maximum hoop
   stress, psi 400
Thermal expansion in/in/$^\circ$F x 10-5   10
Thermal conductivity
   Btu/hr/sq.ft/$^\circ$F/in. 2.3
Resistance to sunlight ...... Poor except
     in black.
Flammability............ Slow-burning.

CHEMICAL RESISTANCE

Weak acids....... Resistant
Strong acids...... Attacked by oxidizing acids
Weak bases ...... Resistant
Strong bases ..... Resistant
Petroleum products Attacked; swells
Inorganic salts .... Resistant
Organic solvents... Attacked by some. Fittings dissolve in aromatic and chlorinated hydrocarbons.

SIZES AND WORKING PRESSURES

Pipe Size	I.D.	O.D.	Weight Lb/Ft.	Recommended Working Pressure at 73.4°F	Standard Coil Length
				Schedule 40 IPS*	
1/2"	.622	.840	.10	104#	100'-400'
3/4"	.824	1.050	.13	86#	100'-400'-600'
1"	1.049	1.315	.20	81#	100'-300'-600'
1 1/4"	1.380	1.660	.27	68#	100'-300'-600'
1 1/2"	1.610	1.900	.32	61#	100'-250'
2"	2.067	2.375	.43	52#	100'-200'
3"	3.068	3.500	.89	50#	100'
4"	4.026	4.500	1.27	42#	25' Straight
6"	6.065	6.625	2.23	31#	25' Straight

Pipe Size	I.D.	O.D.	Weight Lb/Ft.	Recommended Working Pressure at 73.4°F	Standard Coil Length
				Special 100# Pipe (Schedule 40 IPS I.D.)	
1/2"	.622	.842	.103	100#	400'
3/4"	.824	1.114	.178	100#	400'
1"	1.049	1.410	.281	100#	300'
1 1/4"	1.380	1.860	.493	100#	300'
1 1/2"	1.610	2.170	.671	100#	250'
2"	2.067	2.777	1.09	100#	100'

*Iron pipe sizes.

162

HEATING SURFACE IN STANDARD PIPE

Length of Pipe in Ft.	Size of Pipe									
	$3/4$	1	$1\frac{1}{4}$	$1\frac{1}{2}$	2	$2\frac{1}{2}$	3	4	5	6
1	.275	.346	.434	.494	.622	.753	.916	1.175	1.455	1.739
2	.5	.7	.9	1.	1.2	1.5	1.8	2.4	2.9	3.5
3	.8	1.	1.3	1.5	1.9	2.3	2.7	3.5	4.4	5.2
4	1.1	1.4	1.7	2.	2.5	3.	3.6	4.7	5.8	7.
5	1.4	1.7	2.2	2.4	3.1	3.8	4.6	5.8	7.3	7.7
6	1.6	2.1	2.6	2.9	3.7	4.5	5.5	7.	8.7	10.5
7	1.9	2.4	3.	3.4	4.4	5.3	6.4	8.2	10.2	12.1
8	2.2	2.8	3.5	3.9	5.	6.	7.3	9.4	11.6	13.9
9	2.5	3.1	3.9	4.4	5.6	6.8	8.2	10.6	13.1	15.7
10	2.7	3.5	4.3	4.9	6.2	7.5	9.1	11.8	14.6	17.4
11	3.	3.8	4.8	5.4	6.8	8.3	10.	12.9	16.	19.1
12	3.3	4.1	5.2	5.9	7.5	9.	11.	14.1	17.4	20.9
13	3.6	4.5	5.6	6.4	8.1	9.8	11.9	15.3	18.9	22.6
14	3.8	4.8	6.1	6.9	8.7	10.5	12.8	16.5	20.3	24.3
15	4.1	5.2	6.5	7.4	9.3	11.3	13.7	17.6	21.8	26.1
16	4.4	5.5	6.9	7.9	10.	12.	14.6	18.8	23.2	27.8
17	4.7	5.9	7.4	8.4	10.6	12.8	15.5	20.	24.7	29.5
18	5.	6.2	7.8	8.9	11.2	13.5	16.5	21.2	26.2	31.3
19	5.2	6.6	8.3	9.4	11.8	14.3	17.4	22.3	27.6	33.1
20	5.5	6.9	8.7	9.9	12.5	15.	18.3	23.5	29.1	34.8
25	6.9	8.6	10.9	12.3	15.6	18.8	22.9	29.3	36.3	43.5
30	8.3	10.4	13.	14.8	18.7	22.5	27.5	35.3	43.6	52.1
35	9.6	12.1	15.2	17.3	21.8	26.3	32.	41.1	50.9	60.8
40	11.	13.8	17.4	19.8	24.9	30.1	36.6	47.	58.2	69.5
45	12.4	15.6	19.5	22.2	28.	33.8	41.2	52.9	65.5	78.2
50	13.8	17.3	21.7	24.7	31.1	37.6	45.8	58.7	72.7	87.
55	15.2	19.0	23.9	27.1	34.3	41.3	50.4	64.6	80.1	95.6
60	16.6	20.8	26.0	29.6	37.3	45.2	55.	70.5	87.3	104.3
65	18.0	22.6	28.2	32.1	40.5	48.8	59.5	76.4	94.5	112.9
70	19.4	24.2	30.4	34.6	43.5	52.7	64.1	82.3	101.9	121.7
75	20.7	26.0	32.6	37.1	46.6	56.5	68.7	88.1	109.1	130.4
80	22.	27.7	34.7	39.6	49.8	60.2	73.3	94.0	116.4	139.1
85	23.4	29.4	36.9	42.0	53.4	63.9	77.8	99.9	123.7	147.9
90	24.8	31.1	39.1	44.5	56.	67.8	82.4	105.8	130.9	156.5
95	26.2	32.9	41.2	46.9	59.6	71.5	87.2	111.6	138.2	165.2
100	27.5	34.3	43.4	49.4	62.2	75.3	91.6	117.5	145.5	173.9

Courtesy Posey Iron Works, Lancaster, Pa.

PART SEVEN
ELECTRICAL DATA

GRAPHIC SYMBOLS FOR ELECTRICAL DIAGRAMS

(American Standard)

Disconnecting Switch, Single Throw	
Disconnecting Switch, Gang Operated	Full Wave Rectifier
Disc. Sw., Single Blade, Double Throw	Oil Circuit Breaker, Automatic, Single Throw
Automatic Throw-Over	Oil Circuit Breaker, Double Throw
Disconnecting Fuse	Oil Circuit Breaker, Removable Type
Reactor (Non-Magnetic Core)	Air Circuit Breaker, Automatic
Reactor (Magnetic Core)	Air Circuit Breaker, Motor Operated
Resistor	Air Circuit Breaker, Solenoid Operated
Static Condenser	
Valve Type Lightning Arrester	Drawout Air Circuit Breaker
Rheostat, Hand Operated	Network Protector
Rheostat, Motor Operated	Squirrel Cage Motor
Shunt	
Fuse	Synchronous Motor
Battery	3-Phase "Wye" Connection
Ground	3-Phase "Delta" Connection
Pothead, Non-Disconnecting	Wound Rotor Induction Motor
Magnetic Contactor	
Half Wave Rectifier	D.C. Motor with Shunt Field

GRAPHIC SYMBOLS FOR ELECTRICAL DIAGRAMS

(Continued)

D.C. Motor with Series Field	2-conductor non-polarized connector with male contacts		
1-Phase Power Transformer	2-conductor polarized connector with female contacts		
3-Phase Power Transformer, Connected "Delta-Delta"	2-conductor polarized connector with male contacts		
3—Single Phase Trans. in 3-Ph. Bank, Grounded Neutral	Closed contact (break)		
	Open contact (make)		
	Open contact with time closing feature (TC or TDC)		
Potential Transformer	Closed contact with time opening feature (TO or TDO)		
Current Transformer	Time sequential closing		
2-conductor non-polarized connector with female contacts			

METER AND INSTRUMENT DESIGNATION

Letter combination within a circle

A	Ammeter	N	Noise meter
AH	Ampere-hour meter	OHM	Ohmmeter
CMA	Contact-making (or breaking) ammeter	OP	Oil pressure
		OSCG	Oscillograph, string
CMC	Contact-making (or breaking) clock	PH	Phase meter
		PI	Position indicator
CMV	Contact-making (or breaking) voltmeter	PF	Power-factor meter
		RD	Recording demand meter
CRO	Oscilloscope or cathode-ray oscillograph	REC	Recording
		RF	Reactive-factor meter
D	Demand meter	S	Synchroscope
DB	DB (decibel) meter	TLM	Telemeter
DBM	DBM (decibels referred to 1 milliwatt) meter	T	Temperature meter
		TT	Total time
DTR	Demand-totalizing relay	VH	Varhour meter
F	Frequency meter	V	Voltmeter
G	Galvanometer	VA	Volt-ammeter
GD	Ground detector	VAR	Varmeter
I	Indicating	VI	Volume indicator
M	Integrating	VU	Standard volume indicator
μA or UA	Microammeter	W	Wattmeter
MA	Milliammeter	WH	Watthour meter

167

ELECTRICAL SYMBOLS FOR ARCHITECTURAL PLANS

(American Standards Association)

General Outlets

Ceiling Wall

O	–O	Outlet
Ⓑ	–Ⓑ	Blanked Outlet
Ⓓ		Drop Cord
Ⓔ	–Ⓔ	Electric Outlet; for use only when circle used alone might be confused with columns, plumbing symbols, etc
Ⓕ	–Ⓕ	Fan Outlet
Ⓙ	–Ⓙ	Junction Box
Ⓛ	–Ⓛ	Lamp Holder
Ⓛ_PS	–Ⓛ_PS	Lamp Holder with Pull Switch
Ⓢ	–Ⓢ	Pull Switch
Ⓥ	–Ⓥ	Outlet for Vapor Discharge Lamp
Ⓧ	–Ⓧ	Exit Light Outlet
Ⓒ	–Ⓒ	Clock Outlet (Specify Voltage)

Convenience Outlets

⊐⊖	Duplex Convenience Outlet
⊐⊖_{1,3}	Convenience Outlet other than Duplex 1 = Single, 3 = Triplex, etc
⊐⊖_WP	Weatherproof Convenience Outlet
⊐⊖_R	Range Outlet
⊐⊖_S	Switch and Convenience Outlet
⊐⊖Ⓡ	Radio and Convenience Outlet
⬤	Special Purpose Outlet (Des. in Spec.)
⊙	Floor Outlet

Switch Outlets

S	Single Pole Switch
S_2	Double Pole Switch
S_3	Three Way Switch
S_4	Four Way Switch
S_D	Automatic Door Switch
S_E	Electrolier Switch
S_K	Key Operated Switch
S_P	Switch and Pilot Lamp
S_CB	Circuit Breaker
S_WCB	Weatherproof Circuit Breaker
S_MC	Momentary Contact Switch
S_RC	Remote Control Switch
S_WP	Weatherproof Switch
S_F	Fused Switch
S_WF	Weatherproof Fused Switch

Special Outlets

O_{a,b,c,etc}
⊐⊖_{a,b,c,etc}
S_{a,b,c,etc}

Any standard symbol as given above with the addition of a lower case subscript letter may be used to designate some special variation of standard equipment of particular interest in a specific set of architectural plans.

When used they must be listed in the Key of Symbols on each drawing and if necessary further described in the specifications.

ELECTRICAL SYMBOLS FOR ARCHITECTURAL PLANS

Panels, Circuits, and Miscellaneous

▰ Lighting Panel

▨ Power Panel

— Branch Circuit; Concealed in Ceiling or Wall

– · – Branch Circuit; Concealed in Floor

- - - - Branch Circuit; Exposed

►→ Home Run to Panel Board. Indicate number of circuits by number of arrows.
Note: Any circuit without further designation indicates a two-wire circuit. For a greater number of wires indicate as follows: –///– (3 wires) –//–//– (4 wires), etc.

— Feeders. Note: Use heavy lines and designate by number corresponding to listing in Feeder Schedule.

⊒□⊏ Underfloor Duct and Junction Box. Triple System. Note: For double or single systems eliminate one or two lines. This symbol is equally adaptable to auxiliary system layouts.

Ⓖ Generator

Ⓜ Motor

Ⓘ Instrument

Ⓣ Power Transformer (Or draw to scale.)

⊠ Controller

⊡' Isolating Switch

Auxiliary Systems

⊡ Pushbutton

⊏⊐ Bell   □⁄ Buzzer

◇ Annunciator

◄ Outside Telephone

◁ Interconnecting Telephone

◁| Telephone Switchboard

Ⓣ Bell-Ringing Transformer

D Electric Door Opener

F⊃ Fire Alarm Bell

F Fire Alarm Station

☒ City Fire Alarm Station

FA Fire Alarm Central Station

FS Automatic Fire Alarm Device

W Watchman's Station

W Watchman's Central Station

H Horn

N Nurse's Signal Plug

M Maid's Signal Plug

R Radio Outlet

SC Signal Central Station

▯ Interconnection Box

⊣⊢⊣⊢ Battery

- · - · - Auxiliary System Circuits

Note: Any line without further designation indicates a 2-wire system. For a greater number of wires designate with numerals in manner similar to – – 12-No. 18W-3/4"C., or designate by number corresponding to listing in Schedule.

□a,b,c Special Auxiliary Outlets. Subscript letters refer to notes on plans or detailed description in specifications.

FORMULAE FOR DETERMINING AMPERES, HP., KW. AND KVA

To Find	Direct Current	Alternating Current	
		Single Phase	Three Phase
Amperes when Horsepower is known	$\dfrac{Hp. \times 746}{V \times \% \text{ Eff.}}$	$\dfrac{Hp. \times 746}{V \times \% \text{ Eff.} \times P.F.}$	$\dfrac{Hp. \times 746}{1.73 \times V \times \% \text{ Eff.} \times P.F.}$
Amperes when Kilowatts is known	$\dfrac{Kw \times 1000}{V}$	$\dfrac{Kw \times 1000}{V \times P.F.}$	$\dfrac{Kw \times 1000}{1.73 \times V \times P.F.}$
Amperes when Kva is known		$\dfrac{Kva \times 1000}{V}$	$\dfrac{Kva \times 1000}{1.73 \times V}$
Kilowatts	$\dfrac{I \times V}{1000}$	$\dfrac{I \times V \times P.F.}{1000}$	$\dfrac{I \times V \times 1.73 \times P.F.}{1000}$
Kva		$\dfrac{I \times V}{1000}$	$\dfrac{I \times V \times 1.73}{1000}$
Horsepower (output)	$\dfrac{I \times V \times \% \text{ Eff.}}{746}$	$\dfrac{I \times V \times \% \text{ Eff.} \times P.F.}{746}$	$\dfrac{I \times V \times 1.73 \times \% \text{ Eff.} \times P.F.}{746}$

V = volts; I = amperes; P.F. = power factor; Hp = horsepower; Kw = kilowatts; Kva. = kilovolt amperes; % Eff. = per cent efficiency.

Approximate Motor Amperes per Terminal:
230 V. d-c—4 amperes per Hp.; 3-phase, 220 V. a-c—2.5 amperes per Hp.; 3-phase, 440 V. a-c—1.25 amperes per Hp.;
3-phase, 550 V. a-c—1 ampere per Hp.

170

BASIC ELECTRICITY
What Electricity Is

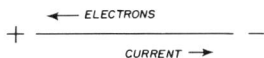

CURRENT FLOW is normally measured from (+) to (−); electrons go reverse

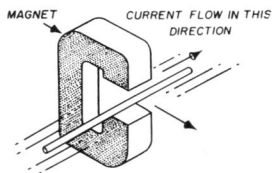

MAGNETISM induces voltage in any conductor kept moving within magnetic field

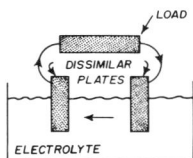

ELECTROLYTIC current flows when two dissimilar metals are put in an electrolyte

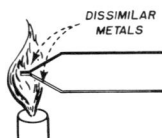

THERMOELECTRIC voltage is generated by heating dissimilar metals at junction

The smallest particle a chemical *element* can exist as, and still keep its physical and chemical characteristics, is an *atom.* Each atom has a *nucleus* at center made up of *protons* and *neutrons. Electrons* move around the nucleus.

Protons carry positive (+) charges and electrons carry negative (−) charges. *Electricity* is present when electrons are kept away from protons. They will aways try to get together . . . the electrons moving toward the protons. When electrons find a path to move along, *current* is flowing. Materials through which current flows easily (electrons are easily separated from protons) are called *conductors.* Materials through which current *does not* flow easily (protons hold electrons tightly) are *non-conductors* or *insulators.*

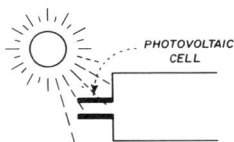

PHOTOVOLTAIC cell (lightmeter) causes slight voltage when exposed to light

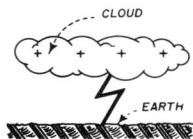

STATIC electricity is charge built up on clouds, moving belts: flash discharge.

Circuit Components

RESISTANCE, like friction, is always present. Long wires have more resistance than short ones; big wires have less resistance than small ones. Copper, highly conductive, is most commonly used wire .

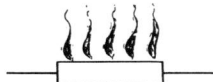

All circuits contain resistance, inductance, capacitance either as separate elements or distributed throughout. Resistors give off energy as heat; inductors store it in their magnetic fields; capacitors store energy on their plates. *Electronic* tubes act like valves to control flow of current in electronic circ

INDUCTANCE stems from shaping wire into a coil. Resulting magnetic fields will join forces and induce a counter voltage in coil as a whole. Induced voltage will be in opposition to that impressed on coil

MAGNETIC FIELD

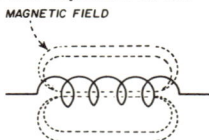

CAPACITANCE depends on presence of two plates separated by insulator called *dielectric*. Energy can be stored on plates as an electrical charge. If well-insulated, a charge takes several hours to leak off

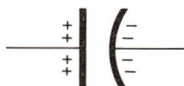

Electrical Units

Since electricity hinges on the presence and flow of electrons, let's define units in terms of electrons:

Coulomb (Q) is basic quantity of electricity (electrical charge). One coulomb equals 6.25 billion billion electrons.

Ampere (I) is the unit of current. One ampere current means that one coulomb flows past a point in a circuit every second.

Volt (V or E) is the unit of pressure that pushes current through a circuit. One volt will push one ampere through a resistance of one *ohm.*

OHM (R) is unit of resistance to current flow. One ohm is quantity of resistance producing a potential drop of 1 volt when the current in it is 1 ampere. The ohm (X_c or X_1) is also the unit for *reactance* of condensers and inductors. The *mho* is the unit of *conductance* (the reciprocal of resistance: mho $= 1/$ohm). A conductance of 1 mho will pass a current of 1 amp when subjected to 1 volt. Ohm's Law: $C = E/R$, where $C =$ current strength (amperes), $E =$ electromotive force (volts), and $R =$ resistance (ohms).

Watt (W) measures power in a circuit. Watts equal current squared times resistance (I^2R). One watt is the power used for 1 ampere to flow through 1 ohm.

Watthour measures energy or work done in a circuit. Simply multiply watts by time in hours that power is flowing.

Farad (C) is the unit of capacitance. A condenser has a capacitance of one farad when a charge of one coulomb produces a potential difference of one volt. Condensers are rated in *microfarads* (millionths of farads).

Henry (L) is unit of inductance. A circuit has inductance of 1 henry if a current *change* of 1 ampere per sec causes one volt to be induced in it.

KILOWATTS TO AMPERES CONVERSION TABLES

115 VOLTS D.C. AND A.C., SINGLE PHASE, UNITY P. F.

K.W.	0	1	2	3	4	5	6	7	8	9
0 : : :		8.70	17.39	26.09	34.78	43.48	52.17	60.87	69.56	78.26
0.1 : : :	0.87	9.57	18.26	26.95	35.65	44.35	53.04	61.74	70.43	79.13
0.2 : : :	1.74	10.43	19.13	27.82	36.52	45.22	53.91	62.61	71.30	80.00
0.3 : : :	2.61	11.30	20.00	28.69	37.39	46.09	54.78	63.48	72.17	80.87
0.4 : : :	3.48	12.17	20.87	29.56	38.26	46.96	55.65	64.35	73.04	81.74
0.5 : : :	4.35	13.04	21.74	30.43	39.13	47.83	56.52	65.22	73.91	82.61
0.6 : : :	5.22	13.91	22.61	31.30	40.00	48.75	57.39	66.09	74.78	83.48
0.7 : : :	6.09	14.78	23.48	32.17	40.87	49.56	58.26	66.96	75.65	84.35
0.8 : : :	6.96	15.65	24.35	33.04	41.74	50.43	59.13	67.83	76.52	85.22
0.9 : : :	7.83	16.52	25.22	33.91	42.61	51.30	60.00	68.70	77.39	86.09

208 VOLTS, 3-PHASE, UNITY P. F.

K.W.	0	1	2	3	4	5	6	7	8	9
0 : : :		2.78	5.56	8.34	11.12	13.90	16.67	19.45	22.23	25.01
0.1 : : :	.28	3.06	5.84	8.61	11.39	14.17	16.95	19.73	22.51	25.29
0.2 : : :	.56	3.33	6.11	8.89	11.67	14.45	17.23	20.01	22.79	25.57
0.3 : : :	.83	3.61	6.39	9.17	11.95	14.73	17.51	20.29	23.07	25.84
0.4 : : :	1.11	3.89	6.67	9.45	12.23	15.01	17.79	20.56	23.34	26.12
0.5 : : :	1.39	4.17	6.95	9.73	12.51	15.28	18.06	20.84	23.62	26.40
0.6 : : :	1.67	4.45	7.23	10.00	12.78	15.56	18.34	21.12	23.90	26.68
0.7 : : :	1.95	4.72	7.50	10.28	13.06	15.84	18.62	21.40	24.18	26.96
0.8 : : :	2.22	5.00	7.78	10.56	13.34	16.12	18.90	21.68	24.46	27.23
0.9 : : :	2.50	5.28	8.06	10.84	13.62	16.40	19.18	21.95	24.73	27.51

For power factor different from unity, divide the current given in the Table by the power factor expressed as a decimal.

HORSEPOWER-TO-AMPERES CONVERSION TABLES

220 VOLTS DC 90% EFFICIENCY

H.P.	0	10	20	30	40	50	60	70	80	90
0 ...		37.68	75.35	113.0	150.7	188.4	226.1	263.7	301.4	339.1
1 ...	3.77	41.44	79.12	116.8	154.5	191.2	229.8	267.5	305.2	342.9
2 ...	7.54	45.21	82.88	120.6	158.2	195.9	233.6	271.3	309.0	346.3
3 ...	11.30	48.98	86.66	124.3	162.0	199.7	237.4	275.0	312.7	350.4
4 ...	15.07	52.75	90.42	128.1	165.8	203.5	241.1	278.8	316.5	354.2
5 ...	18.84	56.52	94.19	131.9	169.6	207.2	244.9	282.6	320.2	357.9
6 ...	22.61	60.28	97.96	135.6	173.3	212.0	248.7	286.4	324.0	361.7
7 ...	26.37	64.05	101.7	139.4	177.1	214.8	252.4	290.1	327.8	365.5
8 ...	30.14	67.82	105.5	143.2	180.9	218.5	256.2	293.9	331.6	369.2
9 ...	33.91	71.59	109.3	146.9	184.6	222.3	260.0	297.7	335.3	373.0

220 VOLTS, 3-PHASE, 90% EFF. 85% P. F.

H.P.	0	10	20	30	40	50	60	70	80	90
0 ...		25.56	51.12	76.68	102.2	127.8	153.4	178.9	204.5	230.3
1 ...	2.56	28.12	53.68	79.24	104.8	130.4	155.9	181.5	207.0	232.6
2 ...	5.11	30.67	56.23	81.79	107.4	132.9	158.5	184.0	209.6	235.2
3 ...	7.67	33.23	58.79	84.34	109.9	135.5	161.0	186.6	212.1	237.7
4 ...	10.22	35.78	60.34	86.91	112.5	138.0	163.6	189.1	214.7	240.3
5 ...	12.78	38.34	64.90	89.46	115.0	140.6	166.1	191.7	217.3	242.8
6 ...	15.34	40.90	66.46	92.02	117.6	143.1	168.7	194.3	219.8	245.4
7 ...	17.89	43.45	69.01	94.57	120.1	145.7	171.3	196.8	222.4	247.9
8 ...	20.45	46.01	71.57	97.13	122.7	148.2	173.8	199.4	224.9	250.5
9 ...	23.00	48.56	74.12	99.68	125.2	150.8	176.4	201.9	227.5	253.0

208 VOLTS, 3-PHASE, 90% EFF. 85% P. F.

H.P.	0	10	20	30	40	50	60	70	80	90
0 ...		26.96	53.92	80.89	107.8	134.8	161.8	188.7	215.7	242.7
1 ...	2.69	29.66	56.62	83.58	110.5	137.5	164.5	191.4	218.4	245.4
2 ...	5.39	32.35	59.32	86.28	113.2	140.2	167.2	194.1	221.1	248.1
3 ...	8.09	35.05	62.01	88.97	115.6	142.9	169.9	196.8	223.8	250.7
4 ...	10.78	37.75	64.71	91.67	118.6	145.6	172.6	199.5	226.5	253.4
5 ...	13.48	40.44	67.41	94.37	121.3	148.3	175.3	202.2	229.2	256.1
6 ...	16.18	43.14	70.10	97.06	124.0	151.0	177.9	204.9	231.9	258.8
7 ...	18.87	45.84	72.80	99.76	126.7	153.7	180.6	207.6	234.6	261.5
8 ...	21.57	48.53	75.49	102.5	129.4	156.4	183.3	210.3	237.3	264.2
9 ...	24.27	51.23	78.19	105.2	132.1	159.1	186.0	213.0	240.0	266.9

FULL-LOAD CURRENTS IN AMPERES

HP	115V	230V	550V
¼	3	1.5	...
⅓	3.8	1.9	...
½	5.4	2.7	...
¾	7.4	3.7	1.6
1	9.6	4.8	2.0
1½	13.2	6.6	2.7
2	17	8.5	3.6
3	25	12.5	5.2
5	40	20	8.3
7½	58	29	12
10	76	38	16
15	112	56	23
20	148	74	31
25	184	92	38
30	220	110	46
40	292	146	61
50	360	180	75
60	430	215	90
75	536	268	111
100		355	148
125		443	184
150		534	220
200		712	295

DIRECT-CURRENT MOTORS

These values of full-load currents are for motors running at usual speeds and motors with normal torque characteristics. Motors built for especially low speeds or high torques may have higher full-load currents, in which case the nameplate current ratings should be used.

To obtain full-load currents of 208 and 200-volt motors, increase corresponding 230-volt motor full-load currents by 10 and 15 per cent, respectively.

HP	115V	230V	440V
⅙	4.4	2.2	...
¼	5.8	2.9	...
⅓	7.2	3.6	...
½	9.8	4.9	...
¾	13.8	6.9	...
1	16	8	...
1½	20	10	...
2	24	12	...
3	34	17	...
5	56	28	...
7½	80	40	21
10	100	50	26

SINGLE-PHASE ALTERNATING-CURRENT MOTORS

WEIGHTS OF MOTORS AND TRANFORMERS,

AC, 60-CYCLE, 3-PHASE (motor only, inpounds)

H.P.	3500 rpm (2-pole)	1750 rpm (4-pole)	1150 rpm (6-pole)	875 rpm (8-pole)
1		70	80	115
5	115	155	180	240
10	180	240	265	450
25	450	450	620	650
50	620	650	970	1100
100	970	1100	1700	2500
150	1300	1700	2500	2500
200	1700	2500	2500	3100

2300 volts, 60-cycle, 3-phase

50		970	1100	1300
100	1100	1300	2500	2500
150	1700	2800	2800	2800
200	2800	2800	2800	3800

DC, 115 OR 230 VOLTS, CONSTANT SPEED

H.P.	3500 rpm	1750 rpm	1150 rpm	850 rpm	690 rpm	575 rpm
1		85	85	155	165	195
5	165	195	255	475	500	500
10	255	475	545	785	785	880
25	585	785	980	1020	1320	1555
50	850	1020	1585	1945	2280	2675
75		1550	2280	2675	2675	2925
100		1930	2675	2925	2925	3725
150		2675	3675	3840	3840	4860
200		3150	3870	4985	5950	6800

TRANSFORMERS—SINGLE-PHASE, 60-CYCLE (lbs.)
440, 550, or 600 volts to 115/230 volts

Kva	Air-Cooled*	Oil-Cooled
3	85	155
5	120	180
7.5	155	
10	195	275
15	225	330
25	395	460
37.5	515	670
50	665	820
75	940	1115
100	1400	1250

*3 to 50 kva, Class H Insulation, 75 and 100 kva, Class B Insulation.

MOTOR APPLICATION DATA: HP REQUIRED

Pumps

$$\text{Water Hp.} = \frac{\text{GPM} \times \text{IDH (in feet)}}{3960}$$

$$= \frac{\text{GPM} \times \text{IDH (in lbs./sq.in.)}}{1715}$$

$$\text{Motor Hp.} = \frac{\text{Water Hp.}}{\text{Pump Efficiency}}$$

$$\text{KW Input} = \frac{\text{GPM} \times \text{IDH (in feet)}}{5308 \times \text{pump eff.} \times \text{motor eff.}}$$

GPM = gallons per minute of water
IDH = total dynamic head in feet of water.

The above formulae are for cold water of density (specific gravity) equal to 1. The horsepower for liquids of different densities is obtained by multiplying the above water horsepower by the density of the liquid.

1 lb./sq.in.	= 2.31 ft. of water
1 lb./sq.in.	= 2.04 ins. of mercury
1 ft. of water	= 0.433 lb./sq.in.
1 gallon	= 231 cu. ins. = 3.785 liters
1 cu. ft.	= 7.48 gallons
1 U.S. gallon	= 8.33 pounds
1 cu. ft. water	= 62.4 pounds
1 cu. ft./sec.	= 448.8 GPM

Fans and Blowers

$$\text{Motor Hp.} = \frac{\text{CFM} \times \text{pressure in ins. of water}}{6356 \times \text{Fan Efficiency}}$$

An average ventilating fan has a typical efficiency of about 65 per cent.

Elevators

$$\text{Approx. Hp.} = \frac{(L - W) S}{33,000 \times \text{Efficiency}}$$

L = rated elevator load in pounds without counterweight.
W = weight in excess of that required to counterbalance empty car.
S = lift speed in feet per minute.

Escalators

For the usual stairway speeds, a 3-foot stairway with a rise of 17 ft. requires about 12 hp. when fully loaded.

Hoists

$$\text{Approx. Hp.} = \frac{W \times S \times \text{sine } A}{33,000 \times \text{Efficiency}}$$

W = weight in pounds
S = feet per minute
A = angle of hoist with horizontal

Air Conditioning

Multiply the number of tons of refrigeration required by:

1.25 Hp per ton for ½ to 5 tons capacity.
1.1 Hp per ton for 5 to 50 tons capacity.
1.0 Hp per ton for capacity above 50 tons.

Tons of air conditioning required to remove a lighting system heat load is equal to

$$\frac{\text{Lighting Kilowatts} \times 3414}{12000}$$

(Equivalent to: one ton of air conditioning capacity will remove the heat for a lighting load of 3500 watts).

Ice Making, Main Compressor

Multiply the number of tons of ice required per 24 hour day by:

3.5 Hp per ton for capacity up to 50 tons capacity.

3.25 Hp per ton for 50 60 200 tons capacity.

3.1 Hp per ton for capacity over 200 tons.

TYPICAL DATA ON LIGHT SOURCES

Number and Type of Lamps	Weight (lbs)	Line Current (amps)	Watts Consumed Ballast	Watts Consumed Per Lamp*	Lumens per Lamp	Lumens per Watt**
FOR 60 CYCLE, 110–125-VOLT CIRCUITS						
2–20	3.4	.42	9	24.5	1000	40.8
2–30	6.2	.70	18	39.0	1890	48.5
2–40	5.5	.85	16	48.0	2500	52.1
2–40T17IS	9.5	.95	30	55.0	2500	45.4
2–48T12	9.5	.95	30	53.0	2300	43.4
2–72T12	13.8	1.60	34	72.0	3600	50.0
2–96T12	13.8	1.60	34	91.0	5050	55.4
2–48T12RS	4.0	.85	12	46.0	2500	54.4
2–48T12RS/800	10.0	1.30	30	75.0	3100	41.4
2–72T12RS/800	14.0	1.70	30	100.0	4800	48.0
2–96T12RS/800	14.0	2.00	20	115.0	7250	63.0
2–90T17	10.0	1.00	21	100.5	5150	51.2
FOR 60 CYCLE, 220–250-VOLT CIRCUITS						
2–40	5.7	.45	18	49.0	2500	51.0
2–90T17	14.3	.93	31	105.5	5150	48.8
2–48T12RS	5.5	.43	13	46.5	2500	53.8
FOR 60 CYCLE, 240–280-VOLT CIRCUITS						
2–40	5.3	.37	18	49.0	2500	51.0
2–48T12	10.0	.43	28	52.0	2300	49.2
2–72T12	9.5	.74	30	70.0	3600	51.4
2–96T12	9.5	.74	30	89.0	5050	56.8
2–48T12RS	4.0	.39	12	46.0	2500	54.3
3–48T12RS	11.0	.55	18	46.0	2500	54.3
2–96T12RS/800	14.0	.88	20	115.0	7250	63.0
2–90T17	14.3	.83	31	105.5	5150	48.7
4–90T17	16.5	1.65	36	99.0	5150	52.0

*Includes lamp wattage plus watts loss in ballast.
**Overall efficiency, including ballast watts loss.

WATTAGE LOADS FOR HOUSEHOLD APPLIANCES

Appliance	Typical Load in Watts
Air Conditioner–3/4 hp	1200 W
,, ,, –1 1/2 hp	2400
Dishwasher	1200
Broiler	1500
Coffee Maker	1000
Freezer	350
Fryer	1300
Ironer	1650
Washing Machine	1200
Dryer	5000
Range	12000 W
Built In Oven	4500
Range Top	3000
Refrigerator	300
Waste Disposer	300
Water Heater	3000
Hand Iron	1000
Portable Heater	1300
Television	300

TYPICAL DATA ON LIGHT SOURCES

INCANDESCENT LAMPS

Lamp Designation	Rated Life (Hours)	Initial Output (Lumens)	Mean Output (Lumens)	Burnouts Per BLH●
100-watt A21	750	1,630	–	–
150-watt A23	750	2,700	–	–
200-watt A25	750	3,700	3,500	381
300-watt PS35	1,000	5,650 ·	5,100	196
500-watt PS40*	1,000	11,200	10,200	98
750-watt PS52*	1,000	17,100	15,800	63
1000-watt 5S52*	1,000	23,400	21,300	47
500-watt R52	2,000	7,500	6,900	73
750-watt R52	2,000	12,500	10,000	50

*Coiled-coil filament axially mounted.

FLUORESCENT LAMPS

Lamp Designation	Rated Life (Hours)*	Initial Output (Lumens)	Mean** Output (Lumens)	Burnouts Per BLH●
F40T12/CW	7,500	2,500	2,150	62
F40T12/D	7,500	2,300	2,000	· 67
F90T17/CW	7,500	5,150	4,250	31
F90T17/D	7,500	4,800	4,000	33
F48T12/CW/RS (800 ma)	7,500	3,100	–	–
F72T12/CW/RS (800 ma)	7,500	4,800	–	–
F96T12/CW/RS (800 ma)	7,500	7,250	6,150	22
F48T12/CW Slimline	7,500	2,300	2,000	67
F96T12/CW Slimline	7,500	5,050	4,500	30

*Based on 3 burning hours per start.
**Approximate mean output at 40% life.

MERCURY VAPOR LAMPS

Lamp Designation	Rated Life* (Hours)	Initial Output (Lumens)	Mean Output (Lumens)	Burnouts Per BLH●
H250A5	6,000	11,000	8,900	18.7
H400E1	6,000**	21,000	16,400	10.2
H400J1	6,000**	20,000	15,600	11.7
H400R1	6,000**	18,000	14,900	11.2
H400RC1	6,000**	20,500	17,000	9.8
H1000A15	6,000	54,000	35,100	4.8
H3000A9	6,000	132,000	103,000	1.6

*Rated life data shown are averages from tests of lamps burning five hours per start in appropriate industrial type reflectors.
**Designates economic life of the lamp under typical average operating conditions.
●Average lamp burnouts per billion lumen hours (calculated).

179

RIGID STEEL CONDUIT*

DIMENSIONS AND WEIGHTS

1	2	3	4	5	6
Nominal or Trade Size of Conduit (Ins.)	Inside Diam. (Ins.)	Outside Diam. (Ins.)	Wall Thickness (Ins.)	Length Without Coupling (Ft. & Ins.)	Min. Wt. of 10 Unit Lengths with Couplings Attached (Lbs.)
1/4	0.364	0.540	0.088	9–11 1/2	38.5
3/8	0.493	0.675	0.091	9–11 1/2	51.5
1/2	0.622	0.840	0.109	9–11 1/4	79.0
3/4	0.824	1.050	0.113	9–11 1/4	105.0
1	1.049	1.315	0.133	9–11	153.0
1 1/4	1.380	1.660	0.140	9–11	201.0
1 1/2	1.610	1.900	0.145	9–11	249.0
2	2.067	2.375	0.154	9–11	334.0
2 1/2	2.469	2.875	0.203	9–10 1/2	527.0
3	3.068	3.500	0.216	9–10 1/2	690.0
3 1/2	3.548	4.000	0.226	9–10 1/4	831.0
4	4.026	4.500	0.237	9–10 1/4	982.0
5	5.047	5.563	0.258	9–10	1344.0
6	6.065	6.625	0.280	9–10	1770.0

DIMENSIONS OF THREADS

1	2	3	3a	4	5
Nominal or Trade Size of Conduit (Inches)	Threads per Inch	Pitch Diam. End of Thread E_0 (Inches)		Length of Thread (Inches)	
		Taper Per Foot		Effective L_2	Overall L_4
		3/4 inch	3/8 inch		
1/4	18	0.4774	0.4865	0.40	0.59
3/8	18	0.6120	0.6213	0.41	0.60
1/2	14	0.7584	0.7706	0.53	0.78
3/4	14	0.9677	0.9803	0.55	0.79
1	11 1/2	1.2136		0.68	0.98
1 1/4	11 1/2	1.5571		0.71	1.01
1 1/2	11 1/2	1.7961		0.72	1.03
2	11 1/2	2.2690		0.76	1.06
2 1/2	8	2.7195		1.14	1.57
3	8	3.3406		1.20	1.63
3 1/2	8	3.8375		1.25	1.68
4	8	4.3344		1.30	1.73
5	8	5.3907		1.41	1.84
6	8	6.4461		1.51	1.95

*Tables courtesy of American Iron and Steel Institute.

ELBOWS AND WEIGHT OF NIPPLES PER 100

Nominal or Trade Size of Conduit (Inches)	ELBOWS AND BENDS		NIPPLES	
	Minimum Radius to Center of Tube (Inches)	Minimum Straight Length Ls at Each End (Inches)	A	B
1/4				
3/8				
1/2	4	1 1/2	0.065	2
3/4	4 1/2	1 1/2	0.090	4
1	5 3/4	1 7/8	0.125	9
1 1/4	7 1/4	2	0.164	10
1 1/2	8 1/4	2	0.202	11
2	9 1/2	2	0.269	14
2 1/2	10 1/2	3	0.430	60
3	13	3 1/8	0.561	70
3 1/2	15	3 1/4	0.663	90
4	16	3 3/8	0.786	115
5	24	3 5/8	1.060	170
6	30	3 3/4	1.410	200

Each lot of 100 nipples shall weigh not
less than the no. of lbs. determined by
the formula: $W = 100 \times L \times A - B$
Where: W = wt. of 100 nipples in lbs.;
$\qquad L$ = length of one nipple in ins.;
$\qquad A$ = wt. of nipple per in. in lbs.;
$\qquad B$ = wt. in lbs., lost in threading 100 nipples.

DIMENSIONS AND WEIGHTS OF COUPLINGS

Nominal or Trade Size of Conduit (Inches)	Outside Diameter (Inches)	Length (Inches)	Minimum Weight (Pounds)
1/4	0.719	13/16	.055
3/8	0.875	13/16	.075
1/2	1.010	1 9/16	.115
3/4	1.250	1 5/8	.170
1	1.525	2	.300
1 1/4	1.869	2 1/16	.370
1 1/2	2.155	2 1/16	.515
2	2.730	2 1/8	.875
2 1/2	3.250	3 1/8	1.675
3	4.000	3 1/4	2.825
3 1/2	4.500	3 3/8	3.400
4	5.000	3 1/2	3.800
5	6.296	3 3/4	7.500
6	7.390	4	9.750

RADIUS OF CONDUIT BENDS

Size of Conduit	Conductors Without Lead Sheath	Conductors With Lead Sheath
½ in.	4 in.	6 in.
¾ in.	5 in.	8 in.
1 in.	6 in.	11 in.
1¼ in.	8 in.	14 in.
1½ in.	10 in.	16 in.
2 in.	12 in.	21 in.
2½ in.	15 in.	25 in.
3 in.	18 in.	31 in.
3½ in.	21 in.	36 in.
4 in.	24 in.	40 in.
5 in.	30 in.	50 in.
6 in.	36 in.	61 in.

Section 3470 of the NEC prescribes that the radius of the curve of the inner edge of any field bend shall not be less than shown in the table:

WEIGHTS OF CABINETS AND BOXES

Size (inches)	Gauge Steel	Approx. Wt. (lbs.)
12 × 12 × 4	14	12
12 × 18 × 4	14	17
12 × 18 × 8	14	22
12 × 24 × 4	14	21
12 × 24 × 8	14	28
18 × 24 × 4	14	29
18 × 24 × 8	14	37
18 × 30 × 4	14	35
18 × 30 × 8	14	44
18 × 30 × 12	14	53
24 × 24 × 4	14	37
24 × 24 × 8	14	46
24 × 24 × 12	14	55
24 × 30 × 4	14	45
24 × 30 × 8	14	54
24 × 30 × 12	14	64
24 × 36 × 8	12	88
24 × 36 × 12	12	104
24 × 42 × 8	12	100
24 × 42 × 12	12	117
30 × 30 × 8	12	90
30 × 30 × 12	12	106
30 × 36 × 8	12	105
30 × 36 × 12	12	122
36 × 36 × 8	12	122
36 × 36 × 12	12	140
36 × 36 × 16	12	158
36 × 42 × 8	10	178
36 × 42 × 12	10	204
36 × 42 × 16	10	230

Size (inches)	Gauge Steel	Approx. Wt. (lbs.)
36 × 48 × 8	10	200
36 × 48 × 12	10	230
36 × 48 × 16	10	260
42 × 42 × 8	10	194
42 × 42 × 12	10	221
42 × 42 × 16	10	248
42 × 48 × 8	10	227
42 × 48 × 12	10	256
42 × 48 × 16	10	286
42 × 60 × 12	10	310
42 × 60 × 16	10	348
42 × 60 × 20	10	382
48 × 48 × 12	10	285
48 × 48 × 16	10	317
48 × 48 × 20	10	348
48 × 60 × 16	10	379
48 × 60 × 20	10	415
48 × 72 × 16	10	440
48 × 72 × 20	10	480
60 × 60 × 20	10	475
60 × 60 × 24	10	515
60 × 72 × 20	8	675
60 × 72 × 24	8	715

Weights per square foot of steel:
No. 14—3.2 lbs., No. 12—4.5 lbs.
No. 10—5.75 lbs.

UNIT LOADS AND DEMAND FACTORS FOR GENERAL LIGHTING
(Related Material in Code Article 220)

Type of Occupancy	Unit Load Per Sq. Ft. (Watts)	Load to which Demand Factor Applies (Watts)	Demand Factor
Armories and Auditoriums	1	Total Wattage	100%
Banks	2	Total Wattage	100%
Barber Shops and Beauty Parlors	3	Total Wattage	100%
Churches	1	Total Wattage	100%
Clubs	2*	Total Wattage	100%
Court Rooms	2	Total Wattage	100%
Dwellings—(Other Than Hotels)	3*	3,000 or less Next 117,000 Over 120,000	100% 35% 25%
Garages—Commercial (storage)	½	Total Wattage	100%
Hospitals	2	50,000 or less Over 50,000	40%† 20%
Hotels, including apartment houses without provisions for cooking by tenants	2*	20,000 or less Next 80,000 Over 100,000	50%† 40% 30%
Industrial Commercial (Loft) Buildings	2	Total Wattage	100%
Lodge Rooms	1½	Total Wattage	100%
Office Buildings	3	30,000 or less Over 30,000	100% 70%
Restaurants	2	Total Wattage	100%
Schools	3	Total Wattage	100%
Stores	3	Total Wattage	100%
Warehouses Storage	¼	12,500 or less Over 12,500	100% 50%

In any of above occupancies except single-family dwellings and individual apartments of multi-family dwellings:
  Assembly Halls and
    Auditoriums
  Halls, Corridors, Closets
  Storage spaces
	
	1
	½
	¼
		
		Total Wattage as
		specified for the
		specific occupancy	

STANDARD COLOR CODE — RESISTORS AND CAPACITORS

INSULATED UNINSULATED Color	FIRST RING BODY COLOR First Figure	SECOND RING END COLOR Second Figure	THIRD RING DOT COLOR Multiplier
BLACK	0	0	None
BROWN	1	1	0
RED	2	2	00
ORANGE	3	3	,000
YELLOW	4	4	0,000
GREEN	5	5	00,000
BLUE	6	6	000,000
VIOLET	7	7	0,000,000
GRAY	8	8	00,000,000
WHITE	9	9	000,000,000

DISC CERAMIC RMA CODE
5-Dot — Temp. Coeff., Capacity, Multiplier, Tolerance
3-Dot — Capacity, Multiplier, Tolerance

EXTENDED RANGE TC CERAMIC HICAP
Temp. Coeff., Capacity, TC Multiplier, Multiplier, Tolerance

AXIAL LEAD CERAMIC CAPACITOR
Capacity, Multiplier, Tolerance

5-DOT RADIAL LEAD CERAMIC CAPACITOR
Temp. Coeff., Capacity, Multiplier, Tolerance

BY-PASS COUPLING CERAMIC CAPACITOR
Capacity, Multiplier, Tolerance, Voltage (Opt.)

AXIAL LEAD RESISTOR
Brown = Insulated
Black = Non-insulated
Tolerance, Multiplier, 1st and 2nd Significant Figures
Wire wound resistors have 1st digit band double width

RADIAL LEAD DOT RESISTOR
Multiplier, 2nd Figure, 1st Figure, Tolerance

RADIAL LEAD (BAND) RESISTOR
Multiplier, 2nd Figure, 1st Figure, Tolerance

The standard color code provides all necessary information required to properly identify color coded resistors and capacitors. Refer to the color code for numerical values and the zeroes or multipliers assigned to the colors used. A fourth color band on resistors determines tolerance rating as follows: Gold = 5%, silver = 10%. Absence of the fourth band indicates a 20% tolerance rating.

The physical size of carbon resistors is determined by their wattage rating. Carbon resistors most commonly used in Heath-kits are ½ watt. Higher wattage rated resistors when specified are progressively larger in physical size. Small wire wound resistors ½ watt, 1 or 2 watt may be color coded but the first band will be double width.

MOLDED MICA TYPE CAPACITORS

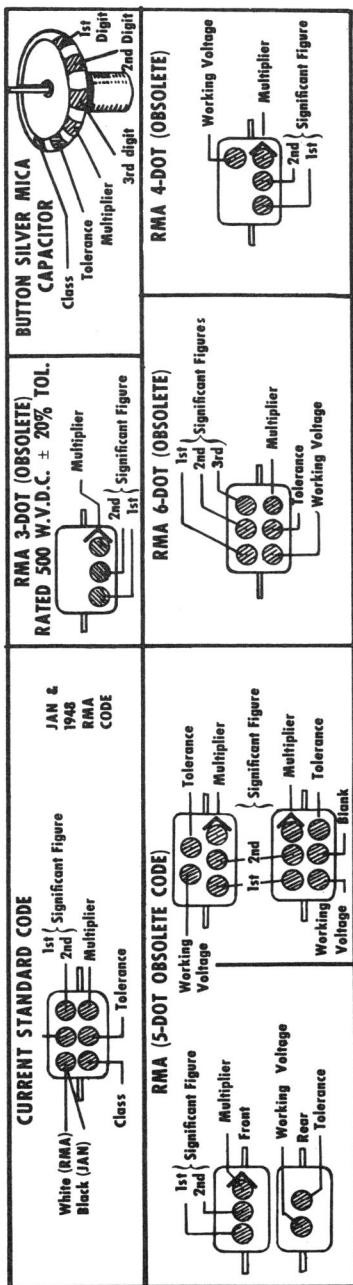

CURRENT STANDARD CODE

White (RMA)
Black (JAN)

1st } Significant Figure
2nd
Multiplier

Class

Tolerance

RMA (5-DOT OBSOLETE CODE)

1st } Significant Figure
2nd

Multiplier

Front

Working Voltage

Working Voltage

Rear

Tolerance

Tolerance

Multiplier

Significant Figure

1st 2nd

Working Voltage

Blank

Multiplier

Tolerance

TUBULAR CAPACITOR

1st } Significant Figure
2nd

Multiplier

Tolerance

2nd } Voltage Figure
1st

Significant
Figure

Normally stamped for value

A 2 digit voltage rating indicates more than 900 V.
Add 2 zeros to end of 2 digit number.

RMA 3-DOT (OBSOLETE)
RATED 500 W.V.D.C. ± 20% TOL.

Multiplier

2nd } Significant Figure
1st

RMA 6-DOT (OBSOLETE)

1st
2nd } Significant Figures
3rd

Multiplier

Tolerance

Working Voltage

JAN & 1948 RMA CODE

BUTTON SILVER MICA CAPACITOR

1st Digit
2nd Digit

3rd digit

Class

Tolerance

Multiplier

Working Voltage

RMA 4-DOT (OBSOLETE)

1st } Significant Figure
2nd

Multiplier

MOLDED PAPER TYPE CAPACITORS

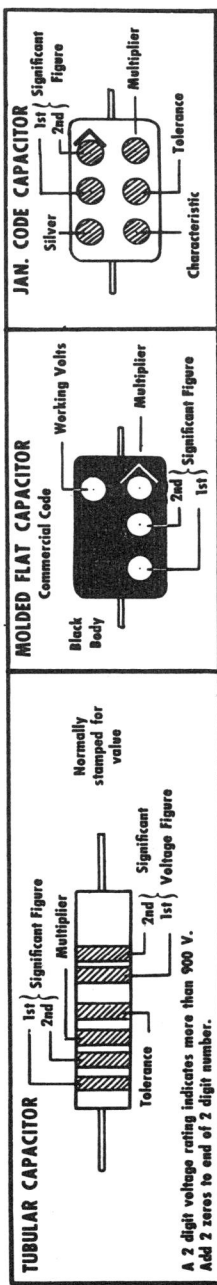

MOLDED FLAT CAPACITOR
Commercial Code

Black Body

Working Volts

Multiplier

2nd } Significant Figure
1st

JAN. CODE CAPACITOR

1st } Significant Figure
2nd

Multiplier

Tolerance

Silver

Characteristic

The tolerance rating of capacitors is determined by the color code. For example: red = 2%, green = 5%, etc. The voltage rating of capacitors is obtained by multiplying the color value by 100. For example: orange = 3 × 100 or 300 volts. Blue = 6 × 100 or 600 volts.

ELECTRONIC SIGNS AND SYMBOLS

Receptacle two-conductor	Battery	Fuse	Piezoelectric Crystal	1000 = **K**	1,000,000 = **M**	OHM = Ω	Microfarad = **MF**	Micro Microfarad = **MMF**	Binding post Terminal strip / Wiring between like letters is understood
Neon Bulb	Illuminating Lamp	Switch Single pole Single throw	Switch double pole single throw	Switch Triple pole Double throw	Switch Multipoint or Rotary	Speaker	Rectifier	Microphone	Typical tube symbol — Plate, screen, suppressor, Grid, cathode, filament
Resistor General	Resistor Tapped	Resistor Variable	Potentiometer	Thermistor	Jack two conductor	Jack three conductor	Wires connected	Wires Crossing but not connected	A. Ammeter V. Voltmeter G. Galvanometer MA. Milliammeter uA. Microammeter, etc.
Antenna General	Loop	Ground	Inductor General	Air core Transformer General	Adjustable Powdered Iron Core	Magnetic Core Variable Coupling	Iron Core Transformer	Capacitor General	Capacitor Electrolytic	Capacitor Variable

Courtesy Institute of Radio Engineers

PART EIGHT

BUSINESS METHODS

INTEREST TABLES

Compound Interest Table

Showing the amount of $1.00 from 1 to 15 years at compound interest, interest added semi-annually, at different rates. This table will be found valuable in computing interest on savings bank deposits.

YEARS.	3 Per Cent.	4 Per Cent.	5 Per Cent.	6 Per Cent.	7 Per Cent.	8 Per Cent.	10 Per Cent.
¼	1.015000	1.020000	1.025000	1.030000	1.035000	1.040000	1.050000
1	1.030225	1.040400	1.050625	1.060900	1.071225	1.081600	1.102500
1¼	1.045678	1.061208	1.079890	1.092727	1.108718	1.124864	1.157625
2	1.061363	1.082432	1.103813	1.125509	1.147523	1.169858	1.215506
2¼	1.077284	1.104081	1.131408	1.159274	1.187686	1.216653	1.276281
3	1.093443	1.126162	1.159693	1.194052	1.229255	1.265319	1.340095
3½	1.109845	1.148685	1.188685	1.229874	1.272279	1.315931	1.407100
4	1.126492	1.171659	1.218403	1.226770	1.316809	1.368569	1.477455
4½	1.143390	1.195092	1.248863	1.304773	1.363897	1.423312	1.551328
5	1.160541	1.218994	1.280084	1.343916	1.410598	1.480244	1.628894
5½	1.177949	1.243374	1.312086	1.384234	1.459969	1.539454	1.710339
6	1.195618	1.268241	1.344888	1.425761	1.511068	1.601032	1.795856
6½	1.213552	1.293606	1.378511	1.468533	1.563956	1.665073	1.885649
7	1.231755	1.319478	1.412973	1.512589	1.618694	1.731676	1.979931
7½	1.250232	1.345868	1.448298	1.557967	1.675349	1.800943	2.078923
8	1.268985	1.372785	1.484505	1.604706	1.733986	1.872981	2.182874
8½	1.288020	1.400241	1.521618	1.652847	1.794675	1.947900	2.292019
9	1.307340	1.428246	1.559658	1.702433	1.857489	2.025816	2.406619
9½	1.326950	1.456811	1.598650	1.753506	1.922501	2.106849	2.526950
10	1.346855	1.485947	1.638616	1.806111	1.989789	2.191123	2.653297
10½	1.367058	1.515666	1.679581	1.860294	2.059431	2.278768	2.785962
11	1.387563	1.545980	1.721571	1.916103	2.131511	2.369919	2.925260
11½	1.408377	1.567899	1.764610	1.973586	2.206114	2.464715	3.071523
12	1.429503	1.608437	1.808726	2.032794	2.283328	2.563304	3.225100
12½	1.450945	1.640606	1.853944	2.093778	2.363245	2.665836	3.386355
13	1.472709	1.673418	1.900292	2.156591	2.445959	2.772470	3.555672
13½	1.494800	1.706886	1.947800	2.221289	2.531567	2.883368	3.733456
14	1.517222	1.741024	1.996595	2.287927	2.620172	2.998703	3.920129
14½	1.539980	1.775845	2.046407	2.356565	2.711878	3.118651	4.116135
15	1.563080	1.811361	2.097567	2.427262	2.806793	3.243397	4.321940

Example.—What will $400 amount to in 8 years and 6 months at 4 per cent compound interest, interest added semi-annually? Referring to table it is found $1 in 8 years and 6 months at 4 per cent will amount to $1.400241. The amount of $400 will be 400 times this or $560.0964.

Note.—If the interest only be wanted, deduct the principal, $400, from $560.0964.

The Lightning Method for Calculating Interest

Where the Time is For Days Only.

RULE: To find the interest on any given sum for any number of days, multiply the principal by the number of days, point off the two right-hand figures in the product and then divide as follows:

At 4 per cent, divide by 90
At 4½ per cent, divide by 80

INTEREST TABLES

At 5 per cent, divide by 72
At 6 per cent, divide by 60
At 7 per cent, divide by 52
At 7½ per cent, divide by 48
At 8 per cent, divide by 45
At 9 per cent, divide by 40
At 10 per cent, divide by 36
At 12 per cent, divide by 30

EXAMPLE:—What is the interest on $900 for 8 days at 6%?
SOLUTION:—900×8÷60=$1.20 interest.

When the Time Consists of Years, Months, and Days

1. RULE:—Reduce years to months, adding the number of months, then place 1/3 of the number of days to the right of the months with a decimal point between.
2. Now move the decimal point two places to the left in the principal and divide by 2 ; the result will equal the interest for one month at 6% per cent.
3. Multiply the interest for one month by the number of months and the product will be the interest at 6% for the given time.

Then:	For	4	per	cent	decrease	product	1/3
	For	4½	per	cent	decrease	product	1/4
	For	5	per	cent	decrease	product	1/6
	For	5½	per	cent	decrease	product	1/12
	For	7	per	cent	increase	product	1/6
	For	7½	per	cent	increase	product	1/4
	For	8	per	cent	increase	product	1/3
	For	8½	per	cent	increase	product	5/12
	For	9	per	cent	increase	product	1/2
	For	10	per	cent	increase	product	2/3
	For	11	per	cent	increase	product	5/6
	For	12	per	cent	double	the	product.

EXAMPLE:—What is the interest on $150 at 9% for 1 year, 4 months, and 12 days?

Solution: One year equals 12 months
  Add   4 months
  12 days ÷3 equal   .4
  ─────────
          16.4 months

$1.50÷2=.75 Interest for 1 month at 6%.
.75x16.4=12.30 Interest at 6%.
$12.30 plus 6.15 ($12.30 increased by ½ itself)=$18.45 Interest 9%.

Another Simple Six Per Cent Method

Rule: Multiply the principal by the interest on $1.00 for the given time at the 6% rate and then increase or decrease the interest as per above table for any other rate.

Interest 6% on $1.00 for 1 year equals .06
                       ”   1 mo.   ”   .005
                       ”   1 day   ”   .000 1/6

Example: Find the interest on $180 for 3 years 5 months and 21 days at 7½%.

Solution: $180×3 × .06 equals $32.40
           180×5 × .005 ”   4.50
           180×21×.000 1/6 “   .6$
                              ──────
           Interest at 6%   37.53
           Increased by ¼   9.38
                              ──────
           Interest at 7½% $46.91

189

INTEREST TABLES

Bankers' 60 Day Interest Method

In banking a great many loans are made and interest figured on 30, 60, and 90 days time. The following is a simple method:

RULE 1. To find the interest on any amount for 60 days, move the decimal point two places to the left in the principal and the result will be the interest at 6%.

    2. For 30 days divide by 2; for 15 days divide by 4; for 90 days increase by ½; for 120 days multiply by 2.

    3. For any other rate than 6% increase or decrease result as shown in previous table.

EXAMPLE: What is the interest on $350 for 90 days at 7%?

SOLUTION:
$350 at 6% for 60 days..........	$3.50
For 90 days increased by ½......	1.75
Interest for 90 days at 6%......	5.25
For 7% increase by 1/6..........	.88
Interest at 7%....................	$6.13

NOTE: The above rules are based on 360 days to the year, whereas it actually contains 365 days. To find the exact or accurate interest decrease the result obtained by 1/73 of itself and the answer will be as though the interest had been originally figured on the basis of 365 days to the year. But in sums of $500 or less or with times of 30 days or less, the difference between the 360 and 365 days basis is too small to make appreciable difference. Besides, 360 days are now generally accepted as a basis.

How to Use the Interest Tables

1. The interest on any sum of money, and for any length of time, may be obtained, by adding to or doubling any certain sum, or length of time in the tables, viz: If the interest on a certain sum of money at 8 per cent for a given time should be $28, one-half of $28 or $14 would equal the interest at 4 per cent, etc.

2. If the interest at 6 per cent should amount to $26 on a certain sum of money for a given time, twice that amount or $52 would equal the interest at 12 per cent, and half that amount would equal the interest at 3 per cent.

3. The tables are computed on the principle of 360 days in a year, the rule adopted by bankers and merchants throughout the entire country.

4. When the fraction of interest is a half cent or more, a whole cent is taken, but when less than a half cent, nothing is charged.

EXAMPLE: Find the interest on $150.00 for 9 mos., 19 days at 5½%. From Table,

Interest	on	$100.00 for	9 mo.	@			5 per	cent,	$3.75
Interest	on	100.00 for	9 mo.	@	½ of 1 per			cent,	.38
Interest	on	50.00 for	9 mo.	@			5 per	cent,	1.90
Interest	on	50.00 for	9 mo.	@	½ of 1 per			cent,	.20
Interest	on	100.00 for	19 da.	@			5 per	cent,	.26
Interest	on	100.00 for	19 da.	@	¼ of 1 per			cent,	.03
Interest	on	50.00 for	19 da.	@			5 per	cent,	.10
Interest	on	50.00 for	19 da.	@	½ of 1 per			cent,	.00

Interest on amount................... $6.62

INTEREST TABLES

Interest at ½ of One Per Cent

TIME	$1	$2	$3	$4	$5	$6	$7	$8	$9	$10	$100	$1000
1 Day	.00	.00	.00	.00	.00	.00	.00	.00	.00	$.00	$.00	$ .01
2 "	.00	.00	.00	.00	.00	.00	.00	.00	.00	.00	.00	.03
3 "	.00	.00	.00	.00	.00	.00	.00	.00	.00	.00	.00	.04
4 "	.00	.00	.00	.00	.00	.00	.00	.00	.00	.00	.00	.06
5 "	.00	.00	.00	.00	.00	.00	.00	.00	.00	.00	.00	.07
6 "	.00	.00	.00	.00	.00	.00	.00	.00	.00	.00	.00	.08
7 "	.00	.00	.00	.00	.00	.00	.00	.00	.00	.00	.00	.10
8 "	.00	.00	.00	.00	.00	.00	.00	.00	.00	.00	.01	.11
9 "	.00	.00	.00	.00	.00	.00	.00	.00	.00	.00	.01	.13
10 "	.00	.00	.00	.00	.00	.00	.00	.00	.00	.00	.01	.14
11 "	.00	.00	.00	.00	.00	.00	.00	.00	.00	.00	.02	.15
12 "	.00	.00	.00	.00	.00	.00	.00	.00	.00	.00	.02	.17
13 "	.00	.00	.00	.00	.00	.00	.00	.00	.00	.00	.02	.18
14 "	.00	.00	.00	.00	.00	.00	.00	.00	.00	.00	.02	.19
15 "	.00	.00	.00	.00	.00	.00	.00	.00	.00	.00	.02	.21
16 "	.00	.00	.00	.00	.00	.00	.00	.00	.00	.00	.02	.22
17 "	.00	.00	.00	.00	.00	.00	.00	.00	.00	.00	.02	.24
18 "	.00	.00	.00	.00	.00	.00	.00	.00	.00	.00	.03	.25
19 "	.00	.00	.00	.00	.00	.00	.00	.00	.00	.00	.03	.26
20 "	.00	.00	.00	.00	.00	.00	.00	.00	.00	.00	.03	.28
21 "	.00	.00	.00	.00	.00	.00	.00	.00	.00	.00	.03	.29
22 "	.00	.00	.00	.00	.00	.00	.00	.00	.00	.00	.03	.31
23 "	.00	.00	.00	.00	.00	.00	.00	.00	.00	.00	.03	.32
24 "	.00	.00	.00	.00	.00	.00	.00	.00	.00	.00	.03	.33
25 "	.00	.00	.00	.00	.00	.00	.00	.00	.00	.00	.03	.35
26 "	.00	.00	.00	.00	.00	.00	.00	.00	.00	.00	.04	.36
27 "	.00	.00	.00	.00	.00	.00	.00	.00	.00	.00	.04	.38
28 "	.00	.00	.00	.00	.00	.00	.00	.00	.00	.00	.04	.39
29 "	.00	.00	.00	.00	.00	.00	.00	.00	.00	.00	.04	.40
1 Month	.00	.00	.00	.00	.00	.00	.00	.00	.00	.00	.04	.42
2 "	.00	.00	.00	.00	.00	.00	.00	.00	.00	.00	.08	.83
3 "	.00	.00	.00	.00	.00	.00	.00	.01	.01	.01	.13	1.25
4 "	.00	.00	.00	.00	.00	.01	.01	.01	.02	.02	.17	1.67
5 "	.00	.00	.00	.00	.01	.01	.01	.02	.02	.02	.21	2.08
6 "	.00	.00	.00	.01	.01	.02	.02	.02	.02	.03	.25	2.50
7 "	.00	.00	.00	.01	.01	.02	.02	.02	.03	.03	.30	2.97
8 "	.00	.00	.01	.01	.02	.02	.02	.03	.03	.03	.33	3.33
9 "	.00	.00	.01	.02	.02	.02	.03	.03	.03	.04	.38	3.75
10 "	.00	.00	.01	.02	.02	.03	.03	.03	.04	.04	.42	4.17
11 "	.00	.00	.01	.02	.02	.03	.03	.04	.04	.05	.46	4.58
1 Year	.00	.01	.02	.02	.03	.03	.04	.04	.05	.05	.50	5.00

INTEREST TABLES

Interest at Five Per Cent

TIME	$1	$2	$3	$4	$5	$6	$7	$8	$9	$10	$100	$1000
1 Day	.00	.00	.00	.00	.00	.00	.00	.00	.00	$.00	$ .01	$ .14
2 "	.00	.00	.00	.00	.00	.00	.00	.00	.00	.00	.03	.28
3 "	.00	.00	.00	.00	.00	.00	.00	.00	.00	.00	.04	.42
4 "	.00	.00	.00	.00	.00	.00	.00	.00	.01	.01	.06	.56
5 "	.00	.00	.00	.00	.00	.00	.01	.01	.01	.01	.07	.69
6 "	.00	.00	.00	.00	.00	.01	.01	.01	.01	.01	.08	.83
7 "	.00	.00	.00	.00	.00	.01	.01	.01	.01	.01	.10	.97
8 "	.00	.00	.00	.00	.01	.01	.01	.01	.01	.01	.11	1.11
9 "	.00	.00	.00	.01	.01	.01	.01	.01	.01	.01	.13	1.25
10 "	.00	.00	.00	.01	.01	.01	.01	.01	.01	.01	.14	1.39
11 "	.00	.00	.00	.01	.01	.01	.01	.01	.01	.02	.15	1.53
12 "	.00	.00	.01	.01	.01	.01	.01	.01	.01	.02	.17	1.67
13 "	.00	.00	.01	.01	.01	.01	.01	.01	.02	.02	.18	1.81
14 "	.00	.00	.01	.01	.01	.01	.01	.02	.02	.02	.19	1.94
15 "	.00	.00	.01	.01	.01	.01	.01	.02	.02	.02	.21	2.08
16 "	.00	.00	.01	.01	.01	.01	.02	.02	.02	.02	.22	2.22
17 "	.00	.00	.01	.01	.01	.01	.02	.02	.02	.02	.24	2.36
18 "	.00	.01	.01	.01	.01	.02	.02	.02	.02	.03	.25	2.50
19 "	.00	.01	.01	.01	.01	.02	.02	.02	.02	.03	.26	2.64
20 "	.00	.01	.01	.01	.01	.02	.02	.02	.03	.03	.28	2.78
21 "	.00	.01	.01	.01	.01	.02	.02	.02	.03	.03	.29	2.92
22 "	.00	.01	.01	.01	.01	.02	.02	.02	.03	.03	.31	3.06
23 "	.00	.01	.01	.01	.02	.02	.02	.03	.03	.03	.32	3.19
24 "	.00	.01	.01	.01	.02	.02	.02	.03	.03	.03	.33	3.33
25 "	.00	.01	.01	.01	.02	.02	.02	.03	.03	.03	.35	3.47
26 "	.00	.01	.01	.01	.02	.02	.03	.03	.03	.04	.36	3.61
27 "	.00	.01	.01	.02	.02	.02	.03	.03	.03	.04	.38	3.75
28 "	.00	.01	.01	.02	.02	.02	.03	.03	.04	.04	.39	3.80
29 "	.00	.01	.01	.02	.02	.02	.03	.03	.04	.04	.40	4.03
1 Month	.00	.01	.01	.02	.02	.03	.03	.03	.04	.04	.42	4.17
2 "	.01	.02	.03	.04	.04	.05	.06	.07	.08	.08	.83	8.33
3 "	.01	.03	.04	.05	.06	.08	.09	.10	.11	.13	1.25	12.50
4 "	.02	.03	.05	.07	.08	.10	.12	.13	.15	.17	1.67	16.67
5 "	.02	.04	.06	.08	.10	.13	.15	.17	.19	.21	2.08	20.83
6 "	.03	.05	.08	.10	.13	.15	.18	.20	.23	.25	2.50	25.00
7 "	.03	.06	.09	.12	.15	.18	.20	.23	.26	.29	2.92	29.17
8 "	.03	.07	.10	.13	.17	.20	.23	.27	.30	.33	3.33	33.33
9 "	.04	.08	.11	.15	.19	.23	.26	.30	.34	.38	3.75	37.50
10 "	.04	.08	.13	.17	.21	.25	.29	.33	.38	.42	4.17	41.67
11 "	.05	.09	.14	.18	.23	.28	.32	.37	.41	.46	4.58	45.83
1 Year	.05	.10	.15	.20	.25	.30	.35	.40	.45	.50	5.00	50.00

INTEREST TABLES

Interest at Six Per Cent

TIME	$1	$2	$3	$4	$5	$6	$7	$8	$9	$10	$100	$1000
1 Day	.00	.00	.00	.00	.00	.00	.00	.00	.00	$.00	$ .02	$ .17
2 "	.00	.00	.00	.00	.00	.00	.00	.00	.00	.00	.03	.33
3 "	.00	.00	.00	.00	.00	.00	.00	.00	.00	.01	.05	.50
4 "	.00	.00	.00	.00	.00	.00	.01	.01	.01	.01	.07	.67
5 "	.00	.00	.00	.00	.00	.01	.01	.01	.01	.01	.08	.83
6 "	.00	.00	.00	.00	.01	.01	.01	.01	.01	.01	.10	1.00
7 "	.00	.00	.00	.00	.01	.01	.01	.01	.01	.01	.12	1.17
8 "	.00	.00	.00	.01	.01	.01	.01	.01	.01	.01	.13	1.33
9 "	.00	.00	.00	.01	.01	.01	.01	.01	.01	.02	.15	1.50
10 "	.00	.00	.01	.01	.01	.01	.01	.01	.02	.02	.17	1.67
11 "	.00	.00	.01	.01	.01	.01	.01	.01	.02	.02	.18	1.83
12 "	.00	.00	.01	.01	.01	.01	.01	.02	.02	.02	.20	2.00
13 "	.00	.00	.01	.01	.01	.01	.02	.02	.02	.02	.22	2.17
14 "	.00	.00	.01	.01	.01	.01	.02	.02	.02	.02	.23	2.33
15 "	.00	.01	.01	.01	.01	.02	.02	.02	.02	.03	.25	2.50
16 "	.00	.01	.01	.01	.01	.02	.02	.02	.02	.03	.27	2.67
17 "	.00	.01	.01	.01	.01	.02	.02	.02	.03	.03	.28	2 83
18 "	.00	.01	.01	.01	.02	.02	.02	.02	.03	.03	.30	3.00
19 "	.00	.01	.01	.01	.02	.02	.02	.03	.03	.03	.32	3.17
20 "	.00	.01	.01	.01	.02	.02	.02	.03	.03	.03	.33	3 33
21 "	.00	.01	.01	.01	.02	.02	.02	.03	.03	.04	.35	3.50
22 "	.00	.01	.01	.01	.02	.02	.03	.03	.03	.04	.37	3.67
23 "	.00	.01	.01	.02	.02	.02	.03	.03	.03	.04	.38	3.83
24 "	.00	.01	.01	.02	.02	.02	.03	.03	.04	.04	.40	4.00
25 "	.00	.01	.01	.02	.02	.03	.03	.03	.04	.04	.42	4.17
26 "	.00	.01	.01	.02	.02	.03	.03	.03	.04	.04	.43	4.33
27 "	.00	.01	.01	.02	.02	.03	.03	.04	.04	.05	.45	4.50
28 "	.00	.01	.01	.02	.02	.03	.03	.04	.04	.05	.47	4.67
29 "	.00	.01	.01	.02	.02	.03	.03	.04	.04	.05	.48	4.83
1 Month	.01	.01	.02	.02	.03	.03	.04	.04	.05	.05	.50	5.00
2 "	.01	.02	.03	.04	.05	.06	.07	.08	.09	.10	1.00	10.00
3 "	.02	.03	.05	.06	.08	.09	.11	.12	.14	.15	1.50	15.00
4 "	.02	.04	.06	.08	.10	.12	.14	.16	.18	.20	2.00	20.00
5 "	.03	.05	.08	.10	.13	.15	.18	.20	.23	.25	2.50	25.00
6 "	.03	.06	.09	.12	.15	.18	.21	.24	.27	.30	3.00	30.00
7 "	.04	.07	.11	.14	.18	.21	.25	.28	.32	.35	3.50	35.00
8 "	.04	.08	.12	.16	.20	.24	.28	.32	.36	.40	4.00	40.00
9 "	.05	.09	.14	.18	.23	.27	.32	.36	.41	.45	4.50	45.00
10 "	.05	˙10	.15	.20	.25	.30	.35	.40	.45	.50	5.00	50.00
11 "	.06	.11	.17	.22	.28	.33	.39	.44	.50	.55	5.50	55.00
1 Year	.06	.12	.18	.24	.30	.36	.42	.48	.54	.60	6.00	60.00

INTEREST TABLES

Interest at Eight Per Cent

TIME		$1	$2	$3	$4	$5	$6	$7	$8	$9	$10	$100	$1000
1	Day	.00	.00	.00	.00	.00	.00	.00	.00	.00	$.00	$ .02	$ .22
2	"	.00	.00	.00	.00	.00	.00	.00	.00	.00	.00	.04	.44
3	"	.00	.00	.00	.00	.00	.00	.00	.01	.01	.01	.07	.67
4	"	.00	.00	.00	.00	.00	.01	.01	.01	.01	.01	.09	.89
5	"	.00	.00	.00	.00	.01	.01	.01	.01	.01	.01	.11	1.11
6	"	.00	.00	.00	.01	.01	.01	.01	.01	.01	.01	.13	1.33
7	"	.00	.00	.00	.01	.01	.01	.01	.01	.01	.02	.16	1.56
8	"	.00	.00	.01	.01	.01	.01	.01	.01	.02	.02	.18	1.78
9	"	.00	.00	.01	.01	.01	.01	.01	.02	.02	.02	.20	2.00
10	"	.00	.00	.01	.01	.01	.01	.02	.02	.02	.02	.22	2.22
11	"	.00	.00	.01	.01	.01	.01	.02	.02	.02	.02	.24	2.44
12	"	.00	.01	.01	.01	.01	.02	.02	.02	.02	.03	.27	2.67
13	"	.00	.01	.01	.01	.01	.02	.02	.02	.03	.03	.29	2.89
14	"	.00	.01	.01	.01	.02	.02	.02	.02	.03	.03	.31	3.11
15	"	.00	.01	.01	.01	.02	.02	.02	.03	.03	.03	.33	3.33
16	"	.00	.01	.01	.01	.02	.02	.02	.03	.03	.04	.36	3.56
17	"	.00	.01	.01	.02	.02	.02	.03	.03	.03	.04	.38	3.78
18	"	.00	.01	.01	.02	.02	.02	.03	.03	.04	.04	.40	4.00
19	"	.00	.01	.01	.02	.02	.03	.03	.03	.04	.04	.42	4.22
20	"	.00	.01	.01	.02	.02	.03	.03	.04	.04	.04	.44	4.44
21	"	.00	.01	.01	.02	.02	.03	.03	.04	.04	.05	.47	4.67
22	"	.00	.01	.01	.02	.02	.03	.03	.04	.04	.05	.49	4.89
23	"	.01	.01	.02	.02	.03	.03	.04	.04	.05	.05	.51	5.11
24	"	.01	.01	.02	.02	.03	.03	.04	.04	.05	.05	.53	5.33
25	"	.01	.01	.02	.02	.03	.03	.04	.04	.05	.06	.56	5.56
26	"	.01	.01	.02	.02	.03	.03	.04	.05	.05	.06	.58	5.78
27	"	.01	.01	.02	.02	.03	.04	.04	.05	.05	.06	.60	6.00
28	"	.01	.01	.02	.02	.03	.04	.04	.05	.06	.06	.62	6.22
29	"	.01	.01	.02	.03	.03	.04	.05	.05	.06	.06	.64	6.44
1	Month	.01	.01	.02	.03	.03	.04	.05	.05	.06	.07	.67	6.67
2	"	.01	.03	.04	.05	.07	.08	.09	.11	.12	.13	1.33	13.33
3	"	.02	.04	.06	.08	.10	.12	.14	.16	.18	.20	2.00	20.00
4	"	.03	.05	.08	.11	.13	.16	.19	.21	.24	.27	2.67	26.67
5	"	.03	.07	.10	.13	.17	.20	.23	.27	.30	.33	3.33	33.33
6	"	.04	.08	.12	.16	.20	.24	.28	.32	.36	.40	4.00	40.00
7	"	.05	.09	.14	.19	.23	.28	.33	.37	.42	.47	4.67	46.67
8	"	.05	.11	.16	.21	.27	.32	.37	.43	.48	.53	5.33	53.33
9	"	.06	.12	.18	.24	.30	.36	.42	.48	.54	.60	6.00	60.00
10	"	.07	.13	.20	.27	.33	.40	.47	.53	.60	.67	6.67	66.67
11	"	.07	.15	.22	.29	.37	.44	.51	.59	.66	.73	7.33	73.33
1	Year	.08	.16	.24	.32	.40	.48	.56	.64	.72	.80	8.00	80.00

PRINTING*

1. Every business man resorts to some form of printing in order to carry on his business. When the average man orders stationery, or plans an advertising campaign the conversation with the printer or the written quotation strikes him as being a meaningless jumble of picas, ems, points, layouts, zincs, screens, reams, and equally unintelligible terms. The following pages have been prepared with special reference to the needs of the beginner, athough even the skilled craftsman will find them a source of convenient reference.

2. **Type Measurement.**—The pica is 12 points long or 1/6 of an inch. The em is a unit of measurement based on the square of the size of the individual type. It is a unit of area to determine the amount of matter set in a page of type. The point is measured up and down, not by width. An inch of type space measured up and down contains 72 points. Dividing 72 by the size of any type in points gives us the number of lines of that type which can be set solid, to an inch. For example, by dividing 72 by 8 we find that 9 lines of 8 point can be set, solid, in a single inch.

3. **Copy and Layout.**—By copy is meant such matter as is to be arranged in type form. The layout consists of a dummy indicating the position of the headings, text and illustrations, which the finished product shall contain.

4. **Illustrations.**—A half-tone is a reproduction of a photograph or wash drawing, on copper plates, to be used in printing. The design is first photographed thru a screen of fine lines, and the negative then printed on a copper plate and etched in acid. Rough paper requires coarse screen; highly finished stock takes a fine screen. Zinc etchings are reproduced from pen drawings, wood engravings, and printed pages, by exactly the same process as half tones except that no screen is used in making the negative. The Ben Dey process is one by which zinc plates are shaded and tinted for printing purposes. By the color process plates can be

*Much of the material used in this chapter is by special permission of the W. B. Conkey Company from their book "What a Business Man should Know about Printing and Bookmaking."

made to reproduce in several different colors. **An electro-type is not an engraving.** It is a metal reproduction of a half tone, etching, cut or type page for printing purposes.

5. How to Determine the Dimensions of a Cut.—Suppose you have a photograph to be reduced to a certain width and you want to know how high the cut will be. Draw a figure having the same dimensions as the photograph in this manner:

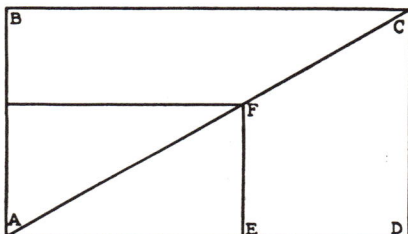

Now draw the diagonal line A C. Next mark off on the bottom line the width A E of the cut you desire made. The point at which the perpendicular F E touches the diagonal A C will give you the height of your cut when reduced. If the height is known the width can be determined in the same way.

TABLES OF TYPE SIZES.—The following tables will be found convenient in estimating the amount of space required for a certain amount of words or pages when set in different sizes of type.

Handy Information on Type

Size of Type	Words in 1000 ems		Square inches in 1,000 ems	Number of ems in 1 pound
	Solid	Leaded		
5 point	305	207	3.91	1,024
6 point	312	222	6.94	576
8 point	370	259	12.35	324
10 point..........	385	289	19.29	207
11 point	373	303	23.34	171
12 point	389	306	27.78	144

The above figures are approximate and vary slightly with different styles of type face; they are based on the solid slug.

Relative Sizes of Type in Ems

A page set in 12 point contains 1000 ems.
The same page set in 11 point contains 1190 ems.
The same page set in 10 point contains 1440 ems.
The same page set in 9 point contains 1778 ems.
The same page set in 8 point contains 2250 ems.
The same page set in 7 point contains 2939 ems.
The same page set in 6 point contains 4000 ems.

Number of Ems to Running Inch

In Columns 10 to 30 Picas Wide

Column Width in Picas	10	11	12	13	14	15	16	17	18	19	20
12 pt.................. Pica	60	66	72	78	84	90	96	102	108	114	120
11 pt.............Small Pica	72	78	86	93	100	107	114	121	128	136	143
10 pt...........Long Primer	86	95	104	112	121	129	138	147	155	164	173
9 pt............. Bourgeois	107	117	128	139	149	160	171	181	192	203	213
8 pt............... Brevier	135	148	162	175	189	202	216	229	243	256	270
7 pt............... Minion	177	194	212	229	247	265	282	300	318	335	353
6 pt............. Nonpareil	240	264	288	312	336	360	384	408	432	456	480
5½ pt................ Agate	288	316	344	372	400	428	456	484	512	544	572

Column Width in Picas	21	22	23	24	25	26	27	28	29	30
12 pt...................... Pica	126	132	138	144	150	156	162	168	174	180
11 pt................Small Pica	150	157	164	171	178	185	192	200	207	214
10 pt..............Long Primer	181	190	199	207	216	225	233	242	250	259
9 pt................. Bourgeois	224	235	246	256	267	277	288	299	309	320
8 pt................... Brevier	283	297	310	324	337	351	364	378	391	405
7 pt................... Minion	371	388	406	424	441	459	477	494	512	529
6 pt................ Nonpareil	504	528	552	576	600	624	648	672	696	720
5½ pt.................... Agate	600	628	656	684	712	740	768	800	828	856

Words to the Square Inch

5 point, leaded	50	9 point, solid	28
5 point, solid	69	10 point, leaded	16
6 point, leaded	34	10 point, solid	21
6 point, solid	47	11 point, leaded	14
7 point, leaded	27	11 point, solid	17
7 point, solid	38	12 point, leaded	11
8 point, leaded	23	12 point, solid	14
8 point, solid	32	14 point, solid	11
9 point, leaded	21	18 point, solid	7

Measurement of Composition Set in Standard Book Measures

Table showing the number of ems to a line, and the number of lines contained in 1,000 ems of matter, standard book measures. Also the space in inches, filled by 1,000 ems of matter in the different measures.

STYLE OF TYPE	21 Ems Pica			23 Ems Pica			25 Ems Pica		
	No. ems in a line	No. lines 1000 ems	No. in. 1000 ems	No. ems in a line	No. lines 1000 ems	No. in. 1000 ems	No. ems in a line	No. lines 1000 ems	No. in. 1000 ems
6 point................	42	24	2	46	21⅔	1¾	50	20	1⅔
8 point................	31⅔	32¼	3½	35	28⅝	3¼	37½	26½	3
10 point................	25¼	39½	5½	27⅝	36	5	30	33⅓	4⅝
11 point................	23	43½	6¾	25	40	6⅛	27¼	36¾	5⅝
12 point................	21	48	8	23	43½	7¼	25	40	6⅔

PRINTING

NAMES, SIZES, AND WEIGHTS OF PAPER.—**Antique finished paper** is practically unfinished. **Laid** has a low finish but is watermarked. **Eggshell** is antique finished paper which has been ironed. **Machine finish** is smoother than antique having been calendered or ironed. **English finish** gives a smooth surface without gloss. S & SC means that the paper has been sized to make it glossy, and super-calendered to make it smooth. **Enameled** paper is coated to fill up the pores. **Dull Coated is made in** the same way but is dull instead of glossy. The following tables give detailed information as to names, sizes, and weights:

Names and Sizes of Paper Sheets

Name	Size
Flat letter	10 x 16 inches
Double Flat Letter	16 x 20 "
Flat Cap	14 x 17 "
Double Cap	17 x 28 "
Flat Foolscap	13 x 16 "
Legal Cap	13 x 16 "
Crown	15 x 19 "
Demy	16 x 21 "
Double Demy	21 x 32 "
Folio Post	17 x 22 "
Extra Size Folio	19 x 23 "
Check Folio (Royal)	19 x 24 "
Double Royal	24 x 38 "
Super Royal	20 x 28 "
Medium Writing	18 x 23 "
Medium Printing	18 x 24 "
Double Medium	23 x 36 "
Regular Bank	19 x 24 "
Elephant	23 x 28 "
Double Elephant	27 x 40 "
Columbian	23 x 34 "
Imperial	22 x 30 "
Imperial	22 x 32 "
Book	24 x 36 "
Atlas	26 x 33 "
Antiquarian	31 x 53 "
Cardboard	22 x 28 "

COMPARATIVE SIZES AND WEIGHTS BONDS, LEDGERS, AND FLAT WRITINGS

SHOWING STANDARD SUBSTANCE WEIGHTS

Double sizes are figured at double the weight of single sizes.

Size	| Substance Weight in Pounds, Basis 17x22								
	13 lbs.	16 lbs.	20 lbs.	24 lbs.	28 lbs.	32 lbs.	36 lbs.	40 lbs.	44 lbs.
16 x21	11½	14½	18	21½	25	28½	32½	36	39½
16 x42	23	29	36	43	50	57	65	72	79
17 x22	13	16	20	24	28	32	36	40	44
17 x28	16½	20½	25½	30½	35½	40½	46	51	56
18 x23	14½	17½	22	26½	31	35½	40	44½	48½
18 x46	29	35	44	53	62	71	80	89	97
19 x24	16	19½	24½	29½	34	39	44	49	53½
19 x26	17	21	26½	31½	37	42½	47½	53	58
20 x28	19½	24	30	36	42	48	54	60	66
21 x32	23	29	36	43	50	57	65	72	79
22 x25½	19½	24	30	36	42	48	54	60	66
22 x34	26	32	40	48	56	64	72	80	88
22½x22½	17½	21½	27	32½	38	43½	48½	54	59½
22½x24½	19	23½	29½	35½	41½	47	53	59	65
22½x28½	22½	27½	34½	41	48	55	61½	68½	75½
22½x34	26½	32½	41	49	57½	65½	73½	82	90
22½x34½	27	33	41	50	58	66½	74½	83	91½
23 x24½	19½	24	30	36	42	48	54	60½	66½
23 x36	29	35	44	53	62	71	80	89	97
24 x38	32	39	49	59	68	78	88	98	107
24½x24½	21	25½	32	38½	45	51½	58	64	70½
24½x28½	24½	30	37½	45	52½	59½	67	74½	82
24½x29	24½	30½	38	45½	53	61	68½	76	83½
24½x38½	33	40½	50½	60½	70½	80½	91	101	111
25½x44	39	48	60	72	84	96	108	120	132
28 x34	33	41	51	61	71	81	92	102	112
34 x44	52	64	80	96	112	128	144	160	176

PROOFREADERS' MARKS

∧ Make correction indicated in margin.

Stet Retain crossed-out word or letter; let it stand.

.... Retain words under which dots appear; write "Stet" in margin.
Stet

✗ Appears battered; examine.

≡ Straighten lines.

✓√✓ Unevenly spaced; correct spacing.

‖ Line up; i.e., make lines even with other matter.

run in Make no break in the reading; no ¶

No ¶ No paragraph; sometimes written "run in."

Out-see copy Here is an omission; see copy.

¶ Make a paragraph here.

tr. Transpose words or letters as indicated.

✑ Take out matter indicated; dele.

✑ Take out character indicated and close up.

✗ Line drawn through a cap means lower case.

⊘ Upside down; reverse.

⌣ Close up; no space.

Insert a space here.

⊥ Push down this space.

□ Indent line one em.

[Move this to the left.

] Move this to the right.

⌐ Raise to proper position.

⌊⌋ Lower to proper position.

//// Hair space letters.

wf. Wrong font; change to proper font.

Qu? Is this right?

lc. Set in lower case (small letters).

S.C. Set in small capitals

Caps Set in capitals.

c+sc. Set in caps and small caps.

rom. Change to Roman.

ital. Change to Italic.

≡ Under letter or word means caps.

≡ Under letter or word, small caps.

— Under letter or word means Italic.

〰 Under letter or word, bold face.

⋀ Insert comma.

;/ Insert semicolon.

:/ Insert colon.

⊙ Insert period.

/?/ Insert interrogation mark.

/!/ Insert exclamation mark.

=/ Insert hyphen.

ᐯ Insert apostrophe.

ᐯᐯ Insert quotation marks.

ᐯ Insert superior letter of figure.

⋀ Insert inferior letter or figure.

[/] Insert brackets.

(/) Insert parentheses.

—m One-em dash.

≡m Two-em parallel dash.

NUMERALS .

ROMAN NUMERALS

I 1	IX 9	XVII ..17	LXX.. 70	D 500
II 2	X 10	XVIII .18	LXXX	DC 600
III 3	XI 11	XIX ...19	or XXC 80	DCC ..700
IV 4	XII 12	XX 20	XC ... 90	DCCC .800
V 5	XIII ...13	XXX ..30	C 100	CM ...900
VI 6	XIV ...14	XL 40	CC ...200	M or
VII 7	XV 15	L 50	CCC 300	cIc ...1000
VIII ...8	XVI ...16	LX 60	CCCC 400	MM ..2000

Note. A dash line over a numeral multiplies the value by 1,000. Thus, $\overline{X} = 10,000$; $\overline{L} = 50,000$; $\overline{C} = 100,000$; $\overline{D} = 500,000$; $\overline{M} = 1,000,000$; $\overline{CLIX} = 159,000$; $\overline{DLIX} = 559,000$.

GENERAL RULES IN ROMAN NUMERALS

(1) Repeating a letter repeats its value: XX = 20; CCC = 300.
(2) A letter placed after one of greater value adds thereto: VIII = 8; DC = 600.
(3) A letter placed before one of greater value subtracts therefrom: IX = 9; CM = 900.

ARABIC NUMERALS

Trillions	Billions	Millions	Thousands	Hundreds
7,	256,	423,	896,	384

Note: In the United States and France a billion is a thousand millions 1,000,000,000). In Britain and Germany a billion is a million millions 1,000,000,000,000).

COUNTRY		RATE
	Africa	
Algeria......................	New Franc.....................	.2050
Angola.......................	Angolar.......................	.0352
British West Africa..........	Pounds........................	2.84
Cameroons (Br.)..............	Pounds........................	2.84
Cameroons (Fr.)..............	C.F.A. Francs.................	.0042
Canary Islands...............	Peseta........................	.0145
Cape Verde Islands...........	Escudo........................	.0352
Central African Republic.....	C.F.A. Francs.................	.0045
Chad.........................	C.F.A. Francs.................	.0045
Congo Republic...............	C.F.A. Francs.................	.0045
Dahomey......................	C.F.A. Francs.................	.0045
Egypt........................	Pounds........................	2.35
Eritrea......................	Ethiopian $...................	.4200
Gabon........................	C.F.A. Francs.................	.0045
Guinea.......................	C.F.A. Francs.................	.0045
Ivory Coast..................	C.F.A. Francs.................	.0045
Kenya........................	Shilling......................	.1410
Libya........................	Pound.........................	2.83
Liberia......................	Dollar........................	1.00
Madagascar...................	C.F.A. Francs.................	.0045
Madeira......................	Escudo........................	.0352
Mauritius....................	Rupee.........................	.18
Mauritanian Islamic Republic...	C.F.A. Francs.................	.0045
Morocco......................	Derham (100 Francs)...........	.205
Niger........................	C.F.A. Francs.................	.0045
Portuguese East Africa.......	Escudo........................	.0352
Congo (Brazzaville)..........	Franc.........................	.0045
Congo (Kinshasa).............	Zaire.........................	2.00
Rhodesia.....................	Pound.........................	2.83
Senegal......................	C.F.A. Francs.................	.0045
Somalia......................	Shilling......................	.1410
Sudan........................	Pound.........................	2.90
Sudanese Republic............	C.F.A. Francs.................	.0045
Tanzania.....................	Shilling......................	.1410
Tunisia......................	Dinar.........................	1.95
Uganda.......................	Shilling......................	.1410
South Africa (Republic)......	Raad..........................	1.41
Voltaic Republic.............	C.F.A. Francs.................	.0045
	Asia:-Middle East	
Aden.........................	Dinar.........................	2.42
Afghanistan..................	Afghani.......................	.025
Bahrain Island...............	Dinar.........................	2.15
Cyprus.......................	Pound.........................	2.42
Iran.........................	Rial..........................	.0135
Iraq.........................	Dinar.........................	2.85
Israel.......................	Pound.........................	.30
Jordan.......................	Dinar.........................	2.85
Kuwait.......................	Dinar.........................	2.85
Lebanon......................	Pound.........................	.33
Saudi Arabia.................	Riyal.........................	.23
Syria........................	Pound.........................	.25
Turkey.......................	Pound.........................	.12

* As of October 1, 1968

COUNTRY		RATE
	Australasia	
Australia.....................	Dollars......................	1.12
New Zealand...................	Dollars......................	1.12

	Far East	
Brunei........................	Local $......................	.33
Burma.........................	Kyat.........................	.2115
Cambodia......................	Riel.........................	.03
Ceylon........................	Rupee........................	.17
Fiji Islands..................	Fiji Pounds..................	2.35
China.........................	Taiwan $.....................	.025
Hong Kong.....................	Hong Kong $..................	.17
India.........................	Rupee........................	.14
Republic of Indonesia.........	Rupiah.......................	.004
Japan.........................	Yen..........................	.0029
Korea (Rep.)..................	Won..........................	.004
Macao.........................	Pataca.......................	.17
Malaysia......................	Malayan$.....................	.3300
New Caledonia.................	C.F.P. Franc.................	.014
New Guinea....................	Local $......................	1.15
Pakistan......................	Rupee........................	.2115
The Philippines...............	Peso.........................	.30
Singapore.....................	Sing. $......................	.3300
Thailand......................	Baht (Tical).................	.05
Vietnam.......................	Piastre......................	.009

	Europe	
Austria.......................	Schilling....................	.0400
Azores........................	Escudos......................	.0355
Belgium.......................	Franc........................	.020075
Crete.........................	Drachma......................	.035
Denmark.......................	Krone........................	.135
Faroe Island.................	Krone........................	.135
Finland.......................	Markka.......................	.25
France........................	New Franc....................	.2042
Germany.......................	Deutsche Mark................	.2520
Gibraltar.....................	Pounds.......................	2.42
Great Britain.................	Pounds.......................	2.42
Greece........................	Drachma......................	.035
Iceland.......................	Krona........................	.018
Italy.........................	Lira.........................	.001617
Jugoslavia....................	Dinar........................	$ Only
Liechtenstein.................	Swiss Franc..................	.2325
Luxembourg....................	Belgian Franc................	.0201
Malta.........................	Pound........................	$ Only
Netherlands...................	Guilders (Florin)............	.2755
Norway........................	Krone........................	.1407
Portugal......................	Escudo.......................	.0352
Spain.........................	Peseta.......................	.0145
Sweden........................	Krona........................	.1942
Switzerland...................	Franc........................	.2325
Vatican City..................	Lire.........................	.001617

COUNTRY   RATE

Central America

British Honduras................ Local $........................ .65
Costa Rica..................... Colon......................... $ Only
Guatemala...................... Quetzal....................... $ Only
Honduras....................... Lempira....................... $ Only
Nicaragua...................... Cordoba....................... $ Only
El Salvador.................... Colon......................... $ Only

North America

Canada......................... Canadian $.................... .9325
Mexico......................... Peso.......................... .0805

South America

Argentina...................... Peso.......................... $ Only
Bolivia........................ Boliviano..................... $ Only
Brazil......................... Cruzeiro...................... $ Only
Chile.......................... Escudo........................ $ Only
Colombia....................... Peso.......................... $ Only
Ecuador........................ Sucre......................... $ Only
Guyana......................... Local $....................... .51
Dutch Guiana................... Guilder....................... .5400
French Guiana.................. Franc......................... .2042
Panama......................... Balboa........................ 1.00
Paraguay....................... Guarani....................... $ Only
Peru........................... Sol........................... .0375
Uruguay........................ Peso.......................... $ Only
Venezuela...................... Bolivar....................... .3000

West Indies

Antigua........................ Local $....................... .51
Bahamas........................ Dollar........................ .99
Barbados....................... Local $....................... .51
Bermuda........................ Pound......................... 2.42
Cuba........................... Peso.......................... 1.00
Dominica (Br.)................. Local $....................... .51
Dominican Republic............. Peso.......................... 1.00
Grenada........................ Local $....................... .51
Guadeloupe..................... Franc......................... .2042
Haiti.......................... Gourde........................ .2025
Jamaica........................ Pound......................... 2.42
Martinique..................... Franc......................... .2042
Montserrat..................... Local $....................... .51
Netherlands Antilles........... Guilder....................... .5400
Puerto Rico.................... Dollars....................... 1.00
St. Kitts...................... Local $....................... .51
St. Lucia...................... Local $....................... .51
St. Vincent.................... Local $....................... .51
Trinidad....................... Local $....................... .51

SOME GEOGRAPHICAL STATISTICS

Great Ship Canals of the World	Opened, year	Length, miles	Depth, feet	Width,* feet	Cost
Cape Cod	1914	8	25	150	$ 12,000,000
Corinth (Greece)	1893	4	26.25	72	5,000,000
Kronstadt-Petrograd (Russia).	1890	16	20.50	220	10,000,000
Elbe and Trave (Germany).	1900	41	10	72	5,831,000
Kaiser Wilhelm or Kiel (Germany)†.	1895	61	45	150	94,818,000
Manchester ship (English)	1894	35.5	26	120	75,000,000
New Orleans Industrial (U.S.).	1921	6	30	150	20,000,000
Panama (U.S.)	1914	50.5	45	300	375,000,000
Sault St. Marie (U.S.)	1855	1.6	22	100	10,000,000
Sault Ste. Marie (Canada).	1895	1.11	20.25	142	2,791,873
Suez (Egypt)	1869	90	31	108	100,000,000
Welland (Canada)	1887	26.75	14	100	25,000,000

*At the bottom.   †Rebuilt.

Longest Rivers in the World

River	Miles	River	Miles	River	Miles	River	Miles
Mississippi-Mo.	4,194	Yangtze	3,000	Amur	2,700	Volga	2,325
Nile	3,670	La Plata	2,950	Mekong	2,600	Hwangho	2,300
Amazon	3,300	Lena	2,860	Niger	2,600	Yukon	2,050
Ob	3,235	Kongo	2,800	Yenesei	2,500	Colorado	2,000

Largest Lakes in the United States
[From U.S. geological survey report.]

Following is a list of lakes in the United States each of which is more than 100 square miles in area at high water:

Lake	Sq. miles	Lake	Sq. miles
Lake Superior, Wis., Minn. and Canada	31,200	Lake St. Clair, Mich. and Canada	410
Lake Huron, Mich, and Canada . .	23,800	Rainy lake, Minn. and Canada.	310
Lake Michigan, Ill., Wis., Mich., Indiana	22,450	Leech lake, Minn. (high water)	234
		Leech lake, Minn. (low water)	173
Lake Erie, O., Pa., N.Y. and Can.	9,960	Mille Lacs, Minn.	207
Lake Ontario, N.Y. and Canada . .	7,240	Lake Winnebago, Wis.	215
Great Salt lake, Utah (in 1912) . .	1,800	Lake Tahoe, Cal.	193
Lake of the Woods, Minn. and Canada	1,500	Flathead lake, Mont.	188
Tulare lake, Cal. . . . . Nothing to	800	Upper Klamath lake, Ore. (including swamp)	156
Lake Okechogee, Fla.	730	Upper Klamath lake, Ore. (excluding	
Lake Pontchartrain, La.	625	swamp)	87
Salton sea, Cal. (Jan. 1, 1909), shrinking	443	Utah lake, Utah . . . . :	145
		Tule lake, Cal.	144
Red lake, Minn. (both lakes)	441	Lake Pen d'Oreille, Idaho	124
Lake Champlain, N.Y. and Vt.	436	Lake Winnibigoshish, Minn.	117
		Moosehead lake, Maine	115

Largest Islands in the World

Name	Sq. miles	Name	Sq. miles	Name	Sq. miles
Greenland	827,300	Honshiu	87,500	Luzon	41,000
New Guinea	330,000	Celebes	72,000	Newfoundland.	40,200
Borneo	280,000	Prince Albert land.	60,000	Iceland	40,000
Baffin land	236,000	South Island, N.Z.	58,500	Ellesmere land	40,000
Madagascar	228,000	Java	48,400	Mindanao	37,000
Sumatra	160,000	North Island, N.Z.	44,500	Hokkaido.	36,500
Great Britain.	88,603	Cuba	44,164	Ireland	32,600

Areas of Oceans and Great Lakes

Oceans	Sq. miles		Sq. miles
Antarc	5,731,350	Gt. Slave	12,000
Arctic	4,781,000	Huron	23,800
Atlant.	34,801,400	Michigan.	22,450
Indian	17,084,000	Nyassa	12,000
Pacific.	67,699,630	Ontario	7,240
Lakes—		Superior	31,200
Baikal	13,000	Tanganyika	15,000
Chad	50,000	Vic. Nyanza.	26,500
Erie	9,960	Winnipeg.	9,000
Gt. Bear.	70,000		

Average Depth of Oceans and Seas

	Feet.		Feet.
Antarctic	10,800	Caribbean	7,614
Arctic	5,160	China	402
Atlantic	12,200	Gulf Mexico.	4,632
Indian.	11,136	Japan.	7,320
Pacific.	12,960	Mediter.	4,560
Baltic.	122	North	300
Bering	900	Okhotsk	5,040

The mean depth of all the oceans and seas is estimated to be from 2 to 2½ miles.

205

INDEX

A

Acetone, 13
Acid Cleaners, xiii
Acidity and alkalinity, 82
AE 1009, xi
Age-compressive-strength, cement, 136
Air-conditioning data, 76
Air velocity, 73
Alkaline Cleaners
  Liquid, viii
  Powdered, ix
Alkalinity, 82
All-purpose cleaner, viii, ix
Alternating-current motors, 175
American Conference of Governmental
  Industrial Hygienists, 7, 33
American National thread, 95
Ampere, 172
Amperes, formula for, 170
Angles, natural functions of, 51
Angular measure, 44
Annulus, 56
Antidote, universal, 25
Antidotes for common poisons, 26-27
Anti-slip, xv
A.P.I. gravity, 66, 75
Apothecaries' measure, 42
AQUA SEAL, x
Arabic numerals, 201
Arches, brick and stone, 126
Architectural plans, electrical symbols
  for, 168-169
Area, 54-55
Area-volume-weight conversion, 62
Artificial respiration, 28-31
Atmosphere data, standard, 69
Atom, 171
Atomic weight table, 80
Auto-ignition temperatures, 16
Avoirdupois measure, 41

B

Back-pressure arm-lift resuscitation, 30-31
Barrels, 103
Basic electricity, 171-172
Bearing capacities of soils, 138
Benzene, 13
Bland, viii
Board feet, 116, 118-119
Boiling point, 64-65
Bolts and nuts, 102

Borax hand cleaner, xii
Brass pipe, 158
BRAWN, x
Brick masonry, 122-126
Brinell scale, 86
BRITE SIL SILICATES, xv
BRITE SORB SILICATES, xv
British thermal unit, 89
British weights and measures, 44
BTU, 89
Building and construction, 115 ff.
Burns, chemical, 23
Bursting pressure, 112
Business machines cleaner, ix
Business methods, 187 ff.
BUXITE, xii

C

Cabinets and boxes, 182
Canals, 205
Capacitance, 172
Capacitors, 184, 185
Capacity, tanks, 103-113
Cap screws, 96, 97
Carbon Removers, x
Carbon stain remover, x
Carbon stripper, x
Carbon tetrachloride, ix, 13
  replacement for, xii
  toxicity of, 10
Cargo Capacity Conversions, 157
Carnauba wax, xv
Carrying capacity of refrigeration lines, 159
Car wash,
  liquid, viii
Cement, 129 ff.
Centigrade scale, 71
Chemical burns, 23
Chest-pressure arm-lift resuscitation, 29
Chloroform, 13
Circle, 56
Circuits, electrical, 171
Circular or angular measure, 44
Circumference, 54-55
Cisterns, 103
Cleaner, all-purpose, viii
  business machines, ix
  disinfectant, viii
Cleaners, acid xiii
Cold tank stripper, x •
Color code, resistors and capacitors, 184
Compound interest, 188

INDEX

INDEX

INDEX

INDEX

INDEX

212